SECOND EDITION # APPLIED BOOLEAN ALGEBRA

An Elementary Introduction

FRANZ E. HOHN

Professor of Mathematics

University of Illinois

THE MACMILLAN COMPANY,
New York

COLLIER-MACMILLAN LIMITED,
London

First Printing

Earlier editions © copyright 1958 and 1960 by
Franz E. Hohn and David E. Muller

Library of Congress catalog card number: 66–13973

THE MACMILLAN COMPANY, NEW YORK
COLLIER-MACMILLAN CANADA, LTD., TORONTO, ONTARIO

Printed in the United States of America

Preface

A simple introduction to the basic facts of Boolean algebra and some of its applications, this book is intended for both mathematicians and engineers, and hence assumes no special engineering or mathematical background. Anyone who has had high school mathematics and physics and has also a modest degree of mathematical maturity should be able to read the entire volume with profit. Explanations have been given in great detail to help make this possible.

The book begins with the algebra of relay circuits, not because relays have primary importance but rather for historical reasons and because the physical reasons for the mathematical laws are so elegantly clear in this case. This chapter provides a thorough introduction to the manipulative aspects of elementary Boolean algebra. The algebra of the subsets of a set is developed in Chapter 2. Chapter 3 presents an intuitive development of the algebra of propositional functions and of the application of the algebra of truth functions in the design of what are called logic circuits. A treatment of NAND and NOR logic circuits has been introduced in this edition. In Chapter 4 there is an introduction to the map method and to the Quine–McCluskey procedure for simplifying Boolean functions. These are intended to provide an introduction to a study of the minimization problem, of which a selected bibliography is given. The book proper is concluded with a summary of the principal properties of Boolean algebra, out of the context of any application. The increase in size of this edition relative to the first results from more detailed exposition and from a greatly increased number of exercises rather than from any significant enlargement of scope.

The notation for Boolean operations used in Chapters 1 and 3 is that employed in the Department of Computer Science of the University of Illinois. The use of the symbol " $\vee$ " instead of the symbol "+" for the "or" operation has a distinct pedagogical advantage: the student is not saddled with incorrect or limiting notions of what "+" might mean. In this edition the notation in the chapter on sets has been changed so as to conform to more of the literature. In Chapter 3 the symbols for implication and equivalence are now familiar mathematical symbols for these relations, namely " $\Rightarrow$ " and " $\Leftrightarrow$." The conditional and the biconditional are denoted by " $\rightarrow$ " and " $\leftrightarrow$," respectively to distinguish them from the corresponding relations. A symmetrical notation is used in Chapter 5 to emphasize the duality of the two basic binary operations. Certain changes in terminology have been made (for example, "complete products" in place of "fundamental products") in order to provide a more descriptive term or in order to conform to usages employed by other authors.

Since rather frequent references are made to binary numbers, an appendix on binary arithmetic is included. For those who wish to develop some idea of how the various logical operations can be realized physically, there is an appendix on semiconductor logic elements. Finally, there is an appendix on the cardinality of a finite set.

None of the chapters pretends to be "complete." Each goes just far enough to establish the connection between the application in question and the basic rules of Boolean algebra, and each, therefore, leaves important issues untreated and important questions unraised and unanswered. However, I hope that despite its limitations this book will make the way easier for those who need to learn Boolean algebra—particularly for those who need to study the subject by themselves—because of its applications to computer and switching circuit design. I also hope that this book will invite other readers, whose interest may be casual, to study more seriously this interesting and increasingly important subject.

Those who have an interest in a particular chapter will find it essentially self-contained. This is intended to make the book more useful for reference and for independent study, but it results in extensive repetition in Chapters 1, 2, 3, and 5. When the book is used as a text, it is naturally not necessary to repeat the details in full each time they appear in a new context.

Relay circuit diagrams have, throughout, a peculiarity that should be explained. Extreme terminals and terminals of springs are identified by open circles. All other connections, except as noted, are identified by solid circles.

I wish to thank Mrs. Carolyn Bloemker for typing the manuscript and Professor Zamir Bavel of Southern Illinois University for a critical reading of the manuscript. Professor Bavel's efforts resulted in many suggestions for improvement and in additional, **excellent exercise material.** They each gave loyal and, indeed, indispensable aid for which I am most grateful. They should, however, not be held accountable for remaining faults, which are solely my responsibility. A special word of thanks is due Professor Bavel and Miss Lois Minning for their particularly conscientious help with the final reading of the proof. Finally, I wish to thank those readers of the first edition who forwarded corrections, suggestions for improvement, and additional exercises. I hope that readers of this edition will feel free to do the same.

My interest in Boolean algebra was aroused during a very happy year spent as a research guest at Bell Telephone Laboratories. Indeed, much of the credit for such merit as these pages may possess belongs to my friends there. Therefore, as an expression of gratitude, this book is dedicated to Mr. Clarence Lovell and to Mr. John Meszar whose interest made my stay at Bell Laboratories possible.

Philo, Illinois   F. E. H.

Contents

INTRODUCTION

1. The Purpose of This Book   xi
2. The Nature of the Mathematical Method   xi

1

THE ALGEBRA OF COMBINATIONAL RELAY CIRCUITS

1.1 Bistable Devices   1
1.2 Circuit Variables and Their Complements   2
1.3 Two-Terminal Switching Circuits   5
1.4 The Operations OR and AND   5
1.5 The Switching Function of a Two-Terminal Circuit   7
1.6 The Postulates of Switching Algebra   11
1.7 Comment on Lack of Independence of the Postulates   14
1.8 The Principle of Duality   15
1.9 Switching Functions of Series-Parallel and of Bridge Circuits   16
1.10 Some Useful Identities   19
1.11 Concerning Identity Elements, Inverses, and Cancellation   23
1.12 Applications of the Identities   25
1.13 Exercises   28
1.14 The Relations of Inclusion and Less-Than-or-Equal-to   34
1.15 Switching Algebra as a Boolean Algebra   39
1.16 Exercises   39
1.17 Complete Products and Complete Unions   41

1.18 The Disjunctive Normal Form   44
1.19 Further Applications of the Disjunctive Normal Form   48
1.20 The Conjunctive Normal Form   51
1.21 Don't-Care Combinations   55
1.22 Further Examples of Circuit Simplification   57
1.23 Exercises   63
1.24 Other Problems   68
1.25 References   70

2

THE ALGEBRA OF THE SUBSETS OF A SET

2.1   The Concept of a Set   71
2.2   Operations on Sets   73
2.3   Basic Theorems Concerning Equality and Inclusion   76
2.4   Basic Theorems Concerning Union and Intersection   78
2.5   The Algebra of the Subsets of U as a Boolean Algebra   80
2.6   The Principle of Duality, Some Useful Identities   81
2.7   Further Properties of the Inclusion Relation   83
2.8   Exercises   85
2.9   Partitioning of the Universal Set   91
2.10 Subsets of Finite Sets   93
2.11 Normal Forms of Boolean Set Functions   96
2.12 Boolean Algebras of Set Functions   98
2.13 Fields of Subsets and the Stone Representation Theorem   99
2.14 Exercises   100
2.15 References   101

3

LOGIC AND LOGIC CIRCUITS

3.1   Propositions and Propositional Functions   103
3.2   Quantifiers, Free and Bound Variables   107
3.3   Three Basic Logical Operations   108
3.4   Truth Values and Truth Functions   111
3.5   Equivalence of Propositional Functions   114
3.6   The Tautology and the Inconsistency   115
3.7   An Algebra of Propositional Functions   119
3.8   Exercises   123
3.9   Other Logical Functions and Connectives   126
3.10 Boolean Algebras of Propositional Functions   134

3.11 Boolean Algebras of Truth Functions 135
3.12 Exercises 137
3.13 Electronic Realization of Logical Connectives 141
3.14 Realization of Truth Values of Logical Functions 145
3.15 Logic Circuits and Computation 149
3.16 Generalized NAND and NOR Functions 153
3.17 Further Remarks on Addition 156
3.18 Codes and Translators 158
3.19 Exercises 162
3.20 References 169

4

THE MINIMIZATION PROBLEM

4.1 The Origin of the Problem 170
4.2 The Veitch–Karnaugh Map of a Boolean Function 170
4.3 Exercises 173
4.4 Simplification of Functions 174
4.5 Use of the Complement in Minimization 185
4.6 Don't-Care Combinations and the Minimization Problem 186
4.7 Five-Variable and Six-Variable Maps 189
4.8 A More Compact Notation 192
4.9 Exercises 194
4.10 Quine's Method of Reduction 201
4.11 Exercises 208
4.12 McCluskey's Mechanization of Quine's Method 208
4.13 McCluskey's Method for Determining All Minimal Forms 212
4.14 Don't-Cares in the Quine–McCluskey Procedure 213
4.15 Exercises 215
4.16 Use of Coverings to Reduce the Problem 215
4.17 Exercises 220
4.18 Summary and Conclusions 220
4.19 References 221

5

AN ABSTRACT SUMMARY OF BOOLEAN ALGEBRA

5.1 The Basic Operations of a Boolean Algebra 223
5.2 Exercises 226
5.3 The Inclusion Relation 227
5.4 Definition of a Boolean Algebra 228

5.5   Normal Forms of Boolean Functions   228
5.6   Exercises   231
5.7   References   232

Appendix   **1**
THE BINARY SYSTEM OF NUMERATION

A1.1   The Decimal System of Numeration   233
A1.2   The Binary System of Numeration   234
A1.3   Binary Arithmetic   235
A1.4   Conversion from Binary to Decimal Form   238
A1.5   Conversion from Decimal to Binary Form   239

Appendix   **2**
SEMICONDUCTOR LOGIC ELEMENTS

A2.1   Basic Assumptions   242
A2.2   The Semiconductor Diode   243
A2.3   A Diode AND-Element   244
A2.4   A Diode OR-Element   246
A2.5   An Alternative Procedure: Negative Logic   248
A2.6   Multiple Input Elements   248
A2.7   Some Simple Diode Circuits   249
A2.8   The Transistor   251
A2.9   The Transistor NOT-Element   253
A2.10 Transistor AND- and Stroke-Elements   254
A2.11 Transistor OR-Element   256
A2.12 Transistor-Diode Circuits   256
A2.13 General Comments   257

Appendix   **3**
THE CARDINALITY OF A FINITE SET

A3.1   The Number of Elements in a Union of Disjoint Sets   259
A3.2   Counting Formulas Involving the Positive Intersections   261
A3.3   Other Counting Formulas   263
A3.4   Comments on Counting Problems   265
A3.5   Exercises   266
A3.6   References   268

INDEX   269

Introduction

1. The Purpose of This Book

In the past thirty-five years, Boolean algebra has developed from what was often regarded as just an interesting curiosity into an extensive and mature branch of mathematics. One phase of this development has been inspired by the applications of Boolean algebra to the design of switching circuits for telephone and control systems, and to the design of logic circuits for electronic computers. However, the subject has also developed into a significant branch of abstract algebra with important applications to topology. Thus Boolean algebra is a proper sphere of interest for the pure mathematician as well as for those primarily interested in applications.

The purpose of this book is to give an elementary, intuitive introduction to Boolean algebra as a model of a class of simple switching circuits, then to show that the same algebra may also be interpreted as the algebra of the subsets of a set, and finally to show that the same algebra provides a theory of propositional functions and of the logic circuits of computers. Thus the emphasis is on Boolean algebra as applied mathematics rather than as abstract algebra. However, a brief summary of Boolean algebra as abstract algebra is given in Chapter 5.

2. The Nature of the Mathematical Method

A primary purpose here is to illustrate how observation of a physical or logical system dictates the details of the mathematical system used to describe it. Since in the present instance the resulting mathematical system is sharply different from the familiar ones of algebra, geometry, and the calculus, it is well to pause briefly to consider some of the characteristics of a formal, mathematical description of a physical system.

It is important at the outset to recognize that because we cannot define every word in terms of simpler words, every mathematical system necessarily contains *undefined terms*. Similarly, because we cannot deduce every theorem as a logical consequence of simpler theorems, every mathematical system must also contain unproved theorems or *postulates*. For example, in Euclidean geometry, the undefined terms might include *point, line,* and *pass through*. Then one of the possible postulates is: *Through two distinct points there passes one and only one line*.

From the undefined terms and the postulates, we deduce theorems by means of the rules of logic. Then we introduce definitions of new terms in terms of the undefined terms and prove more theorems. For example, having defined *triangle* and *median,* we prove the theorem: *The medians of a triangle pass through a common point*.

The choice of the undefined terms and the postulates of a mathematical system is by no means simple. Those of Euclidean geometry were the outgrowth of several thousand years' experience with experimental and intuitive geometry. In all other examples of postulational systems — and there are many — the undefined terms, postulates, and definitions are similarly selected, on the basis of physical or mathematical experience, in such a way as to yield useful results.

When mathematics is applied to the world of nature, it is relatively rare that the natural system being studied is understood well enough so that even a reasonably complete set of undefined terms and postulates is suggested by it. To illustrate, no such system has yet been given for the · science of electricity; we simply do not know enough about the subject to reduce the whole of it to a single, formal, postulational kind of mathematical scheme.

Often, however, it is possible to give a set of postulates for a mathematical system which is a useful description of a part of nature. A particularly elegant example of this is the use of Boolean algebra to represent switching circuits. We call such a system a **mathematical model** of the part of nature it represents.

No mathematical model has ever provided all the answers to all of the problems concerning its corresponding physical system. This is because it does not — in fact cannot — take into account *all* of the conditions that affect the physical system in question. Normally we ignore all but what appear to be the most vital factors. Taking the latter into account, we idealize and symbolize our physical concepts and observations, thus building a mathematical model which, if cleverly constructed, produces theorems that correlate closely with what is observed in nature. When this is the case, the model in question is a useful one. Otherwise the model is unsatisfactory and at least one additional factor must be added to the list of vital ones. Newtonian mechanics provides the classical example of this situation. Adequate to explain the mechanical phenomena of ordinary experience, it is inadequate to explain all observable phenomena at either the subatomic or the astronomical levels. Hence the theory of relativity—a generalization of Newtonian mechanics which includes the latter as a special case—was invented to account for the apparently irregular observations.

This same circumstance appears in the mathematical study of switching circuits. The simple model with which we begin is based on certain admittedly incomplete and inaccurate assumptions, which, however, make the mathematical system much more tractable. The resulting system is useful in solving a wide variety of problems because the factors invalidating the *assumptions* in question are not of major significance for the *problems* in question. When they do become significant, theory and observation will no longer correlate satisfactorily, and we must replace our system by a more general one that recognizes the importance of these factors.

In what follows, we shall take care to point out where we make simplifying assumptions, and we shall also indicate the physical origins of the postulates used, so that both the limitations and the naturalness of our mathematics will always be kept in evidence.

1

The Algebra of
Combinational Relay Circuits

The Mathematical Model

1.1   Bistable Devices

In electronic digital computers, telephone switching systems, control systems for automatic factories, and other systems involving the communication or processing of data, we find many examples of electric circuits that employ what are known as **two-state** or **bistable devices.** The simplest example of such a device is a **switch** or **contact** that may be in the **open state** or in the **closed state.** When a contact is operated with the aid of an electromagnet, the combination is called a **relay.** A switch or relay is called a **bilateral circuit element** since it permits the passage of current in either direction when the contact is closed. Devices permitting the passage of current in only one direction are called **unilateral.**

There are various other two-state devices in use or in the process of development. These include rectifying diodes, magnetic cores, transistors, various types of electron tubes, cryotrons, and a variety of others. Magnetic drums and magnetic tapes may be regarded as assemblages of two-state devices. The physical nature of the two stable states of a device varies from one device to another and may take such forms as conducting vs. nonconducting, closed vs. open, charged vs. discharged, positively magnetized vs. negatively magnetized, high potential vs. low potential, and other states.

The methods and results of Boolean algebra and related subjects, such as logic and set theory, have been found useful in discussing circuits that employ two-state devices. In this chapter we use contact networks to

1

illustrate how this is done. The mathematical model is particularly simple in this case and, historically, this is the first application of Boolean algebra to digital circuitry (Shannon: [1], [2]).

Some commonly used symbols for contacts are shown in Figure 1.1.1. In this book we often use the first type of symbol, but frequently without representation of the electromagnet that operates the contact. Each of

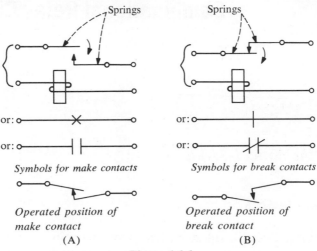

Figure 1.1.1

the contacts illustrated here has two flexible blades called **springs.** One of these springs is forced by the attraction of the electromagnet to move toward or away from the other when current is passed through the coil around the iron core of the magnet. A normally open contact is called a **make** or **front contact** whereas a normally closed one is called a **break** or **back contact.** The wires that conduct (lead) the current through the network are called **leads.** Symbols for other devices are given later as needed.

1.2　Circuit Variables and Their Complements

We introduce two mathematical symbols as the first step in constructing the announced model. With an open contact (or open path) in a circuit we associate the symbol "0" and with a closed contact (or closed path) we associate the symbol "1". Although we call these symbols **zero** and **one,** respectively, they are not to be regarded as the zero and one of ordinary arithmetic. From a mathematical point of view, "0" and "1" are to be regarded as *undefined terms*. The definitions to follow and the postulates of Section 1.6 give 0 and 1 their mathematical meaning. All we have stated here is the particular *physical interpretation* which it is convenient to give to 0 and 1 in this application.

When the condition of a contact is variable in a problem, we represent it by a literal symbol such as *x*, *y*, *a*, *b*, and so on. Such a symbol, called a **circuit variable,** assumes the value 0 when the contact is open, the value 1 when it is closed.

With each symbol *x*, we associate a symbol $\bar{x}$, called the **complement** of *x*, which assumes the value 1 when *x* assumes the value 0, the value 0 when *x* assumes the value 1:

$$
\begin{array}{c|c}
x & \bar{x} \\
\hline
0 & 1 \\
1 & 0
\end{array}
$$

Note that we have in fact defined an **operation of complementation** in terms of the symbols 0 and 1. This is the first step in the process of giving these symbols their mathematical meaning. The definition of the complement is intended to imply that

(1.2.1) $$\bar{0} = 1, \quad \bar{1} = 0.$$

The complement $\bar{x}$ of *x* is employed as the circuit variable associated with a contact which is open when the *x*-contact is closed and is closed when the *x*-contact is open. Thus, if *x* denotes a normally open contact of a certain relay, $\bar{x}$ denotes a normally closed contact of that same relay, as is shown in all three parts of Figure 1.2.1. *Throughout this chapter, an uncomplemented variable refers to a normally open (make) contact and a complemented variable refers to a normally closed (break) contact.*

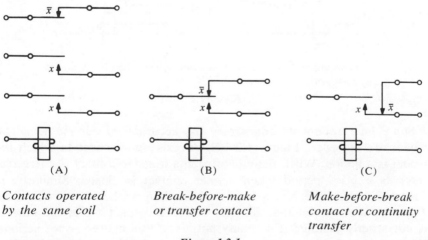

(A)

Contacts operated by the same coil

(B)

Break-before-make or transfer contact

(C)

Make-before-break contact or continuity transfer

Figure 1.2.1

When two or more contacts are assumed to open simultaneously and close simultaneously, we denote them by the same circuit variable. Thus, we ordinarily assume that two make (or two break) contacts actuated by the same electromagnet operate simultaneously, and hence we denote them by the same symbol (Figure 1.2.1). Although this assumption does not strictly hold true, it is nevertheless well justified in the case of a high quality, well-adjusted relay.

Frequently, in order to save one spring, or to eliminate certain types of hazards, a make contact and a break contact operated by the same electromagnet are combined in one device called a **transfer contact.** Two types of transfer contact are illustrated in Figures 1.2.1(B) and 1.2.1(C). In Figure 1.2.1(B), when the relay is operated, the conducting path is transferred from the upper right lead to the lower right lead. In Figure 1.2.1(C), when x closes, the lower right spring is pushed down by the left spring, which thereby opens $\bar{x}$. The conducting path is now transferred from the upper right lead to the left lead.

To observe how our notation describes the behavior of a circuit, the reader should verify that, in Figure 1.2.2, there is a path from t_1 to t_2 if and only if $\bar{x} = \bar{y} = 1$ or $x = y = 1$, and a path from t_3 to t_4 if and only if $x = 0$ and $y = 1$ or $x = 1$ and $y = 0$.

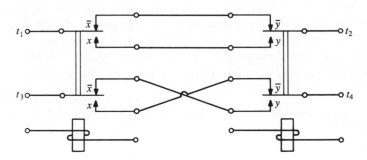

A switching circuit. (The double bars represent a non-conducting mechanical connection.)

Figure 1.2.2

Some final comments concerning the accuracy of our mathematical model are in order. Figure 1.2.1(B) reveals one respect in which the model is a fiction. When the coil of such a transfer contact is energized, there is a brief period when neither contact is closed. Similarly, in Figure 1.2.1(C), there is a brief period when neither contact is open. Thus the assumption that we may call one contact x and the other $\bar{x}$ is not strictly justified. For many purposes, this matter is not serious. When it is serious, we must use design techniques which employ fast-

or slow-acting relays, make-before-break in place of break-before-make contacts, and so on, to eliminate undesirable effects.

Another assumption which we make is that when the coil of a relay is energized, its contacts are instantaneously operated. This assumption too causes difficulties at times. The difficulties may be taken care of by treating the coil as one two-state device (energized or not energized) and a contact on it as another (operated or not operated). In this book, we restrict our attention to circuits such that these difficulties may be ignored as far as the mathematical model is concerned.

1.3   Two-Terminal Switching Circuits

The circuits illustrated in Figure 1.2.2 provide open or closed paths between the terminals t_1 and t_2, t_3 and t_4, depending on the states of the contacts involved. Any circuit consisting of interconnected contacts, whose purpose is to connect two fixed points with a conducting path under specified conditions (open or closed) of the contacts, and to leave the two points unconnected under all other conditions, is called a **combinational two-terminal switching circuit.** In this chapter, we study such two-terminal circuits, assuming that they can be described in terms of a finite number of circuit variables $x_1, x_2, \ldots, x_n$ and their complements.

In order to study these circuits mathematically, we associate with each circuit a function f of the variables $x_1, x_2, \ldots, x_n$, which has the following property: when we substitute any combination of values $\xi_1, \xi_2, \ldots, \xi_n$, where each ξ_j is 0 or 1, for the circuit variables, the function value $f(\xi_1, \xi_2, \ldots, \xi_n)$ will be 1 if the circuit is closed for the given combination, but will be 0 if it is open for that combination. Such a function is called a **switching function** of the two-terminal circuit. In order to be able to write such a function, we must first define what operations, in addition to complementation, are to be used in constructing it. This is done in the next section.

1.4   The Operations OR and AND

One of the characteristics of switching circuits is that there may well be a number of possible paths from one terminal to another. That is, the current may proceed via one path *or* another *or* perhaps a third *or* even via several paths at once. This suggests the introduction of an operation that will make possible the symbolic representation of such alternatives. We shall call the operation OR, or **union,** and denote it by the symbol "∨," which is derived from the first letter of the Latin word "vel" for the **inclusive-or.** When we use the inclusive-or, "*a* or *b*" means "*a* or *b* or both."

Applied to two circuit variables, the operation OR is realized physically by the parallel connection of the contacts corresponding to these variables. In Figure 1.4.1(A), contacts symbolized by *x* and *y* are shown connected in parallel, and this connection is represented by the **union** "*x* ∨ *y*."

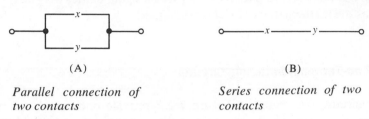

(A)   (B)

Parallel connection of   *Series connection of two*
two contacts   *contacts*

Figure 1.4.1

We read this "*x* or *y*" since the circuit provides a closed path between its endpoints if and only if the *x*-contact is closed *or* the *y*-contact is closed *or both* are closed.

The operation OR is also called **disjunction** or **alternation** or **the join.** In the expression *x* ∨ *y*, *y* is said to be **joined** to *x*.

Another characteristic of switching circuits is that a current may have to pass through one contact *and* another *and* possibly even more in order to proceed along a certain path from one terminal to another. This suggests the introduction of an operation that will make possible the symbolic representation of such sequences. We call the operation AND, or **multiplication,** and denote it by the symbol "·" or simply by juxtaposition. The AND operation is also called **conjunction.**

Applied to two circuit variables, the operation AND is realized physically by the series connection of the contacts corresponding to these variables. In Figure 1.4.1(B), contacts *x* and *y* are shown connected in series, and this connection is represented by the **product** "*xy*." We read this "*x* and *y*" when it is desired to emphasize the fact that the circuit provides a closed path between its endpoints if and only if the *x*-contact is closed *and* the *y*-contact is closed.

The operations OR and AND are also applied to more complicated expressions than just circuit variables. For example, if we connect the circuits corresponding to *xy* and *w* ∨ *z* in parallel, we obtain the result shown in Figure 1.4.2(A), with which we associate the expression *xy* ∨ (*w* ∨ *z*). Again, if we connect the circuits corresponding to *xy* and *w* ∨ *z* in series, we obtain the result shown in Figure 1.4.2(B), with which we associate the expression *xy* · (*w* ∨ *z*).

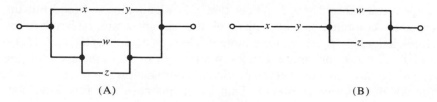

(A)   (B)

Parallel connection of two circuits   Series connection of two circuits

Figure 1.4.2

Later developments will show that more complicated OR and AND relationships can be described symbolically and that their physical realization need not be in terms of series and parallel connections alone. Sometimes, in fact, the non-series-parallel realization requires fewer contacts or fewer springs than the best series-parallel circuit does, as will be illustrated in Section 1.9.

1.5   The Switching Function of a Two-Terminal Circuit

Now let us return to the problem of constructing a switching function for a circuit. First we need a definition of equality of functions. We define two switching functions of the same set of circuit variables to be **identically equal,** more briefly **equal,** and their circuits to be **equivalent,** if and only if both switching functions take on the value 1 for exactly the same combinations of values of the circuit variables, and hence also both take on the value 0 for exactly the same combinations of values of the circuit variables.

The definition of equality just given implies that any two switching functions that correctly describe the behavior of the same circuit are equal. For this reason, it is proper to refer to *the* switching function of a circuit, when such a function exists. There is always, on the other hand, an infinite number of circuits that give rise to a given switching function. Any two of these circuits are closed under exactly the same conditions and hence are said to be equivalent.

The definition of equality of functions also implies that if $f = g$ *and* $h = k$, *where* f, g, h, k *are switching functions of* $x_1, x_2, \ldots, x_n$, *then* $f \lor h = g \lor k$, $fh = gk$, *and* $\bar{f} = \bar{g}$. Indeed, in each equation, both members take on the same value for all combinations of values of the variables. That is, we can "OR" equals with equals, "AND" equals with equals, and complement equals, in each case obtaining equals as results.

When, as here, we write $f = g$ or $f(x_1, x_2, \ldots, x_n) = g(x_1, x_2, \ldots, x_n)$, we always mean *identical* equality. In particular, $f = 0$ means that f

is identically 0 and $g = 1$ means that g is identically 1. Fixed but un-specified combinations of values of the variables are referred to by Greek letters, $\xi_1, \xi_2, \ldots, \xi_n$, for example. Thus, an equation $f(\xi_1, \xi_2, \ldots, \xi_n) = g(\xi_1, \xi_2, \ldots, \xi_n)$, or, more briefly written, $f(\xi) = g(\xi)$, means that the *function values* are equal at the particular combination $\xi = (\xi_1, \xi_2, \ldots, \xi_n)$, but not necessarily at others. That is, in this case, the functions may or may not be identically equal. In particular, $f(\xi) = 0$ means that f takes on the value 0 for the particular combination $\xi_1, \xi_2, \ldots, \xi_n$ but need not necessarily be identically 0. Similarly, if $f(\xi) = 1$, the function takes on the value 1 for the particular combination $\xi_1, \xi_2, \ldots, \xi_n$ but is not necessarily identically 1.

There are some circuits for which we already know the switching functions. For a permanently open circuit, the switching function is identically 0 and, for a permanently closed circuit, the switching function is identically 1. For a circuit containing a single, normally open contact represented by the circuit variable x, the switching function is just x. Similarly, for a single, normally closed contact represented by $\bar{x}$, the switching function is $\bar{x}$ (see Figure 1.5.1).

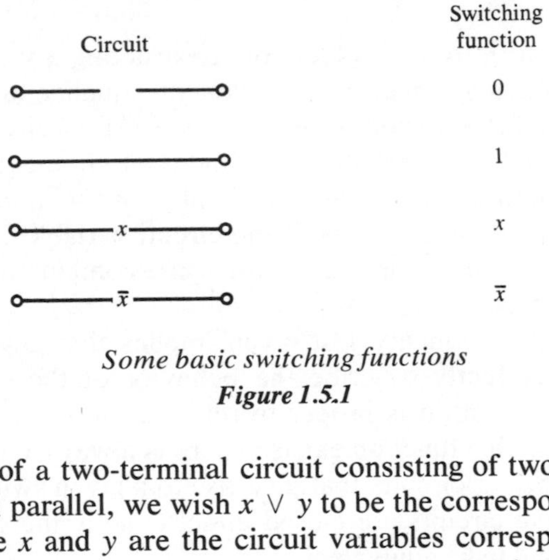

| | Switching |
Circuit	function
	0
	1
x	x
$\bar{x}$	$\bar{x}$

Some basic switching functions
Figure 1.5.1

In the case of a two-terminal circuit consisting of two contacts x and y connected in parallel, we wish $x \lor y$ to be the corresponding switching function where x and y are the circuit variables corresponding to these contacts. Now, only when $x = y = 0$ does the circuit *fail* to provide a closed path between its terminals. Hence, only when $x = y = 0$ should the switching function $x \lor y$ take on the value zero. However, if $x = 1$ and $y = 0$, or $x = 0$ and $y = 1$, or $x = y = 1$, the circuit *does* provide a closed path between its terminals and hence in all these cases the switching function $x \lor y$ should take on the value 1. For all these conditions to be satisfied, we must *define*

$$(1.5.1) \qquad 0 \lor 0 = 0, \qquad 1 \lor 0 = 0 \lor 1 = 1 \lor 1 = 1.$$

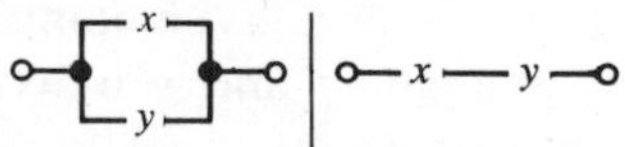

x	y	$x \lor y$	xy
0	0	0	0
0	1	1	0
1	0	1	0
1	1	1	1

Definition of OR *and* AND *operations*
Figure 1.5.2

In the case of a two-terminal circuit consisting of two contacts x and y connected in series, we wish xy to be the corresponding switching function where x and y are circuit variables representing the contacts. If $x = y = 0$, or if $x = 0$ and $y = 1$, or if $x = 1$ and $y = 0$, the circuit fails to provide a closed path and hence the switching function xy should take on the value 0 in all these cases. Only if $x = y = 1$ does the circuit provide a closed path between its terminals and hence only in this case should xy be 1. For all these conditions to be satisfied, we must define

(1.5.2) $$0 \cdot 0 = 0 \cdot 1 = 1 \cdot 0 = 0, \qquad 1 \cdot 1 = 1.$$

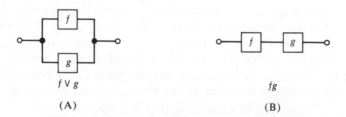

$f \lor g$

(A)

fg

(B)

Parallel and series connections of arbitrary circuits
Figure 1.5.3

These definitions are all summarized conveniently in Figure 1.5.2.

Now suppose we have two given circuits with switching functions f and g respectively and suppose the circuits are connected in parallel (Figure 1.5.3(A)). Then, just as was the case with two contacts connected in parallel, the resulting circuit is closed if either one of the two given circuits is closed or if both are closed. Hence, for exactly those combinations of values $\xi_1, \xi_2, \ldots, \xi_n$ of the circuit variables such that $f(\xi) = 1$ or $g(\xi) = 1$ or both, the switching function of the parallel circuits must take on the value 1 and therefore may be represented by the function

$f \vee g$. To evaluate $f \vee g$ at a given combination of values of the circuit variables, we first evaluate f and g individually and then compute the OR of these values by (1.5.1).

If the two circuits are connected in series (Figure 1.5.3(B)), the resulting circuit is closed only when the two given circuits are both closed. Hence, for exactly those combinations of values $\xi_1, \xi_2, \ldots, \xi_n$ of the circuit variables such that $f(\xi) = g(\xi) = 1$, the switching function of the series circuit must take on the value 1 and thus may be represented by fg. To evaluate fg at any given combination of values of the circuit variables, we multiply the individual values of f and g in accordance with (1.5.2).

We also apply the operation of complementation to arbitrary switching functions. Given a two-terminal circuit C with switching function f, its **complement** $\bar{C}$ is a circuit which is closed when C is open and open when C is closed. The switching function of $\bar{C}$ is denoted by $\bar{f}$. This is consistent with our earlier use of x and $\bar{x}$ as circuit variables to denote normally open and normally closed contacts on the same relay.

We illustrate these ideas by reference to Figure 1.2.2. Here there is a path through the circuit joining t_1 to t_2 if the x-contact *and* the y-contact are closed *or* if the $\bar{x}$-contact and the $\bar{y}$-contact are closed, that is, if $x = y = 1$ or $\bar{x} = \bar{y} = 1$. Each of these paths has two contacts in series so that their switching functions are xy and $\bar{x}\bar{y}$, respectively. The two paths are in parallel. Hence, by the principles just outlined, the switching function of the entire circuit connecting t_1 and t_2 is $xy \vee \bar{x}\bar{y}$.

In the case of the circuit joining t_3 to t_4, there is a closed path if the $\bar{x}$-contact *and* the y-contact are closed *or* if the x-contact *and* the $\bar{y}$-contact are closed, that is, if $\bar{x} = y = 1$ or $x = \bar{y} = 1$. Again, each path has two contacts in series so that their switching functions are $\bar{x}y$ and $x\bar{y}$, respectively. The two paths are in parallel (despite being twisted in the drawing) so·that the switching function of the circuit connecting t_3 and t_4 must be $\bar{x}y \vee x\bar{y}$. These results are summarized in Table 1.5.1.

Table 1.5.1
Exclusive-or and Its Complement

$x\,y$	$xy \vee \bar{x}\bar{y}$	$\bar{x}y \vee x\bar{y}$
0 0	1	0
0 1	0	1
1 0	0	1
1 1	1	0

The reader should now verify arithmetically, by substitution of values for x and y, that the functions $xy \vee \bar{x}\bar{y}$ and $\bar{x}y \vee x\bar{y}$ have indeed the values listed in the table. For example, if $x = 0$, $y = 0$, then $xy \lor \bar{x}\bar{y}$ has the value

$$0 \cdot 0 \lor \bar{0} \cdot \bar{0} = 0 \lor 1 \cdot 1 = 0 \lor 1 = 1.$$

The table shows that $xy \lor \bar{x}\bar{y}$ and $\bar{x}y \lor x\bar{y}$ always have complementary values so that each of these functions is the complement of the other. The corresponding circuits are therefore also complementary circuits.

The function $x\bar{y} \lor \bar{x}y$ is called the **exclusive-or function** since it takes on the value 1 if $x = 1$ or $y = 1$ but not when both are 1; that is, it takes on the value 1 when exclusively one or the other of the variables takes on the value 1. Its complement is the **both-or-neither function**.

1.6   The Postulates of Switching Algebra

We are now ready to let physical considerations dictate postulates governing the application of the symbols "$\lor$," "$\cdot$," and "$\bar{}$" to arbitrary switching functions. In the diagrams that follow, equivalence of circuits is denoted by the symbol "$\sim$". The symbols f, g, h denote arbitrary switching functions of n variables and include the functions 0, 1, and symbols for single contacts as special cases.

The **commutative laws:**

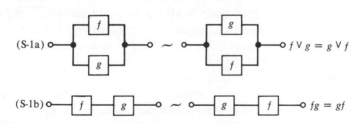

(S-1a) $\quad f \lor g = g \lor f$

(S-1b) $\quad fg = gf$

In each case, the two circuits are equivalent because their behaviors are indistinguishable. The corresponding switching functions must therefore be equal.

The **associative laws:**

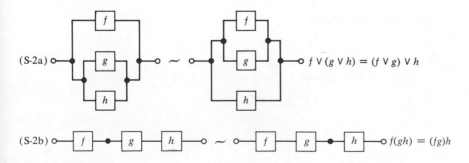

(S-2a) $\quad f \lor (g \lor h) = (f \lor g) \lor h$

(S-2b) $\quad f(gh) = (fg)h$

Here, connecting f in parallel with the parallel connection of g and h gives the same physical circuit as connecting the parallel connection of f and g in parallel with h. A similar observation holds in the series case. Because of the associative laws it is legitimate to write $f \vee g \vee h$ and fgh (*without* parentheses) as switching functions for these circuits: It does not matter whether we first combine g with f or with h in evaluating these expressions.

The **distributive laws:**

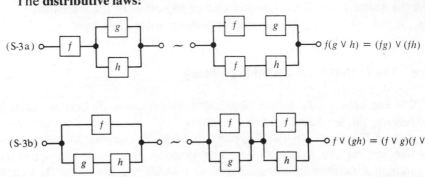

$$(\text{S-3a}) \qquad f(g \vee h) = (fg) \vee (fh)$$

$$(\text{S-3b}) \qquad f \vee (gh) = (f \vee g)(f \vee h)$$

The first of these laws says that multiplication distributes to each term of a union and the second says that union distributes to each factor in multiplication. In the first case, both circuits are closed if and only if the f-circuit is closed *and* at least one of the other two circuits is closed. In the second case, both circuits are closed if and only if the f-circuit is closed *or* both of the other two circuits are closed.

At this point let us agree that, *in the absence of parentheses, multiplication is to be performed before union.* Thus $f \vee gh$ means $f \vee (gh)$, *not* $(f \vee g)h$. This convention operates here just as does the analogous agreement in the algebra of complex numbers. It reduces the number of parentheses required to represent expressions without ambiguity. For example, the distributive laws now become

$$f(g \vee h) = fg \vee fh$$

and

$$f \vee gh = (f \vee g)(f \vee h).$$

The **idempotent laws:**

$$(\text{S-4a}) \qquad f \vee f = f$$

$$(\text{S-4b}) \qquad f \cdot f = f$$

These laws are dictated by the fact that each circuit here is closed if and only if the f-circuit is closed. "Idempotent" means "same power." These laws account for the absence of conventional exponents, and coefficients other than 0 and 1, in switching algebra.

The **laws of operation with 0 and 1:**

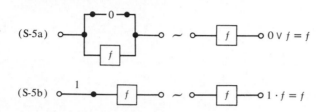

Here a gap designates a permanently open circuit (0) and a solid line designates a permanently closed circuit (1).

Note that 0 with respect to union, and 1 with respect to multiplication, are **identity elements;** that is, they leave the function f unchanged. Contrast this with the behavior of 0 in multiplication and of 1 in union:

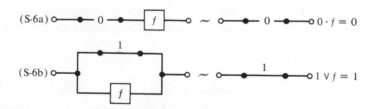

Here 0 and 1 are **dominant elements** with respect to the operations of multiplication and union, respectively; that is, when combined with any other switching function, *they* are unchanged.

The **laws of complementarity:**

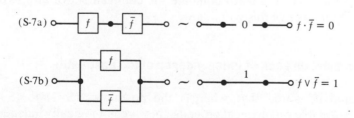

In the first case, one of the circuits corresponding to f and $\bar{f}$ is always open, whereas in the second case one of these circuits is always closed.

DeMorgan's laws:

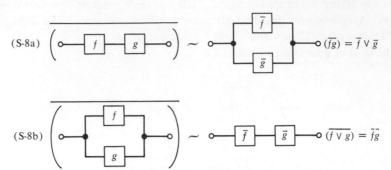

A bar drawn over a circuit denotes the complement of that circuit (see definition of the complement of a circuit in Section 1.5). The reader should check in detail that whenever a circuit drawn under a bar is closed (open), the corresponding complementary circuit shown here is open (closed) and vice versa. These laws, with (S–9), will enable us to compute the complement of an arbitrary switching function. It is well to learn these laws in verbal form:

The complement of a product is the union of the separate complements and *the complement of a union is the product of the separate complements.*

The **law of involution:**

$$(S\text{-}9) \quad \overline{\left(\text{o}\!-\!\boxed{\bar{f}}\!-\!\text{o} \right)} \;\sim\; \text{o}\!-\!\boxed{f}\!-\!\text{o} \quad \overline{(\bar{f})} = f$$

If we form the complement and then form the complement again, we recover the original function.

We shall refer to (S–8a, b) and (S–9) as the **laws of complementation** since these laws enable us to compute the complement of any switching function. Examples of this will follow.

1.7   Comment on Lack of Independence of the Postulates

It should be noted that whereas the postulates (S–1) to (S–9) all appear reasonable on physical grounds, they are not logically independent. As a first illustration of how the postulates may be used, we show how (S–3b) may be derived from other postulates of the list. Full details are given and every step should be checked.

$$(f \vee g)(f \vee h) = (f \vee g)f \vee (f \vee g)h \qquad \text{(S–3a)}$$
$$= f(f \vee g) \vee h(f \vee g) \qquad \text{(S–1b)}$$
$$= (ff \vee fg) \vee (hf \vee hg) \qquad \text{(S–3a)}$$
$$= (f \vee fg) \vee (fh \vee gh) \qquad \text{(S–4b, S–1b)}$$
$$= [(f \vee fg) \vee fh] \vee gh \qquad \text{(S–2a)}$$
$$= [f \vee (fg \vee fh)] \vee gh \qquad \text{(S–2a)}$$
$$= [f \cdot 1 \vee f(g \vee h)] \vee gh \qquad \text{(S–5b, S–1b, S–3a)}$$
$$= f[1 \vee (g \vee h)] \vee gh \qquad \text{(S–3a)}$$
$$= f \cdot 1 \vee gh \qquad \text{(S–6b)}$$
$$= f \vee gh \qquad \text{(S–1b, S–5b)}$$

In practical work, one naturally does not write out the steps in such complete detail. Just as in any other type of mathematics, one omits steps that may properly be regarded as obvious.

An independent set of postulates could have been employed here, but a formal derivation of the other postulates from an independent set is tedious and not particularly rewarding in this context.

1.8 The Principle of Duality

An important fact to note is that the above postulates, except for (S–9), appear in **dual pairs,** each member of a pair being obtainable from the other by replacing each of the operations OR and AND by the other and replacing each of the symbols 0 and 1 by the other, wherever they appear. Thus, if in (S–7a): $f \cdot \bar{f} = 0$ we replace AND by OR and 0 by 1, we obtain (S–7b): $f \vee \bar{f} = 1$. In similar fashion, we may obtain (S–7a) from (S–7b). In these simple cases, such interchanges may be interpreted as the interchange of series and parallel connections and of open and closed circuits. Postulate S–9 may be regarded as its own dual since the required interchanges leave it unaltered.

Suppose now that from our postulates we are able to derive a certain identity. Then the dual of this identity can be derived in the same manner as the original identity by employing dual statements and dual postulates at each step. That is, *we may conclude the truth of the dual identity without bothering to write out an additional proof.* This important fact, which we shall have frequent occasion to use, is known as the **principle of duality.** An illustration of dual proofs is provided by the proofs of (S–10a) and (S–10b) in Section 1.10.

Other, analogous duality principles occur frequently in mathematics. Note that we have *not* defined the dual of a function here, but have defined only the dual of an identity.

1.9 Switching Functions of Series-Parallel and of Bridge Circuits

We have used the symbols "·" and "∨", respectively, to represent the operations AND and OR and have interpreted these physically with the aid of series and parallel connections, respectively. We can build up circuits of arbitrary complexity by suitable successions of series and parallel connections. Such circuits are called **series-parallel circuits.** More precisely, we define each of the circuits in Figure 1.9.1 to be a series-parallel circuit. In this figure, a and b represent single contacts but the names of the circuit variables associated with these contacts

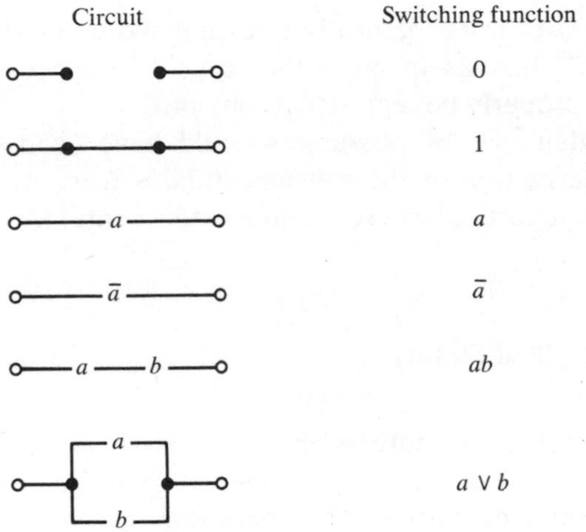

Circuit	Switching function
o—● ●—o	0
o—●——●—o	1
o———a———o	a
o———$\bar{a}$———o	$\bar{a}$
o—a——b—o	ab
(parallel a, b)	$a \vee b$

Basic series-parallel circuits
Figure 1.9.1

are, of course, arbitrary. Any circuit obtainable by substituting a known series-parallel circuit for any contact of a known series-parallel circuit is also defined to be series-parallel. Any circuit not so obtainable is called a **non-series-parallel circuit** or **bridge circuit.** The class of series-parallel circuits has been studied from a combinatorial point of view by Riordan and Shannon [3].

In Figures 1.9.2(A) and 1.9.2(B) we construct a three-contact series circuit and a three-contact parallel circuit by replacing one contact of a two-contact circuit by another two-contact circuit of the same type.

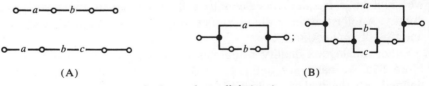

(A)   (B)

Series and parallel circuits
Figure 1.9.2

The *circles within the figures* indicate the details of the substitutions. The results in Figure 1.9.2 are used in Figure 1.9.3 to construct a more complex series-parallel circuit. In Figure 1.9.3(A) we replace the single

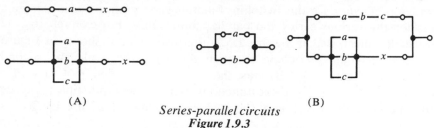

(A)

(B)

Series-parallel circuits
Figure 1.9.3

contact *a* by three contacts in parallel. In Figure 1.9.3(B) we replace the contact *a* by three contacts in series, the contact *b* by the series-parallel circuit obtained in Figure 1.9.3(A). More complex circuits can be developed in similar fashion. Of course, in every circuit, series-parallel or bridge, we represent independent contacts by distinct circuit variables, identically behaving contacts by the same circuit variable, and oppositely behaving contacts by a variable and its complement.

It should be clear at this point that any given switching function can be represented as a series-parallel circuit. One has only to represent all OR's as parallel connections and all AND's as series connections, in the manner suggested by the preceding examples.

The problem of deciding whether or not a given circuit is series-parallel is solved by reversing the synthesis procedure just illustrated. We look for a known series-parallel circuit containing at least two contacts and connecting two terminals of the given circuit. If no such series-parallel subcircuit exists, the given circuit is a bridge circuit. If such a series-parallel circuit does exist, it is replaced by any convenient single contact symbol and the same process is now applied to the reduced circuit. If at any stage the reduced circuit is series-parallel, then the original circuit is series-parallel. If at any stage the reduced circuit is a bridge circuit, then the original circuit is a bridge circuit. Thus, the circuit of Figure 1.9.4(A) is a bridge circuit, as replacement of the central series-parallel subcircuit by a single contact symbol demonstrates (Figure 1.9.4B).

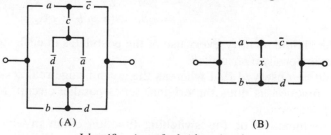

(A)

(B)

Identification of a bridge circuit
Figure 1.9.4

In most cases of importance, we can see at a glance that a circuit is or is not series-parallel.

We can write the switching function of any given series-parallel circuit without difficulty, for the switching function simply expresses in algebraic fashion the various series and parallel connections. For example, by the principles illustrated in Figure 1.5.3, the lower circuit shown in Figure 1.9.2(A) has the switching function $a \cdot (bc) = abc$ while the second circuit of Figure 1.9.2(B) has the switching function $a \lor (b \lor c) = a \lor b \lor c$. Now, using these functions and the same principles, we see that the switching function of the final circuit shown in Figure 1.9.3(B) is

$$abc \lor (a \lor b \lor c)x.$$

In the case of a bridge circuit, the AND and OR relationships of the various paths through the circuit are often less evident than they are in the series-parallel case. However, we can still write a switching function for the bridge circuit by first tracing all possible paths through it. For example, the bridge circuit of Figure 1.9.5 provides paths with switching functions ax, abc, $xbx = (xb)x = (bx)x = b(xx) = bx$, and xc between the terminals 1 and 2. Hence its switching function is

$$ax \lor abc \lor bx \lor xc.$$

However, these paths are equivalent to the paths that are provided by

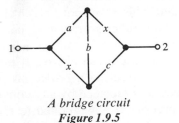

A bridge circuit
Figure 1.9.5

the series-parallel circuit of Figure 1.9.3(B), so that the two switching functions must be equal. The postulates previously listed make this clear:

$$\begin{aligned}
ax \lor abc \lor bx \lor xc &= ax \lor abc \lor bx \lor cx \\
&= abc \lor ax \lor bx \lor cx \\
&= abc \lor (a \lor b \lor c)x.
\end{aligned}$$

The reader should identify every use of the postulates in each step. Some of the uses are easily overlooked.

It should be observed that whereas the given bridge realizes the same switching function as does the original series-parallel circuit, it does so with two fewer contacts.

The determination of the switching function of an involved bridge circuit by this method of inspection can be a difficult matter. A systematic but often tedious method is given later in this chapter (Section 1.19). Another method employs matrices whose elements are switching functions [4], [5].

The general class of circuits for which a switching function may be written is represented diagrammatically in Figure 1.9.6. In this circuit the "load" might be a light, a bell, or the coil of another relay, and so on. In this figure, the box is assumed to contain all the contacts of the circuit. These we represent by $x_1, x_2, \ldots, x_n$ and their complements. The contacts are to be operated by the corresponding electromagnets $X_1, X_2, \ldots, X_n$, which are controlled from outside the box. In this case, after the brief time it takes for the magnets to move the contacts, the open or closed condition of the path between the power supply and the load depends

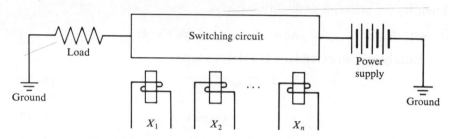

Schematic diagram of a combinational relay circuit

Figure 1.9.6

only on the particular combination of the relays $X_1, X_2, \ldots, X_n$ which are operated. Thus, the open or closed condition of the path ultimately depends only on the combination of values taken on by the circuit variables $x_1, x_2, \ldots, x_n$. Such a circuit is what we have already called a **combinational circuit.** We can always write a switching function $f(x_1, x_2, \ldots, x_n)$ for such a combinational circuit, using only the operations "$\cdot$," "$\vee$," and "$\overline{}$." Systematic ways of doing this have been referred to earlier. However, in many cases of interest, the function may be written by simple inspection, as preceding examples suggest.

1.10   Some Useful Identities

The number of formal Boolean identities that may be derived from (S–1) through (S–9) is unlimited. However, only a few types of these identities are of major usefulness. All such identities may be established by algebraic manipulations or by what is sometimes called **perfect induction,** that is, by checking the correctness of the identity for all possible combinations of values of the variables involved, namely, for all combinations of 0's and 1's. Often such identities are suggested by network considerations. Others have a purely algebraic origin.

We show first how some of the postulates may be extended. Consider the distributive laws. We have

$$f(g \lor h \lor k) = f[g \lor (h \lor k)] \qquad \text{(S-2a)}$$
$$= fg \lor f(h \lor k) \qquad \text{(S-3a)}$$
$$= fg \lor (fh \lor fk) \qquad \text{(S-3a)}$$

so that, finally,

(S-3c) $\qquad\qquad f(g \lor h \lor k) = fg \lor fh \lor fk.$ $\qquad$ (S-2a)

Then, by the principle of duality, we have

(S-3d) $\qquad\qquad f \lor ghk = (f \lor g)(f \lor h)(f \lor k).$

Similarly we can extend the DeMorgan laws:

$$\overline{f \lor g \lor h} = \overline{f \lor (g \lor h)} \qquad \text{(S-2a)}$$
$$= \bar{f} \cdot \overline{g \lor h} \qquad \text{(S-8b)}$$
$$= \bar{f} \cdot (\bar{g}\bar{h}) \qquad \text{(S-8b)}$$

so that, finally,

(S-8c) $\qquad\qquad \overline{f \lor g \lor h} = \bar{f}\bar{g}\bar{h}.$ $\qquad$ (S-2b)

Again, by duality,

(S-8d) $\qquad\qquad \overline{fgh} = \bar{f} \lor \bar{g} \lor \bar{h}.$

It is clear that these laws can be extended to an arbitrary number of functions (see Exercise 4, Section 1.13).

We now turn to six identities that are often used in simplifying switching functions. The first of these **absorption laws** is

(S-10a) $\qquad\qquad f \lor fg = f.$

This is proved algebraically with the aid of (S-5b), (S-1b), (S-3a), and (S-6b) as follows:

$$f \lor fg = 1 \cdot f \lor fg \qquad \text{(S-5b)}$$
$$= f \cdot 1 \lor fg \qquad \text{(S-1b)}$$
$$= f(1 \lor g) \qquad \text{(S-3a)}$$
$$= f \cdot 1 \qquad \text{(S-6b)}$$
$$= 1 \cdot f \qquad \text{(S-1b)}$$
$$= f. \qquad \text{(S-5b)}$$

Alternatively, we have the readily computed values of Table 1.10.1.

Table 1.10.1

f g	fg	$f \vee fg$
0 0	0	0
0 1	0	0
1 0	0	1
1 1	1	1

Since the first and fourth columns have the same entries for all combinations of values of f and g, and hence for all combinations of values of the variables of which f and g are functions, we conclude by perfect induction that $f \vee fg = f$.

Finally, the circuits in Figure 1.10.1 are both closed when and only when f takes on the value 1. That is, $f \vee fg = f$.

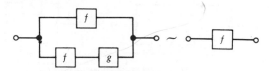

Circuit equivalent of S–10a

Figure 1.10.1

The dual of (S–10a) is

(S–10b) $$f(f \vee g) = f.$$

By the principle of duality, no proof is required, but to illustrate the principle more fully, let us write the step-by-step dual of the preceding proof:

$$
\begin{aligned}
f(f \vee g) &= (0 \vee f)(f \vee g) & \text{(S–5a)}\\
&= (f \vee 0)(f \vee g) & \text{(S–1a)}\\
&= f \vee 0 \cdot g & \text{(S–3b)}\\
&= f \vee 0 & \text{(S–6a)}\\
&= 0 \vee f & \text{(S–1a)}\\
&= f. & \text{(S–5a)}
\end{aligned}
$$

Another extremely useful identity is

(S–11a) $$f \vee \bar{f}g = f \vee g.$$

Here we have

$$
\begin{aligned}
f \vee \bar{f}g &= (f \vee \bar{f})(f \vee g) & \text{(S–3b)}\\
&= 1 \cdot (f \vee g) & \text{(S–7b)}\\
&= f \vee g. & \text{(S–5b)}
\end{aligned}
$$

The proof by perfect induction is accomplished by Table 1.10.2.

Table 1.10.2

f	g	$\bar{f}$	$\bar{f}g$	$f \vee \bar{f}g$	$f \vee g$
0	0	1	0	0	0
0	1	1	1	1	1
1	0	0	0	1	1
1	1	0	0	1	1

The identity also makes sense physically, as Figure 1.10.2 suggests. In fact, when f takes on the value 1, each circuit is closed regardless of the value of g. When f takes on the value 0, then $\bar{f}$ takes on the value 1, and each circuit is now closed only when g assumes the value 1.

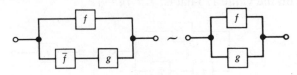

Circuit equivalent of S–11a
Figure 1.10.2

Thus the circuits are closed under precisely the same conditions and hence are equivalent. Therefore they have equal switching functions, that is, $f \vee \bar{f}g = f \vee g$.

The dual of (S–11a) is

(S–11b) $f(\bar{f} \vee g) = fg.$

Two more useful identities are

(S–12a) $(f \vee g)(\bar{f} \vee h)(g \vee h) = (f \vee g)(\bar{f} \vee h)$

and its dual

(S–12b) $fg \vee \bar{f}h \vee gh = fg \vee \bar{f}h.$

We have, in fact,

$(f \vee g)(\bar{f} \vee h)(g \vee h) = (f \vee g)(\bar{f} \vee h)[f\bar{f} \vee (g \vee h)]$ (S–7a, 5a)

$= (f \vee g)(\bar{f} \vee h)[f \vee (g \vee h)][\bar{f} \vee (g \vee h)]$

(S–1a, 3b)

$= (f \vee g)[(f \vee g) \vee h] \cdot (\bar{f} \vee h)[(\bar{f} \vee h) \vee g]$

(S–1a, b; S–2a)

$= (f \vee g) \cdot (\bar{f} \vee h).$ (S–2b, S–10b

The reader should prove (S–12b) by the dual argument, that is, by first replacing the term gh by the equal term $(f \vee \bar{f})gh$. The trick of making use of a redundant zero term $(f\bar{f})$ or of a redundant unit factor $(f \vee \bar{f})$ is often useful.

Another proof, longer but employing different devices, is the following:

$$(f \vee g)(\bar{f} \vee h)(g \vee h) = (f \vee g)(g \vee h) \cdot (\bar{f} \vee h)(g \vee h) \qquad \text{(S–1b, 4b)}$$
$$= (g \vee fh)(h \vee \bar{f}g) \qquad \text{(S–1a, 3b)}$$
$$= fh \vee \bar{f}g \vee gh \qquad \text{(S–1a, b; 3a)}$$
$$= fh \vee \bar{f}g \vee gh \vee f\bar{f} \qquad \text{(S–5a, 7a)}$$
$$= f(h \vee \bar{f}) \vee g(\bar{f} \vee h) \qquad \text{(S–1a, b; 3a)}$$

where only the main reasons are listed. Thus, as before,

$$(f \vee g)(\bar{f} \vee h)(g \vee h) = (f \vee g)(\bar{f} \vee h). \qquad \text{(S–1a, b; 3a)}$$

From the third and sixth lines of the preceding proof we have

$$fh \vee \bar{f}g \vee gh = (f \vee g)(\bar{f} \vee h)$$

so that

$$fh \vee \bar{f}g \vee gh = (f \vee \bar{f}g)(\bar{f} \vee fh) \qquad \text{(S–11a)}$$
$$= fh \vee \bar{f}g. \qquad \text{(S–3a)}$$

Now, exchanging g and h in the first and last members, we obtain (S–12b) again:

$$fg \vee \bar{f}h \vee gh = fg \vee \bar{f}h.$$

As the proofs of S–12a and S–12b suggest, there are often various distinct, correct ways of proving a given identity.

1.11   Concerning Identity Elements, Inverses, and Cancellation

It is an important though simple fact that the identity elements 0 and 1 are *unique*. That is, $f \vee 0 = f$ for all switching functions f, and 0 is the only function that has this property. Similarly, $f \cdot 1 = f$ for all switching functions f, and 1 is the only function that has this property. Indeed, suppose that g is any function such that $f \vee g = f$ for *all f*. Then this relation holds in particular for the function $f = 0$: $0 \vee g = 0$, so $g = 0$. Similarly, if h is any function such that $f \cdot h = f$ for *all f*, then in particular for the function $f = 1$, we have $1 \cdot h = 1$ so that $h = 1$. This proves that the identity elements are unique.

Once one has identity elements, a natural procedure is to search for inverses. Indeed, our experience with negatives, reciprocals, and so on, suggests that inverses should be particularly useful, if they exist. Suppose then that g is an inverse of f with respect to the OR-operation, so that (since 0 is the identity element with respect to the OR-operation), $f \vee g = 0$. Then $f(f \vee g) = f \cdot 0$, or, by (S–10b), $f = 0$, and hence also $g = 0$. Thus 0 is the only switching function that has an inverse with respect to the OR-operation and it is in fact its own inverse: $0 \vee 0 = 0$. Similarly, suppose that h is a multiplicative inverse of f, so that $fh = 1$. Then $f \vee fh = f \vee 1$ or, by (S–10a), $f = 1$, and hence also $h = 1$. Thus 1 is the only switching function that has an inverse with respect to the AND-operation, and it is in fact its own inverse: $1 \cdot 1 = 1$. Our search for inverses is quickly ended: only these two trivial inverses exist.

Now, cancellation is always equivalent to operation with an inverse. For example, when – in the algebra of complex numbers – we conclude from $x + a = b + a$ that $x = b$, we really add a-inverse to each member. Since we have only trivial inverses in switching algebra, we cannot cancel in a manner analogous to that used in the algebra of complex numbers. Thus, since there exists no OR-inverse in general, the identity $f \vee fg = f \vee 0$ does *not* imply an identity $fg = 0$ by cancellation of the term f. Indeed, there may well be combinations at which fg assumes the value 1. Similarly, since there exists no AND-inverse in general, the identity $f(f \vee g) = f \cdot 1$ does *not* imply an identity $f \vee g = 1$, for now there may well be combinations at which $f \vee g$ assumes the value 0. In summary, *there is no cancellation law for either union or multiplication in switching algebra.*

A somewhat subtle question remains. Since 0 is the *unique* element such that $f \vee 0 = f$ for all f, and since $f \vee fg = f$ for all f, should not $f \vee fg = f$ imply after all that $fg = 0$? The answer is, of course, still "No." The point is that in the condition $f \vee 0 = f$, the function f is completely arbitrary, but the identity element 0 is a fixed function. In the identity $f \vee fg = f$, f is still arbitrary, as is also g, but the function fg *varies with* f. Thus we do not have in fg a *fixed* function that can serve as an identity element for all f. The analogous dual question is settled in a similar way.

There are, of course, times when we need to remove a certain function from some expression. Even though there are no inverses to accomplish this, the removal can often be effected by appropriate use of the laws of complementarity: $f \vee \bar{f} = 1$, $f\bar{f} = 0$.

By way of illustration, suppose we wish to solve the equation

(1.11.1) $$f h \vee \bar{f} h = g,$$

where f and g are given functions, for the unknown function h. First we multiply (1.11.1) by $\bar{f}$ and obtain, since $f\bar{f} = 0$,

(1.11.2) $$\bar{f} h = \bar{f} g.$$

This eliminates $\bar{h}$ from the equation, but we cannot cancel the common factor $\bar{f}$. Instead, by complementation in the equation (1.11.1) we obtain (see Table 1.5.1)

(1.11.3) $$ fh \vee \bar{f}\bar{h} = \bar{g}. $$

Next we multiply (1.11.3) by f and obtain

(1.11.4) $$ fh = f\bar{g}, $$

which is also free of $\bar{h}$. Finally we form the unions of corresponding members of (1.11.2) and (1.11.4) so that we can use the fact that $f \vee \bar{f} = 1$:

$$ fh \vee \bar{f}h = f\bar{g} \vee \bar{f}g, $$
$$ (f \vee \bar{f})h = f\bar{g} \vee \bar{f}g, $$
(1.11.5) $$ h = f\bar{g} \vee \bar{f}g. $$

Now the expression (1.11.5) is obtained on the tacit assumption that (1.11.1) has a solution for h, which may or may not be true. All we have shown is that *if there is a solution, (1.11.5) is it.* Moreover, in obtaining (1.11.5) we have performed several irreversible operations, so that (1.11.5) might well be an "extraneous solution," that is, *no* solution of (1.11.1). Hence we must substitute (1.11.5) in (1.11.1) to determine whether or not we actually have a solution. We have

$$ f\bar{h} \vee \bar{f}h = f(\overline{f\bar{g} \vee \bar{f}g}) \vee \bar{f}(f\bar{g} \vee \bar{f}g) = f\bar{g} \vee \bar{f}g = (f \vee \bar{f})g = g. $$

Thus we have indeed a solution.

It can easily occur that an apparent solution of a Boolean equation is not a solution at all, as the final checking process will reveal. (For an example, see Exercise 31, Section 1.13.)

1.12   Applications of the Identities

We now give several examples to illustrate how identities are used. Consider first the simplification of a series-parallel circuit whose switching function is

$$ f = abc \vee a\bar{b}c \vee \bar{a}\bar{b}c. $$

We have

$$ f = c(ab \vee a\bar{b} \vee \bar{a}\bar{b}) $$
$$ = c[a(b \vee \bar{b}) \vee \bar{a}\bar{b}] $$
$$ = c(a \vee \bar{a}\bar{b}) = c(a \vee \bar{b}). \qquad \text{(S–11a)} $$

The circuits are shown in Figure 1.12.1. The simplification saves six

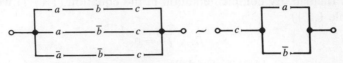

An example of circuit simplification
Figure 1.12.1

contacts. An important thing to notice is that the series-parallel circuit corresponding to $c(a \lor \bar{b})$ is simpler than that corresponding to $ca \lor c\bar{b}$ since one less c-contact is indicated. In the case of a complicated function, it is not always easy to discover the factorizations which are simplest from the point of view of "hardware."

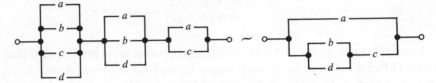

Another example of circuit simplification
Figure 1.12.2

As another example, consider the first circuit of Figure 1.12.2. Its switching function is

$$f = (a \lor b \lor c \lor d)(a \lor b \lor d)(a \lor c).$$

With the aid of (S–3b) and (S–10b) this may be reduced to

$$f = a \lor (b \lor c \lor d)(b \lor d)c$$
$$= a \lor c[c \lor (b \lor d)] \cdot (b \lor d)$$
$$= a \lor c(b \lor d)$$

and the circuit corresponding to this last form has five fewer contacts than the original circuit does.

The use of the complement of a function is at times helpful in solving a problem. For example, let it be required to factor $x\bar{y} \lor \bar{x}y$ into a product of two factors. We have, by the DeMorgan laws,

$$(\overline{x\bar{y} \lor \bar{x}y}) = (\overline{x\bar{y}}) \cdot (\overline{\bar{x}y}) = (\bar{x} \lor y)(x \lor \bar{y}) = \bar{x}\bar{y} \lor xy.$$

Taking complements of the first and last members, we have

(1.12.1) $$x\bar{y} \lor \bar{x}y = \overline{(\bar{x}\bar{y})} \cdot \overline{(xy)} = (x \lor y)(\bar{x} \lor \bar{y}).$$

In exactly the same way, we find

(1.12.2) $$xy \lor \bar{x}\bar{y} = (x \lor \bar{y})(\bar{x} \lor y).$$

These two factored forms are often useful. Note that the second may be obtained from the first simply by interchanging y and $\bar{y}$ throughout, or by the principle of duality.

Similarly, we can factor $x\bar{y} \vee y\bar{z} \vee z\bar{x}$ as follows:

$$\overline{(x\bar{y} \vee y\bar{z} \vee z\bar{x})} = (\bar{x} \vee y)(\bar{y} \vee z)(\bar{z} \vee x)$$
$$= \bar{x}\bar{y}\bar{z} \vee xyz.$$

Hence

$$x\bar{y} \vee y\bar{z} \vee z\bar{x} = \overline{(\bar{x}\bar{y}\bar{z} \vee xyz)}$$
$$= (x \vee y \vee z)\overline{xyz}$$
$$= (x \vee y \vee z)(\bar{x} \vee \bar{y} \vee \bar{z}).$$

A different type of factoring problem is illustrated by the following example:

$$x_1x_2x_3 \vee x_1x_3x_4x_5 \vee x_1x_2x_4x_6 \vee x_4x_5x_6$$
$$= x_1x_3(x_2 \vee x_4x_5) \vee x_4x_6(x_1x_2 \vee x_5).$$

After this first step, it looks as though we are through. However, the two factors in parentheses resemble each other closely. A factor x_1 in the first term of the first of these factors and a factor x_4 in the second term of the second of these factors would make them alike. Could such factors be inserted? If we *do* insert them and expand, then, because of the idempotent law, the original function is obtained. This suggests that we should proceed as follows:

$$x_1x_2x_3 \vee x_1x_3x_4x_5 \vee x_1x_2x_4x_6 \vee x_4x_5x_6$$
$$= x_1x_3{\cdot}x_1x_2 \vee x_1x_3{\cdot}x_4x_5 \vee x_1x_2{\cdot}x_4x_6 \vee x_4x_5{\cdot}x_4x_6$$
$$= x_1x_3(x_1x_2 \vee x_4x_5) \vee x_4x_6(x_1x_2 \vee x_4x_5)$$
$$= (x_1x_3 \vee x_4x_6)(x_1x_2 \vee x_4x_5).$$

This expression would lead to a circuit with eight contacts whereas the original, incomplete factorization would lead to a circuit with ten contacts.

Factors that are legitimate, like the extra factors x_1 and x_4 inserted in the first and fourth terms above, but not necessary for the correct representation of the function, are called **redundant factors.** Similarly, there are **redundant terms.** For example, in $f \vee \bar{f}g, \bar{f}$ is a redundant factor while in $f \vee fg, fg$ is a redundant term. An extreme example of the introduction of redundant terms is the following:

$$x\bar{y} \vee y\bar{z} \vee z\bar{x} = x\bar{y} \vee y\bar{z} \vee z\bar{x} \vee \bar{x}y \vee \bar{y}z \vee x\bar{z} \qquad \text{by (S-12b)}$$
$$= x\bar{x} \vee x\bar{y} \vee x\bar{z} \vee y\bar{x} \vee y\bar{y} \vee y\bar{z} \vee z\bar{x} \vee z\bar{y} \vee z\bar{z}$$
$$= x(\bar{x} \vee \bar{y} \vee \bar{z}) \vee y(\bar{x} \vee \bar{y} \vee \bar{z}) \vee z(\bar{x} \vee \bar{y} \vee \bar{z})$$
$$= (x \vee y \vee z)(\bar{x} \vee \bar{y} \vee \bar{z})$$
$$= (x \vee y \vee z) \cdot (\overline{xyz}),$$

a result that was obtained earlier by complementation.

We emphasize in conclusion that the identities (S–1) through (S–12) and any others we may derive, such as (1.12.1) and (1.12.2), for example, apply just as well to arbitrary switching functions as to individual circuit variables. This observation is illustrated by many of the preceding examples and will be used frequently in what follows. It is particularly important to learn to recognize a basic identity, even when it is disguised by the functions to which it applies. The following exercises provide opportunities for developing this skill.

1.13   Exercises

Throughout this book, exercises marked with an asterisk (*) develop an important part of the theory and should not be overlooked.

1.   Prove the following identities:

*(a) $fg \vee f\bar{g} = f$,
*(b) $(f \vee g)(\bar{f} \vee g) = g$,
*(c) $fg \vee \bar{f}g \vee f\bar{g} \vee \bar{f}\bar{g} = 1$,
*(d) $(f \vee g)(\bar{f} \vee g)(f \vee \bar{g})(\bar{f} \vee \bar{g}) = 0$,
 (e) $(a \vee b \vee c)(abc \vee x) = abc \vee (a \vee b \vee c)x$,
 (f) $ab \vee bc \vee ca = (a \vee b)(b \vee c)(c \vee a)$,
*(g) $fg(h \vee k) = fg(fh \vee gk)$.

2.   Prove the following identities:

*(a) $(f \vee g)(\bar{f} \vee h) = fh \vee \bar{f}g$,
 (b) $x\bar{y} \vee z(\bar{x} \vee y \vee w) = z \vee x\bar{y}$,
 (c) $x\bar{y}w \vee \bar{x}yz = (xw \vee yz)(\bar{x} \vee \bar{y})$
            $= (x \vee y)(\bar{x}z \vee \bar{y}w)$,
 (d) $(x \vee \bar{y})(\bar{x} \vee y)(x \vee z) = (x \vee \bar{y})(\bar{x} \vee y)(y \vee z)$,
 (e) $(x \vee \bar{y})(y \vee \bar{z})(z \vee \bar{x}) = (\bar{x} \vee y)(\bar{y} \vee z)(\bar{z} \vee x)$,
 (f) $(\bar{x}y \vee z) \cdot (\bar{x} \vee z) \vee (\bar{x}y \vee z)(\bar{x} \vee z) = x \vee y \vee z$,
*(g) $(f \vee g)(f \vee gh) = f \vee gh$.

3.   Write the duals of the identities in the two preceding exercises.

*4.   Prove by induction the following generalizations of (S–3a), (S–3b), (S–8a), and (S–8b):

(a) $f\left(\bigvee_{j=1}^{n} g_j\right) = \bigvee_{j=1}^{n}(fg_j)$,   (b) $f \vee \left(\prod_{j=1}^{n} g_j\right) = \prod_{j=1}^{n}(f \vee g_j)$,

(c) $\left(\overline{\prod_{j=1}^{n} f_j}\right) = \bigvee_{j=1}^{n}\bar{f}_j$,   (d) $\left(\overline{\bigvee_{j=1}^{n} f_j}\right) = \prod_{j=1}^{n}\bar{f}_j$.

In these formulas $\overset{n}{\underset{j=1}{\vee}} g_j$ is an abbreviation for the union $g_1 \vee g_2 \vee \cdots \vee g_n$ and $\overset{n}{\underset{j=1}{\Pi}} g_j$ is an abbreviation for the product $g_1 g_2 \cdots g_n$, and so on. These generalizations will be used in what follows.

5.   Give three examples of switching functions f and g, neither of which is the function zero, but such that their product is identically zero. For example, $x\bar{x} = 0$, but neither x nor $\bar{x}$ is the function zero. For your examples, find functions f and g which are *not* complements of each other.

6.   Show by examples (three distinct types in each case) that one may have identities

$$\text{(a)}\quad f \vee h = g \vee h \quad \text{where} \quad h \neq 1, f \neq g,$$

and

$$\text{(b)}\quad fk = gk \quad\quad \text{where} \quad k \neq 0, f \neq g.$$

Here, f, g, h, k may, if you wish, be chosen as specific switching functions of any convenient number of circuit variables. See (S–10) for some ideas.

7.   (a)   Factor each of the following into a product of two factors by introducing redundant expressions:

(i) $x_1 x_2 \bar{x}_3 \vee x_1 \bar{x}_3 \bar{x}_5 x_6 \vee x_1 x_2 x_4 \vee x_2 x_4 \bar{x}_5 x_6,$

(ii) $x_1 x_2 x_3 \vee x_1 x_2 x_4 x_5 \vee x_2 x_3 x_4 \vee x_1 x_3 x_4 x_5.$

(b)   Factor in three different ways into a product of two factors, in no case using more than six variable symbols:

$$x_1 x_2 x_3 \vee \bar{x}_1 \bar{x}_2 x_4.$$

Compare the circuits corresponding to the original and factored forms. Generalize, factoring so that transfer contacts are used as extensively as possible. (See page 50, Figure 1.19.3.)

8.   Compute the complements of the following functions and *then* simplify. The results of Exercises 4(c) and 4(d) are needed here.

(a) $(x \vee \bar{y}z)(\overline{xyz}),$

(b) $x\bar{y} \vee y\bar{z} \vee z\bar{x},$

(c) $(x \vee \bar{y}\bar{z})(y \vee \bar{z}\bar{x})(z \vee \bar{x}\bar{y}),$

(d) $x \vee yz \vee \bar{x} \cdot \bar{y}\bar{z}.$

9.   Prove the following identities with the aid of (S–12):

(a) $\bar{w}z \vee wx \vee \bar{x}\bar{z} = xz \vee \bar{x}\bar{z} \vee xw \vee \bar{x}\bar{w},$

(b) $x\bar{y} \vee \bar{x}y \vee y\bar{z} \vee \bar{y}z = x\bar{y} \vee y\bar{z} \vee z\bar{x}$

$$= \bar{x}y \vee \bar{y}z \vee \bar{z}x,$$

(c) $xz \vee \bar{x}\bar{z} \vee wy \vee \bar{w}\bar{y} \vee \bar{w}\bar{z}$

$$= xz \vee \bar{x}\bar{z} \vee wy \vee \bar{w}\bar{y} \vee xy$$
$$= xz \vee \bar{x}\bar{z} \vee wy \vee \bar{w}\bar{y} \vee \bar{w}x$$
$$= xz \vee \bar{x}\bar{z} \vee wy \vee \bar{w}\bar{y} \vee \bar{z}y,$$

(d) $(f \vee g \vee h)(f \vee h \vee \bar{k})(g \vee k) = (f \vee h \vee \bar{k})(g \vee k).$

10. Why is the circuit in Figure 1.13.1 in fact series-parallel even though it appears to be a bridge?

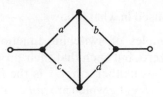

A series-parallel circuit
Figure 1.13.1

11. Prove by induction that the circuits shown in Figure 1.13.2 are series-parallel.

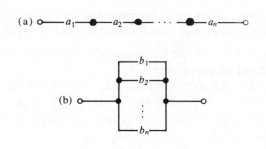

Series-parallel circuits
Figure 1.13.2

Then prove that the circuit of Figure 1.13.3 is series parallel.

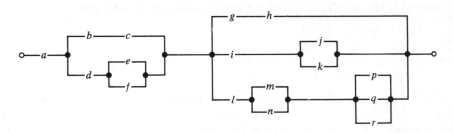

A series-parallel circuit
Figure 1.13.3

12. Show that if f and g are switching functions for arbitrary combinational circuits, then the circuit of Figure 1.13.4(A) is always closed. Under what conditions is the circuit of Figure 1.13.4(B) closed?

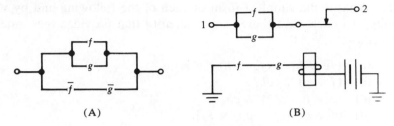

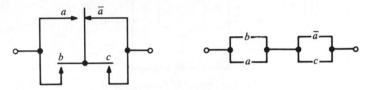

(A)   (B)

Circuits to be analyzed
Figure 1.13.4

13. Write and compare switching functions for the circuits of Figure 1.13.5.

Circuits to be compared
Figure 1.13.5

14. Write and simplify switching functions for the circuits of Figure 1.13.6, then sketch the simplified circuits. In each problem, the minimum possible number of contacts should be sought.

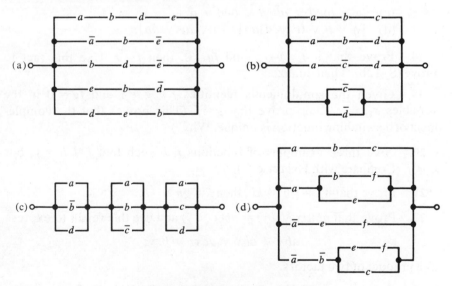

Series-parallel circuit to be simplified
Figure 1.13.6

15. What is the simplest form of each of the following and by what identity? In each case there is one identity that provides the principal explanation.

(a) $(fg \lor h) \lor (fg \lor h)(r \lor st)$,
(b) $(f \lor g) \lor \bar{f}\bar{g}h$,
(c) $fg \lor \bar{f}(\bar{g} \lor h) \lor gh$,
(d) $(f \lor gh)[(f \lor gh) \lor rs]$.

16. Write and simplify the switching function for the bridge circuit of Figure 1.13.7. Then draw the simplified network.

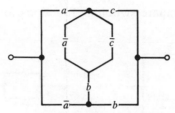

Bridge circuit to be simplified
Figure 1.13.7

17. Obtain the simplest possible relay circuits corresponding to these switching functions:

(a) $(x_1 \lor x_3 \lor x_4)(x_2 \lor x_3 \lor x_4)(x_1 \lor x_5)(x_2 \lor x_5)$,
(b) $x(\bar{z}w \lor x \lor \bar{y}) \lor \bar{x}(z \lor \bar{w})(\bar{x} \lor y)$,
(c) $(a \lor \bar{b})\bar{c}d \lor ab\bar{c}\bar{d} \lor b\bar{c}d \lor \bar{a}$,
(d) $[\bar{a} \lor \bar{b} \lor (c \lor d)ab] \cdot [b \lor ae \lor \bar{a}\bar{b}]$.

18. Prove that if $f \lor g = g$ and $\bar{f}g = 0$, then $f = g$. Use this fact to prove (S–12b). Then dualize.

19. Given the simultaneous identities $f \lor g = 1$ and $fg = 0$ in the variables $x_1, x_2, \ldots, x_n$, prove that $g = \bar{f}$. (This proves that the complement of a switching function is unique. Why?)

20. Give three examples of functions f, h such that $f \lor h = 1$, but $h \neq \bar{f}$. (Compare with Exercise 5.)

*21. Prove that if $f = gh \lor k\bar{h}$, then $\bar{f} = \bar{g}h \lor \bar{k}\bar{h}$.

22. Prove that $ab(ax \lor by) = ab(x \lor y)$ and use this result to express

$$abx \lor aby \lor acxz \lor bcyz$$

as a product of two factors.

23. Prove that $f = g$ if and only if $f\bar{g} \lor \bar{f}g = 0$. (*Hint:* Define $\phi = f\bar{g} \lor \bar{f}g$ and form the function $f\bar{\phi} \lor \bar{f}\phi$.)

24. Given f, g, h, prove that there exists a switching function θ such that

$$f = g\theta \vee h\theta$$

if and only if

$$gh\bar{f} \vee \bar{g}\bar{h}f = 0.$$

25. Given that

$$\begin{aligned} gh\bar{f} \vee \bar{g}\bar{h}f &= 0, \\ hk\bar{f} \vee \bar{h}\bar{k}f &= 0, \\ gk\bar{f} \vee \bar{g}\bar{k}f &= 0, \end{aligned}$$

prove that

$$f = gh \vee hk \vee kg.$$

26. Prove the identities (two lines suffice for each proof):

  (a) $f(x_1, x_2, \ldots, x_n) = \bar{x}_1 f(0, x_2, \ldots, x_n) \vee x_1 f(1, x_2, \ldots, x_n)$,

  (b) $f(x_1, x_2, \ldots, x_n) = [\bar{x}_1 \vee f(1, x_2, \ldots, x_n)] \cdot [x_1 \vee f(0, x_2, \ldots, x_n)]$.

Then apply the same principles to x_2 in $f(0, x_2, \ldots, x_n)$ and $f(1, x_2, \ldots, x_n)$ and obtain analogous expansions involving both x_1 and x_2.

27. Prove the identities

$$\begin{aligned} x_1 \cdot f(x_1, x_2, \ldots, x_n) &= x_1 \cdot f(1, x_2, \ldots, x_n) \\ \bar{x}_1 \cdot f(x_1, x_2, \ldots, x_n) &= \bar{x}_1 \cdot f(0, x_2, \ldots, x_n) \\ x_1 \vee f(x_1, x_2, \ldots, x_n) &= x_1 \vee f(0, x_2, \ldots, x_n) \\ \bar{x}_1 \vee f(x_1, x_2, \ldots, x_n) &= \bar{x}_1 \vee f(1, x_2, \ldots, x_n) \end{aligned}$$

and interpret them in terms of circuits. Then generalize them to 2, 3, $\ldots$, n variables and use the results to solve Exercise 26.

28. Denote the exclusive-or operation by "$\oplus$," that is, define

$$f \oplus g = f\bar{g} \vee \bar{f}g.$$

Then prove, algebraically, the following:

  (a) $f \oplus g = g \oplus f$,

  (b) $f \oplus (g \oplus h) = (f \oplus g) \oplus h$,

  (c) $f(g \oplus h) = fg \oplus fh$,

  (d) $f \oplus 0 = f$,

  (e) $f \oplus 1 = \bar{f}$,

  (f) $f \oplus f = 0$,

  (g) $f \oplus g \oplus fg = f \vee g$.

  (h) The solution for x of $x \oplus a = b$ is $a \oplus b$.

  (i) $f = g$ if and only if $f \oplus g = 0$.

29. (a) Let f, g, h be switching functions of n variables. Given *fixed* functions f and g such that $fh = gh$ for all switching functions h, prove that $f = g$.

(b)   Given that $f(x_1 \cdots x_n) \cdot x_j = g(x_1,\ldots, x_n) \cdot x_j$ for all values of x_j, show by an example that it does *not* necessarily follow that $f = g$. Under what conditions on f and g could we conclude $f = g$? (j is fixed.)

What is the simplest difference between (a) and (b) that accounts for the different conclusions?

30.   Design a circuit in which the operation of a relay X will switch the connection of two impedances (loads) from series to parallel. The relay contacts may be used as part of the path for the current through these impedances. (See Figure 1.13.8.)

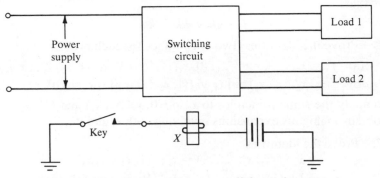

Schematic diagram for series-to-parallel switching circuit

Figure 1.13.8

31.   Show that the equation $fh = \bar{f} \lor g$, in which f and g are regarded as given functions, can be solved for h if and only if $f = 1$, in which case the result is trivial.

Order Relations in Switching Theory

1.14   The Relations of Inclusion and Less-Than-or-Equal-To

In order to complete our mathematical model of combinational switching circuits, we introduce the relation of **inclusion**. Let $f_1(x_1, x_2, \ldots, x_n)$ and $f_2(x_1, x_2, \ldots, x_n)$ be switching functions associated with two-terminal combinational circuits S_1 and S_2. If S_1 is never closed unless S_2 is also closed, we shall say that S_1 is **included** in S_2. This does not mean that the wiring diagram of S_1 is apparent in that of S_2. Rather it means that the ability of S_1 to close a path between its terminals for certain combinations of relays operated is possessed also by S_2, so that S_2 includes *the circuit-closing ability of S_1*.

If S_1 is included in this sense in S_2, then for every combination at which the value of f_1 is 1, the value of f_2 must be 1 also. However, the value of f_2 may well be 1 for some combinations at which the value of f_1 is 0. When f_1 and f_2 are related in this way, we write $f_1 \leqslant f_2$ or $f_2 \geqslant f_1$, reading the symbols "f_1 is **less than or equal to** f_2" and "f_2 is **equal to or greater than** f_1," respectively.

These definitions are illustrated by the circuits shown in Figure 1.14.1. Here S_1 is included in S_2 because if S_1 is closed, so is S_2. Moreover, $f_1 \leqslant f_2$ because, if f_1 has the value 1, then $x_1 = x_2 = 1$, so that the value of f_2 is 1 also.

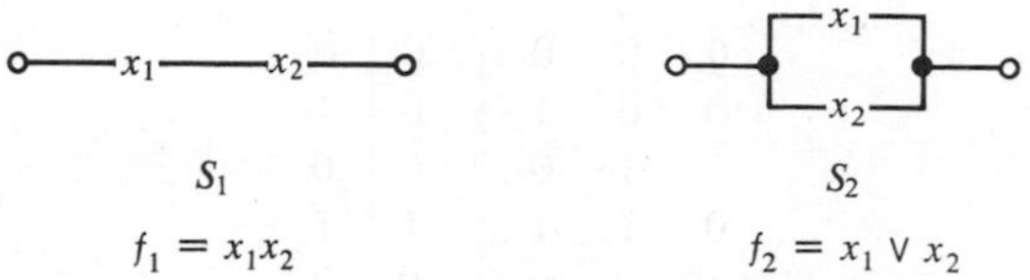

$$S_1 \qquad\qquad\qquad S_2$$
$$f_1 = x_1 x_2 \qquad\qquad\qquad f_2 = x_1 \vee x_2$$

Circuits illustrating the inclusion relation
Figure 1.14.1

The terminology "less-than-or-equal-to" is of course suggested by the resemblance of our notation to that of ordinary arithmetic. It implies in particular that $0 \leqslant 0$, $0 \leqslant 1$, and $1 \leqslant 1$. These three statements are all weaker than is necessary since in fact $0 = 0$, $0 < 1$, and $1 = 1$, but that does not mean that they are incorrect. Indeed, the weaker statements are often more useful than the stronger ones. (The symbol $<$ means "$\leqslant$ but not equal" and is read "is less than.")

The relations *inclusion* and "$\leqslant$" defined here for switching circuits and switching functions respectively are examples of a general class of relations called *order relations*, the relation equal-to-or-less-than of arithmetic being a familiar example.

Given two functions $f_1(x_1, x_2, \ldots, x_n)$ and $f_2(x_1, x_2, \ldots, x_n)$, it often is the case that neither is equal to or less than the other. For example, if

$$f_1(x_1, x_2) = \bar{x}_1, \qquad f_2(x_1, x_2) = x_1 x_2 \vee \bar{x}_1 \bar{x}_2,$$

we have the function values shown in Table 1.14.1.

Table 1.14.1

x_1	x_2	f_1	f_2
0	0	1	1
0	1	1	0
1	0	0	0
1	1	0	1

In this case, we have neither $f_1 \leqslant f_2$ nor $f_2 \leqslant f_1$. When, as in this example, neither of two functions is equal to or less than the other, we say that the functions are **not comparable**. Otherwise they are **comparable**.

As a further example, let

$$g_1(x_1, x_2, x_3) = x_2 x_3, \qquad g_2(x_1, x_2, x_3) = x_1 x_2 \vee \bar{x}_1 x_3.$$

We now have $g_1 \leqslant g_2$, as is shown by Table 1.14.2.

Table 1.14.2

x_1	x_2	x_3	g_1	g_2
0	0	0	0	0
0	0	1	0	1
0	1	0	0	0
0	1	1	1	1
1	0	0	0	0
1	0	1	0	0
1	1	0	0	1
1	1	1	1	1

The fact that the pair of values 1, 0 does not occur for g_1 and g_2, respectively, is what proves that $g_1 \leqslant g_2$.

In theory, an inequality $f_1 \leqslant f_2$ can always be tested, in the manner of the preceding examples, by a complete table of values of the functions f_1 and f_2. However, algebraic procedures also are useful, particularly when the number of variables is not small. They derive from the basic properties of the relation "$\leqslant$," which we now establish. Here f, g, h are arbitrary switching functions of the same circuit variables $x_1, x_2, \ldots, x_n$.

The **universal bounds property:**

(S–13)   For all f, $0 \leqslant f \leqslant 1$.

This is immediate from the definition of $\leqslant$.

The **reflexive property:**

(S–14)   For all f, $f \leqslant f$.

Since in fact $f = f$, the weaker statement, $f \leqslant f$, is certainly true.

The **antisymmetric property:**

(S–15)   If $f \leqslant g$ and $g \leqslant f$,   then $f = g$.

Some relations, such as that of blood-relationship among people, hold symmetrically between distinct objects; that is, if a is related to b then b is also related to a. The present statement says that the relation "$\leqslant$" can never hold symmetrically between *distinct* switching functions. The proof follows from the fact that under the given hypotheses, g takes on the value 1 for each combination for which f takes on the value 1, and also f takes on the value 1 for each combination for which g takes on the value 1. Thus f and g take on the value 1 for exactly the same combinations of values of the circuit variables. Hence, they also take on the value zero for exactly the same combinations and, therefore, having equal values for all combinations, they are in fact equal functions.

The **transitive property:**

(S–16) If $f \leq g$ and $g \leq h$, then $f \leq h$.

Indeed, since g takes on the value 1 for each combination such that f takes on the value 1, and since h takes on the value 1 for each combination such that g takes on the value 1, it follows that h takes on the value 1 for each combination such that f takes on the value 1.

The **consistency principle:**

(S–17a) For all f and g, $f \leq g$ if and only if $fg = f$.
(S–17b) For all f and g, $f \leq g$ if and only if $f \vee g = g$.

Each of (S–17a) and (S–17b) is in fact two statements: a theorem and its converse.

To prove (S–17a) we first assume that $f \leq g$. Then if f takes on the value 0 for any combination of values of the variables, substitution of this combination in $fg = f$ yields $0 = 0$. If, on the other hand, the value of f is 1, then the value of g is also 1 since $f \leq g$. In this case, substitution in $fg = f$ yields $1 = 1$. Thus, if $f \leq g$, the identity $fg = f$ holds true. Next, to prove the converse result, we assume that $fg = f$ holds for all combinations of values of the variables. For every combination at which f takes on the value 1, the value of g must also be 1 since $fg = f$. Hence $f \leq g$. The reader may prove (S–17b) in similar fashion.

To illustrate how (S–13) to (S–17) are used in proofs, let us prove first that for all switching functions f and g,

$$fg \leq f \leq f \vee g.$$

Indeed, since $fg \cdot f = fg$, $fg \leq f$ by (S–17a). Also, since $f \vee (f \vee g) = f \vee g$, $f \leq f \vee g$ by (S–17b). There is an important principle involved here. When factors are multiplied together, there are at least as many combinations at which the product is zero as there are combinations at which only one of the factors is zero. On the other hand, in the case of a union of terms, there are at least as many combinations at which the union is 1 as there are combinations at which only one term is 1. Hence the above inequalities.

As a second example, we prove that $f \vee h = g \vee h$ if and only if $h \geq f\bar{g} \vee \bar{f}g$. First, assume

(α) $\qquad\qquad\qquad\qquad f \vee h = g \vee h.$

Then, multiplying both members by $\bar{f}g$, we obtain

$$\bar{f}gh = \bar{f}g \vee \bar{f}gh = \bar{f}g$$

and multiplying both members by $f\bar{g}$, we obtain

$$f\bar{g} \vee f\bar{g}h = f\bar{g}h,$$

or

$$f\bar{g} = f\bar{g}h.$$

Hence

$$\bar{f}gh \vee f\bar{g}h = \bar{f}g \vee f\bar{g}$$

or

$$(\bar{f}g \vee f\bar{g})h = \bar{f}g \vee f\bar{g}$$

so that, by (S–17a),

(β) $\qquad\qquad\qquad\qquad h \geq \bar{f}g \vee f\bar{g}.$

Now, to prove the converse, assume

$$h \geq f\bar{g} \vee \bar{f}g.$$

Then, by (S–17b),

$$h = h \vee f\bar{g} \vee \bar{f}g,$$

so

$$f \vee h = f \vee h \vee f\bar{g} \vee \bar{f}g$$
$$= f \vee h \vee \bar{f}g$$
$$= f \vee h \vee g.$$

Similarly,

$$g \vee h = g \vee h \vee f\bar{g} \vee \bar{f}g$$
$$= g \vee h \vee f\bar{g}$$
$$= g \vee h \vee f.$$

Hence

$$f \vee h = g \vee h.$$

We have thus shown that (β) defines *only* solutions and *all* solutions of (α), regarded as an equation in the unknown h.

As in this example, it is often useful to multiply both members of an equality by the same Boolean expression, or to join the same function to both members. In addition, it is important to remember that the laws (S–17) give ways of translating inequalities into equalities, and vice versa. These observations will be useful in following exercises.

1.15   Switching Algebra as a Boolean Algebra

Any set of elements for which equality, denoted by "=," means identity is called a Boolean algebra if it possesses the following properties:

1. Two distinct elements may be denoted by "0" and "1."
2. There are two binary operations "∨" and "·" which, when applied to any two elements of the set, yield in each case a unique element of the set.
3. There is a unary operation "‾" which, if applied to any element of the set, yields a unique element of the set.
4. There is a relation "≤" which may or may not exist between any two elements of the set.
5. The elements of the set, the operations "∨," "‾," "·," and the relations "=" and "≤" satisfy the rules (S–1) through (S–9) and (S–13) through (S–17).

What we have done so far is to show that by interpreting "0," "1," "∨," "·," "‾," "=," and "≤" as indicated in preceding sections, we may regard the set of all switching functions of n circuit variables as a Boolean algebra. That is, each positive integer n yields in this way a particular Boolean algebra. An even simpler example is provided by the set of elements $\{0, 1\}$ which, under the rules of operation defined in preceding pages, constitutes a Boolean algebra of two elements.

Since switching functions take on only the values 0 and 1, they provide a very special example of a Boolean algebra. In Chapters 2 and 3 more general sets of elements will be given which also satisfy the requirements of a Boolean algebra.

In discussions of Boolean algebra, functions of n variables built up by a finite number of applications of the operations "∨," "·," and "‾" are called "Boolean functions." We shall continue to call them "switching functions" in this chapter.

It is worthwhile to reflect on how natural the postulates we have set up for switching algebra appear to be, yet how dramatically they differ from those of the more familiar algebra of real and complex numbers. This serves to emphasize the importance of selecting properly and understanding clearly the basic postulates of every mathematical system with which we work.

1.16   Exercises

1. Prove that $f \leq g$ implies $f \vee h \leq g \vee h$ and $fh \leq gh$ for all switching functions h. Is the converse true? Why?

2.   Prove that if $f \leqslant g$, then $(f \vee h)(g \vee h) = f \vee h$.

3.   How should we form the dual of an identity containing the symbol "$\leqslant$"? Prove that your answer is correct. Then give the dual of (S–17a).

4.   Prove that if $g \leqslant h$, then $\bar{f}g \vee fh = g \vee fh$.

5.   Write a switching function for the bridge of Figure 1.16.1 by tracing all possible paths that do not cross or retrace themselves. Then draw an equivalent series-parallel circuit. The problem may also be solved by

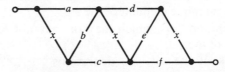

Bridge circuit to be analyzed
Figure 1.16.1

first drawing the circuit with all the x-contacts open and then drawing it with all the x-contacts closed. If f_1 and f_2 are the switching functions of the resulting circuits, respectively, then the required switching function is $\bar{x}f_1 \vee xf_2$, which reduces here to $f_1 \vee xf_2$. Why?

6.   Prove that if $f \vee g \leqslant h$, then $f \leqslant h$ and $g \leqslant h$, and conversely. State and prove the dual result.

7.   Prove that if $f \leqslant h$ and $g \leqslant k$, then $f \vee g \leqslant h \vee k$ and $fg \leqslant hk$.

8.   Prove that if $f \geqslant g \geqslant h$, then $f\bar{g} \vee g\bar{h} = f\bar{h}$.

9.   Prove that $f \leqslant g$ if and only if $f\bar{g} = 0$. Prove also that $f \leqslant g$ if and only if $\bar{f} \vee g = 1$.

10.   Prove with the aid of Exercise 9 that $f = g$ if and only if $f\bar{g} \vee \bar{f}g = 0$.

11.   Given that $fg = f$ and $g \vee h = g$, prove that $(f \vee h)g = f \vee h$.

12.   Given that $f(x_1, x_2, \ldots, x_n) = x_1 f_1(x_2, \ldots, x_n) \vee \bar{x}_1 f_2(x_2, \ldots, x_n)$, show that f can be written free of both x_1 and $\bar{x}_1$ if $f_1 = f_2$, free of x_1 if $f_1 \leqslant f_2$, and free of $\bar{x}_1$ if $f_2 \leqslant f_1$. Show finally that if neither $f_1 \leqslant f_2$ nor

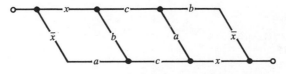

Bridge circuit to be analyzed
Figure 1.16.2

$f_2 \leqslant f_1$, then both x_1 and $\bar{x}_1$ must appear in f. Apply these results to the circuit of Figure 1.16.2.

13. Prove algebraically that $fh = gh$ if and only if $h \leqslant fg \vee \bar{f}\bar{g}$ (see Section 1.14).

14. Prove that, given an arbitrary switching function h, $\bar{f} \leqslant h \leqslant f$ if and only if $f = 1$.

15. Solve each of the equations $fg = 0$ and $f \vee g = 1$ for g. What is the simultaneous solution of these equations for g?

The Normal Forms of a Boolean Function

1.17 Complete Products and Complete Unions

Of particular interest among the switching functions of n variables are the products containing all n of the variables as factors, either complemented or not (but not both complemented and uncomplemented in any one case, of course). When $n = 1$, we consider x_1 and $\bar{x}_1$ to be these "products." When $n = 2$, they are $\bar{x}_1\bar{x}_2$, $\bar{x}_1 x_2$, $x_1\bar{x}_2$, and $x_1 x_2$. Since each of the variables is chosen in complemented or uncomplemented form, the number of such products is 2^n. We call these products the **complete products** of the n variables.

The characteristic property of a complete product is that it takes on the value 1 for exactly one set of values of x_1 through x_n, namely that combination which makes each factor of the product equal to 1.

For example, if $n = 2$, $\bar{x}_1 x_2$ takes on the value 1 only when $x_1 = 0$ and $x_2 = 1$. If $n = 3$, the complete product $x_1\bar{x}_2\bar{x}_3$ takes on the value 1 only when $x_1 = 1$, $x_2 = 0$, $x_3 = 0$, etc.

If we define $x_j^0 = \bar{x}_j$ and $x_j^1 = x_j$, then a complete product of n variables may be represented in the form $x_1^{e_1} x_2^{e_2} \cdots x_n^{e_n}$, where each e_j is either 0 or 1. It is convenient to interpret the sequences of superscripts $e_1 e_2 \cdots e_n$ as integers in *binary notation*. Then we use the corresponding decimal integers to number the complete products as follows:

$$p_i = x_1^{e_1} x_2^{e_2} \ldots x_n^{e_n}$$

where

$$(i)_{\text{decimal}} = (e_1 e_2 \ldots e_n)_{\text{binary}}$$

and where "p_i" means "product number i." For example, when $n = 3$,

$$x_1\bar{x}_2 x_3 = x_1{}^1 x_2{}^0 x_3{}^1 = p_5$$

since

$$101_{\text{bin}} = 5_{\text{dec}}.$$

(That is, the number *five* is written 101 in binary notation and 5 in decimal notation. Those unfamiliar with binary arithmetic will find it treated in Appendix 1.)

A particular advantage of this method of numbering the complete products appears from the following considerations. If we define

$$0^0 = \bar{0} = 1, \quad 1^0 = \bar{1} = 0, \quad 0^1 = 0, \quad 1^1 = 1,$$

we have in every case

$$e^e = 1, \quad \bar{e}^e = 0, \quad e^{\bar{e}} = 0.$$

From this, we see that product p_i takes on the value 1 when each x_j is replaced by e_j; that is,

$$p_i(e_1, e_2, \ldots, e_n) = e_1^{e_1} e_2^{e_2} \cdots e_n^{e_n} = 1; \qquad i_{\text{dec}} = e_1 e_2 \ldots e_{n\text{bin}}.$$

For example, let $n = 7$, $i = 21$. Then, because $21_{\text{dec}} = 10101_{\text{bin}} = 0010101_{\text{bin}}$, we have

$$p_{21}(0, 0, 1, 0, 1, 0, 1) = 1.$$

Note that since $n = 7$, it is necessary to write 0010101 as the translation of 21 into an equivalent sequence of 7 binary digits.

As this example illustrates, *the index i of p_i identifies the unique combination at which the complete product p_i takes on the value 1.*

A complete product is often called a **minimal polynomial** or **minterm** because it takes on the value 1 for only one combination of values of the variables. Every other Boolean function, except the function 0, takes on the value 1 for *more* than one combination. (The word "polynomial" means "Boolean function" here.) Thus, for example, when $n = 2$, the function $x_1 \vee \bar{x}_2$ takes on the value 1 for the combinations 10, 11, and 00. The function $\bar{x}_1$ takes on the value 1 for the combinations 00 and 01. However, when the function is a single complete product, each variable must assume a unique value in order for the function to take on the value 1.

A **complete union** of the variables $x_1, x_2, \ldots, x_n$ is a union containing all n of the variables as terms, either complemented or not. When $n = 1$, these "unions" are x_1 and $\bar{x}_1$. When $n = 2$, the complete unions are $x_1 \vee x_2$, $x_1 \vee \bar{x}_2, \bar{x}_1 \vee x_2$, and $\bar{x}_1 \vee \bar{x}_2$.

The behavior of the complete unions is dual to that of the complete products:

The characteristic property of a complete union is that it takes on the value 0 ("vanishes") for exactly one combination of values of the x's, namely the one which makes each term of the union equal 0.

For example, if $n = 2$, $x_1 \lor \bar{x}_2$ takes on the value 0 only when $x_1 = 0$ and $x_2 = 1$. If $n = 3$, $x_1 \lor x_2 \lor x_3$ takes on the value 0 only when $x_1 = 0$, $x_2 = 0$, and $x_3 = 0$. Similarly in other cases.

A complete union of n variables may be represented in the form $x_1^{e_1} \lor x_2^{e_2} \lor \cdots \lor x_n^{e_n}$ where each e_j is 0 or 1. We number the complete unions according to the scheme

$$u_i = x_1^{e_1} \lor x_2^{e_2} \lor \cdots \lor x_n^{e_n},$$

where

$$(i)_{\text{dec}} = (\bar{e}_1 \bar{e}_2 \ldots \bar{e}_n)_{\text{bin}}$$

and "u_i" means "complete union number i." For example, when $n = 4$,

$$\bar{x}_1 \lor x_2 \lor \bar{x}_3 \lor \bar{x}_4 = x_1^{\,0} \lor x_2^{\,1} \lor x_3^{\,0} \lor x_4^{\,0} = u_{11}$$

since

$$\overline{0100}_{\text{bin}} = 1011_{\text{bin}} = 11_{\text{dec}}.$$

Note that

$$u_i(\bar{e}_1, \bar{e}_2, \ldots, \bar{e}_n) = \bar{e}_1^{\,e_1} \lor \bar{e}_2^{\,e_2} \lor \cdots \lor \bar{e}_n^{\,e_n} = 0.$$

That is, *the index i of the complete union u_i identifies the unique combination for which the union vanishes.*

For example, if $n = 6$, $i = 57$, we have

$$57_{\text{dec}} = 111001_{\text{bin}}$$

so that

$$u_{57} = \bar{x}_1 \lor \bar{x}_2 \lor \bar{x}_3 \lor x_4 \lor x_5 \lor \bar{x}_6$$

and

$$u_{57}(1, 1, 1, 0, 0, 1) = 0.$$

A complete union is often called a **maximal polynomial** or **maxterm** because it takes on the value 1 for all combinations except the one that makes it zero. (Only the function 1 takes on the value 1 for *all* combinations.) For example, if $n = 2$, the complete union $\bar{x}_1 \lor x_2$ takes on the value 0 for the combination 10 but takes on the value 1 for all others. On the other hand, $\bar{x}_1$ takes on the value 0 for the combinations 10 and 11, so that it takes on the value 1 for only two combinations, namely 00 and 01.

The points made in the preceding paragraphs are illustrated for $n = 3$ in Table 1.17.1.

Table 1.17.1
Complete Products and Unions for n = 3.

i	x_1	x_2	x_3	Nonvanishing Product, p_i	Vanishing Union u_i
0	0	0	0	$\bar{x}_1\bar{x}_2\bar{x}_3$	$x_1 \lor x_2 \lor x_3$
1	0	0	1	$\bar{x}_1\bar{x}_2x_3$	$x_1 \lor x_2 \lor \bar{x}_3$
2	0	1	0	$\bar{x}_1x_2\bar{x}_3$	$x_1 \lor \bar{x}_2 \lor x_3$
3	0	1	1	$\bar{x}_1x_2x_3$	$x_1 \lor \bar{x}_2 \lor \bar{x}_3$
4	1	0	0	$x_1\bar{x}_2\bar{x}_3$	$\bar{x}_1 \lor x_2 \lor x_3$
5	1	0	1	$x_1\bar{x}_2x_3$	$\bar{x}_1 \lor x_2 \lor \bar{x}_3$
6	1	1	0	$x_1x_2\bar{x}_3$	$\bar{x}_1 \lor \bar{x}_2 \lor x_3$
7	1	1	1	$x_1x_2x_3$	$\bar{x}_1 \lor \bar{x}_2 \lor \bar{x}_3$

At this point, the reader should practice writing several complete products p_i and complete unions u_i, employing various values of n and i. These should be checked by writing also the combinations that make them 1 and 0, respectively.

1.18　The Disjunctive Normal Form

It is, in principle, a simple matter to express a given switching function as a union of complete products. For example, suppose $n = 3$ and

$$f = (\overline{\bar{x}_1x_2})(x_1 \lor x_3).$$

First we express f as a union of products, not necessarily complete:

$$f = (x_1 \lor \bar{x}_2)(x_1 \lor x_3) = x_1 \lor \bar{x}_2x_3.$$

Then by (S–7b) we have

$$f = x_1(x_2 \lor \bar{x}_2)(x_3 \lor \bar{x}_3) \lor (x_1 \lor \bar{x}_1)\bar{x}_2x_3.$$

Now, expanding and removing duplicate terms by (S–4a), we obtain

$$f = x_1\bar{x}_2\bar{x}_3 \lor x_1\bar{x}_2x_3 \lor x_1x_2\bar{x}_3 \lor x_1x_2x_3 \lor \bar{x}_1\bar{x}_2x_3,$$

which contains only distinct complete products.

The method just illustrated is perfectly general. As the example suggests, a representation of a given switching function f as a union of complete products may be obtained by the following steps:

1.　Express f as a union of products with the aid of DeMorgan's laws, the first distributive law, and any others that aid in simplification.

2. In each product insert a factor $x_j \vee \bar{x}_j$ for each variable x_j that is missing from that product.
3. Expand by the first distributive law again and eliminate duplicate terms by the use of the idempotent law for unions.

Once we have expanded a switching function into a union of complete products, we can read off, by inspection of the terms present, the combinations of values of the n variables at which the function has the value 1, for *they are the combinations that make these terms take on the value 1*. For the given example, these combinations are 100, 101, 110, 111, and 001, respectively. Because a complete product takes on the value 1 for *exactly one combination* of values of the variables, every term in the expanded form of f will take on the value 0 for all other combinations than the five just listed, and hence f too will take on the value 0 for these combinations. These observations enable us to represent f by means of a function table (Table 1.18.1) which lists (in ascending binary order) all eight combinations of values of the variables, together with the corresponding values of the function.

Table 1.18.1
Function Table for Given Function f.

x_1	x_2	x_3	f
0	0	0	0
0	0	1	1
0	1	0	0
0	1	1	0
1	0	0	1
1	0	1	1
1	1	0	1
1	1	1	1

Conversely, we could start with Table 1.18.1 and ask, "What is an algebraic representation of the function defined by this table?" To answer this, we reason thus: There is a 1 in the 001 row of the table. If we let the corresponding complete product $\bar{x}_1\bar{x}_2x_3$ be one term of a function, then that function will take on the value 1 for the combination 001. Similarly, the other rows in which the value of f is shown to be 1 suggest the inclusion of the products $x_1\bar{x}_2\bar{x}_3, x_1\bar{x}_2x_3, x_1x_2\bar{x}_3$, and $x_1x_2x_3$, respectively. (Note how these products are determined by the given combinations: If x_1 has the value 0 in a given combination, we write $\bar{x}_1$ in the corresponding product; if it has the value 1 in the combination, we write x_1 in the product. Similarly for x_2 and x_3.) Finally, let us write the union of these products:

$$\bar{x}_1\bar{x}_2x_3 \vee x_1\bar{x}_2\bar{x}_3 \vee x_1\bar{x}_2x_3 \vee x_1x_2\bar{x}_3 \vee x_1x_2x_3.$$

Now this union takes on the value 1 wherever f does and also takes on the value 0 wherever f does because a complete product is 0 at every combination except the single combination at which it has the value 1. Therefore, the written function is in fact f. Some modest algebraic manipulation then yields the reduced form

$$f = x_1 \lor \bar{x}_2 x_3.$$

The reasoning involved in the example just discussed is general. Suppose we know all the combinations of values of the n x's for which a switching function f is 1. Now each complete product takes on the value 1 for exactly one combination. Hence the products corresponding to the combinations for which f is 1 must all appear in the expansion of f into a union of complete products. Moreover, no other complete products may appear in the expanded form of f since this would imply that f takes on the value 1 for at least one other combination. We therefore have the

Theorem: *Every switching function f of n variables may be expressed uniquely as a union of complete products of those n variables:*

(S–18a) $$f = \bigvee_{i=0}^{2^n-1} f_i p_i,$$

where f_i is the value of the function f at the combination at which p_i takes on the value 1.

The expansion (S–18a) is called the **disjunctive normal form** of f because it is a disjunction (union) of complete products.

In practice, we of course do not write down the complete products whose coefficients f_i are 0. That is, as in the last example, *f may be expressed as the union of exactly those complete products which correspond to the combinations of values of the x_j's at which f takes on the value 1.* To illustrate this point further, consider the function table given in Figure 1.18.1.

x_1	x_2	x_3	x_4	f_i
1	1	1	0	1
1	0	1	0	1
0	0	1	0	1
0	0	1	1	1

($f_i = 0$ otherwise)   *Design using disjunctive normal form*

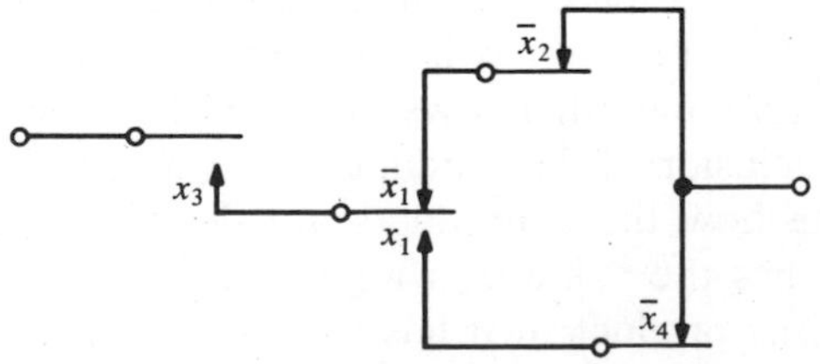

Figure 1.18.1

Here, we have, in disjunctive normal form,

$$f = x_1 x_2 x_3 \bar{x}_4 \ \lor \ x_1 \bar{x}_2 x_3 \bar{x}_4 \ \lor \ \bar{x}_1 \bar{x}_2 x_3 \bar{x}_4 \ \lor \ \bar{x}_1 \bar{x}_2 x_3 x_4$$
$$= x_3 (x_1 x_2 \bar{x}_4 \ \lor \ x_1 \bar{x}_2 \bar{x}_4 \ \lor \ \bar{x}_1 \bar{x}_2 \bar{x}_4 \ \lor \ \bar{x}_1 \bar{x}_2 x_4).$$

By combining the first and last pairs of terms, we obtain

$$f = x_3 (x_1 \bar{x}_4 \ \lor \ \bar{x}_1 \bar{x}_2).$$

An alternative form of this is

$$f = x_3 (x_1 \ \lor \ \bar{x}_2)(\bar{x}_1 \ \lor \ \bar{x}_4).$$

The relay circuit corresponding to f is diagrammed at the right in Figure 1.18.1.

From the theorem summarized in formula (S–18a), we see that an arbitrary switching function f may be defined by examining each complete product p_i and either *rejecting* it (coefficient 0) or *including* it (coefficient 1) in the normal form of f. Since there are 2^n complete products of n variables and since each product p_i admits two choices for the coefficient f_i, there are $2^{(2^n)}$ choices possible for f; that is, we have the

Theorem: *There are $2^{(2^n)}$ switching functions of n variables.*

Formula (S–18a) also suggests a valid and often useful, though not always elegant, means of proving two functions to be identically equal or unequal. Expand both functions into disjunctive normal form; if the results are the same, the functions are identically equal, otherwise not. For example,

$$x_1 \bar{x}_2 \ \lor \ x_2 \bar{x}_3 \ \lor \ x_3 \bar{x}_1 = x_1 \bar{x}_2 x_3 \ \lor \ x_1 \bar{x}_2 \bar{x}_3 \ \lor \ x_1 x_2 \bar{x}_3 \ \lor \ \bar{x}_1 x_2 \bar{x}_3 \ \lor \ \bar{x}_1 x_2 x_3 \ \lor \ \bar{x}_1 \bar{x}_2 x_3.$$

In addition,

$$\bar{x}_1 x_2 \ \lor \ \bar{x}_2 x_3 \ \lor \ \bar{x}_3 x_1 = \bar{x}_1 x_2 x_3 \ \lor \ \bar{x}_1 x_2 \bar{x}_3 \ \lor \ x_1 \bar{x}_2 x_3 \ \lor \ \bar{x}_1 \bar{x}_2 x_3 \ \lor \ x_1 x_2 \bar{x}_3 \ \lor \ x_1 \bar{x}_2 \bar{x}_3.$$

Since the two expansions on the right are the same, we have the identity

$$x_1 \bar{x}_2 \ \lor \ x_2 \bar{x}_3 \ \lor \ x_3 \bar{x}_1 = \bar{x}_1 x_2 \ \lor \ \bar{x}_2 x_3 \ \lor \ \bar{x}_3 x_1.$$

We conclude this section with a list of the sixteen switching functions of two variables in both disjunctive normal form and in simplified form, and show how the coefficients f_0, f_1, f_2, f_3 may be used to number the functions decimally in a convenient fashion (Table 1.18.2).

Table 1.18.2

f	Simplified Form	f_0	f_1	f_2	f_3	Decimal No.
0	0	0	0	0	0	0
x_1x_2	x_1x_2	0	0	0	1	1
$x_1\bar{x}_2$	$x_1\bar{x}_2$	0	0	1	0	2
$x_1\bar{x}_2 \vee x_1x_2$	x_1	0	0	1	1	3
$\bar{x}_1x_2$	$\bar{x}_1x_2$	0	1	0	0	4
$\bar{x}_1x_2 \vee x_1x_2$	x_2	0	1	0	1	5
$\bar{x}_1x_2 \vee x_1\bar{x}_2$	$\bar{x}_1x_2 \vee x_1\bar{x}_2$	0	1	1	0	6
$\bar{x}_1x_2 \vee x_1\bar{x}_2 \vee x_1x_2$	$x_1 \vee x_2$	0	1	1	1	7
$\bar{x}_1\bar{x}_2$	$\bar{x}_1\bar{x}_2$	1	0	0	0	8
$\bar{x}_1\bar{x}_2 \vee x_1x_2$	$\bar{x}_1\bar{x}_2 \vee x_1x_2$	1	0	0	1	9
$\bar{x}_1\bar{x}_2 \vee x_1\bar{x}_2$	$\bar{x}_2$	1	0	1	0	10
$\bar{x}_1\bar{x}_2 \vee x_1\bar{x}_2 \vee x_1x_2$	$x_1 \vee \bar{x}_2$	1	0	1	1	11
$\bar{x}_1\bar{x}_2 \vee \bar{x}_1x_2$	$\bar{x}_1$	1	1	0	0	12
$\bar{x}_1\bar{x}_2 \vee \bar{x}_1x_2 \vee x_1x_2$	$\bar{x}_1 \vee x_2$	1	1	0	1	13
$\bar{x}_1\bar{x}_2 \vee \bar{x}_1x_2 \vee x_1\bar{x}_2$	$\bar{x}_1 \vee \bar{x}_2$	1	1	1	0	14
$\bar{x}_1\bar{x}_2 \vee \bar{x}_1x_2 \vee x_1\bar{x}_2 \vee x_1x_2$	1	1	1	1	1	15

The reader should check the correctness of all the entries. This scheme extends readily to more variables, although it soon becomes cumbersome.

1.19   Further Applications of the Disjunctive Normal Form

The disjunctive normal form is useful for translating verbally stated conditions into algebraic form. Suppose, for example, we wish to design a two-terminal circuit using contacts on three relays and satisfying the following requirements:

"The network is to be closed whenever the relay X_1 is released unless *exactly one* of X_2 or X_3 is operated, in which case the network is to be open. It is also to be closed when X_1 is operated unless X_2 and X_3 are both operated or both released, in which case it is to be open."

Let the circuit variables x_1, x_2, x_3 denote normally open contacts on relays X_1, X_2, X_3, respectively. Then the given conditions are summarized in Table 1.19.1. We have, from the table, with the aid of the above theorem,

$$f = \bar{x}_1\bar{x}_2\bar{x}_3 \vee \bar{x}_1x_2x_3 \vee x_1\bar{x}_2x_3 \vee x_1x_2\bar{x}_3,$$

where the terms of f are the complete products corresponding to the combinations for which the value of f is 1. That is, in this case, $f_0 = f_3 =$

Table 1.19.1

i	x_1	x_2	x_3	f
0	0	0	0	1
1	0	0	1	0
2	0	1	0	0
3	0	1	1	1
4	1	0	0	0
5	1	0	1	1
6	1	1	0	1
7	1	1	1	0

$f_5 = f_6 = 1$ and $f_1 = f_2 = f_4 = f_7 = 0$. (This is an example of a **symmetric function.** It is unchanged by any permutation of x_1, x_2, x_3, where the bars are not permuted along with the variables.)

The series-parallel realization of this function requires twelve contacts unless some simplification is effected. If we write

$$f = \bar{x}_1(\bar{x}_2\bar{x}_3 \vee x_2x_3) \vee x_1(\bar{x}_2x_3 \vee x_2\bar{x}_3),$$

we can obtain a series-parallel realization with only ten contacts, as shown in Figure 1.19.1(A). However, the use of a bridge circuit allows us to realize the function with only eight contacts (Figure 1.19.1(C)).

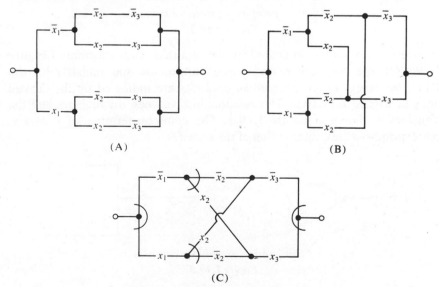

(A)

(B)

(C)

Example of reduction by inspection
Figure 1.19.1

Unfortunately, there seems to be no simple way of looking at the switching function itself and seeing that a bridge circuit is the most economical of contacts. The bridge in this example is obtained by noting first that an x_2-contact and an $\bar{x}_2$-contact each lead to separate x_3-contacts. We connect the x_2-contact and the $\bar{x}_2$-contact to a single x_3-contact and then remove the other one (Figure 1.19.1(B)).

Then we also note that an x_2-contact and an $\bar{x}_2$-contact each lead to separate $\bar{x}_3$-contacts. We connect both to a single $\bar{x}_3$-contact and remove the other one. The next step is to check the operation of the redesigned circuit for all combinations to make sure that it is not, as a result of the changes, closed for any combinations for which it should be open, and vice versa. Finally, we redraw the circuit in as simple a way as possible.

In the actual construction of this circuit, transfer contacts would be employed in order to save springs (Figure 1.19.2). That the use of

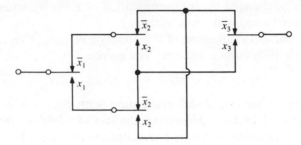

Illustration of use of transfer contacts
Figure 1.19.2

transfers is possible is indicated by the fact that in the diagram of Figure 1.19.1(C), the contacts x_1 and $\bar{x}_1$ are coterminal, and similarly for the other variables. These coterminal contacts are indicated by the curved lines in Figure 1.19.1(C). The relationship between the diagram and the transfers is shown in Figure 1.19.3. The common terminal of $\bar{x}_1$ and x_1 corresponds to the center spring of the transfer.

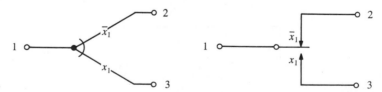

Identification of transfer contacts
Figure 1.19.3

This example suggests a proof for the earlier assertion (Section 1.9) that we can, at least in principle, write a switching function for any combinational circuit. Indeed, we simply observe the behavior of the circuit and record, in a table of combinations of values of the circuit variables, a "1" opposite each combination for which the circuit is closed and a "0" opposite every other combination. Then the disjunctive normal form of the switching function of the circuit is the union of the complete products corresponding to the combinations for which the circuit is closed.

Additional examples of circuit design appear in Section 1.22.

As a second type of application, we prove once more that if $h \geqslant f\bar{g} \vee \bar{f}g$, then $f \vee h = g \vee h$, a result first obtained in Section 1.14. To prove this, we note that since $h \geqslant f\bar{g} \vee \bar{f}g$, we can write h in the form $h = f\bar{g} \vee \bar{f}g \vee k$ where k is the union of all those terms in the disjunctive normal form of h that are not in the disjunctive normal form of $f\bar{g} \vee \bar{f}g$. Then, by (S–10) and (S–11),

$$f \vee h = f \vee f\bar{g} \vee \bar{f}g \vee k = f \vee g \vee k$$

and

$$g \vee h = g \vee f\bar{g} \vee \bar{f}g \vee k = f \vee g \vee k.$$

The result follows.

Note that in this proof we only need to know that the disjunctive normal form *exists* and what its nature is; this enables us to conclude the existence of k and hence the truth of the theorem. This type of proof, which avoids irrelevant computational details, illustrates what one strives for in good mathematics.

1.20 The Conjunctive Normal Form

It is not difficult, in principle, to express a given switching function as a product of complete unions. For example, if $g = x_1\bar{x}_2 \vee \bar{x}_1x_2x_3$, we have

$$
\begin{aligned}
g &= (x_1\bar{x}_2 \vee \bar{x}_1)(x_1\bar{x}_2 \vee x_2)(x_1\bar{x}_2 \vee x_3) && \text{(S–3b)} \\
&= (\bar{x}_1 \vee \bar{x}_2)(x_1 \vee x_2)(x_1 \vee x_3) && \text{(S–11a), (S–3b), (S–12a)} \\
&= (\bar{x}_1 \vee \bar{x}_2 \vee x_3\bar{x}_3)(x_1 \vee x_2 \vee x_3\bar{x}_3) \\
&\quad \cdot (x_1 \vee x_2\bar{x}_2 \vee x_3) && \text{(S–7a), (S–5a)} \\
&= (\bar{x}_1 \vee \bar{x}_2 \vee x_3)(\bar{x}_1 \vee \bar{x}_2 \vee \bar{x}_3)(x_1 \vee x_2 \vee x_3) \\
&\quad \cdot (x_1 \vee x_2 \vee \bar{x}_3)(x_1 \vee \bar{x}_2 \vee x_3). && \text{(S–3b), (S–4b)}
\end{aligned}
$$

The steps here are analogous to those used to obtain the disjunctive normal form but are of dual character. They may be summarized thus:

1. Express g as a product of unions with the aid of DeMorgan's laws, the second distributive law, and any other rules that aid in simplification.

2.   In each union, insert a term $x_j \bar{x}_j$ for each variable x_j that is missing from that union.

3.   Expand again by the second distributive law and eliminate duplicate factors by the use of the idempotent law for products.

Once we have expanded a function into a product of complete unions, we can read off, from the factors of the expansion, the combinations at which the function assumes the value 0. At all other combinations it assumes the value 1 since a complete union vanishes at exactly one combination. Once again, therefore, we can use the expansion to construct a table representing the function. In the case of the preceding example the result is shown in Table 1.20.1. A zero appears in the g-column for each of the five complete unions in the expansion of g.

Table 1.20.1

x_1	x_2	x_3	g
0	0	0	0
0	0	1	0
0	1	0	0
0	1	1	1
1	0	0	1
1	0	1	1
1	1	0	0
1	1	1	0

Conversely, we can start with a given table and find an algebraic representation of the corresponding function as a product of complete unions by the following reasoning: If there is a zero in a row of the table, we form the corresponding complete union and let this be one factor of a product. The product of all the complete unions corresponding to rows in which zero is the function value takes on the value zero at exactly the same combinations as the tabulated function does, for a complete union *vanishes* at exactly one combination. The product in question therefore represents the function. As an example, consider the function defined in Table 1.20.2. Here the number of zeros in the f-column is small so that it is desirable to represent f as a product of unions. Following the rule just outlined, we obtain, from the first and third rows,

$$f = (x_1 \lor x_2 \lor x_3)(x_1 \lor \bar{x}_2 \lor x_3).$$

Table 1.20.2

x_1	x_2	x_3	f
0	0	0	0
0	0	1	1
0	1	0	0
0	1	1	1
1	0	0	1
1	0	1	1
1	1	0	1
1	1	1	1

(Note that where a 0 appears in the table in an x_j-column, x_j appears in the corresponding complete union and that where a 1 appears in an x_j-column, $\bar{x}_j$ appears in the union.) With a single application of the second distributive law, we obtain

$$f = x_1 \lor x_3.$$

The same result would, of course, have been obtained from the representation of f as a union of complete products, but the six terms of the disjunctive normal form would have rendered the reduction to the form $x_1 \lor x_3$ more tedious.

Once again, the reasoning employed in the example is general and may be stated formally:

Theorem: *Every switching function g of n variables $x_1, x_2, \ldots, x_n$ may be expressed uniquely as a product of complete unions:*

(S–18b)
$$g = \prod_{i=0}^{2^n-1} (g_i \lor u_i),$$

where g_i is the value of the function g at the combination at which u_i takes on the value 0.

The theorem is proved by noting that since $1 \lor u_i = 1$, substituting $g_i = 1$ in (S–18b) effectively eliminates u_i from the product and thus *prevents* g from vanishing at the combination at which u_i assumes the value 0. On the other hand, substituting $g_i = 0$ *guarantees* the vanishing of g at that combination. Thus the expansion defined in the theorem correctly represents the function g. Since any other assignment of values to the g_i's would alter the set of combinations at which the function assumes the value 0, for each given function g the expansion is unique.

The expansion (S–18b) is called the **conjunctive normal form** of g because it is a conjunction (product) of complete unions. In writing the conjunctive normal form from a table of values of a function, we in effect ignore those rows in which the function value is 1 and simply write the product of the complete unions corresponding to the rows in which the function value is 0. This is what the theorem in fact calls for.

The conjunctive normal form is generally to be preferred when the number of 0-entries in the function-value column is less than the number of entries which are 1.

As an illustration of these last remarks, consider the function defined by the table in Figure 1.20.1.

x_1	x_2	x_3	x_4	g
0	0	0	0	0
0	0	0	1	0
0	0	1	1	0
0	1	1	1	0

$g_i = 1$ otherwise

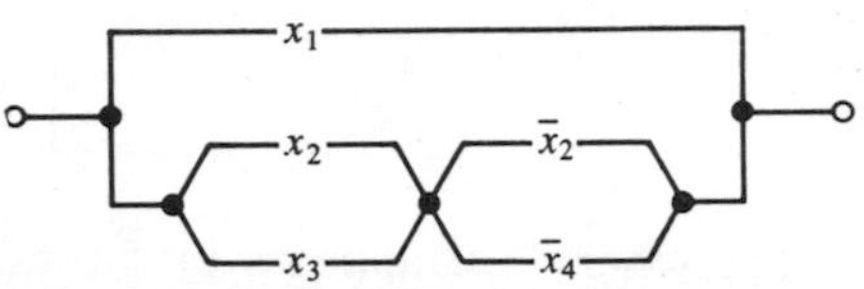

Design using conjunctive normal form

Figure 1.20.1

We have, by (S–18b),

$$g = (x_1 \lor x_2 \lor x_3 \lor x_4)(x_1 \lor x_2 \lor x_3 \lor \bar{x}_4)(x_1 \lor x_2 \lor \bar{x}_3 \lor \bar{x}_4)$$
$$(x_1 \lor \bar{x}_2 \lor \bar{x}_3 \lor \bar{x}_4)$$

$$= x_1 \lor (x_2 \lor x_3 \lor x_4)(x_2 \lor x_3 \lor \bar{x}_4)(x_2 \lor \bar{x}_3 \lor \bar{x}_4)(\bar{x}_2 \lor \bar{x}_3 \lor \bar{x}_4).$$

Combining the first and last pairs of factors, we obtain

$$g = x_1 \lor (x_2 \lor x_3)(\bar{x}_3 \lor \bar{x}_4).$$

An equivalent form is

$$g = x_1 \lor x_2\bar{x}_3 \lor x_3\bar{x}_4.$$

The circuit diagram appears at the right in Figure 1.20.1.

If we go back to the example of Table 1.19.1 and write the conjunctive normal form for f, we obtain

$$f = (x_1 \lor x_2 \lor \bar{x}_3) (x_1 \lor \bar{x}_2 \lor x_3) (\bar{x}_1 \lor x_2 \lor x_3) (\bar{x}_1 \lor \bar{x}_2 \lor \bar{x}_3)$$
$$= [x_1 \lor (x_2 x_3 \lor \bar{x}_2 \bar{x}_3)] [\bar{x}_1 \lor (x_2 \bar{x}_3 \lor \bar{x}_2 x_3)].$$

This leads to the circuit of Figure 1.20.2(A), in which points 2 and 3 are connected to point 1 via x_3-contacts. We connect them to point 1 via a single x_3-contact (upper dotted line), thereafter deleting the two original x_3-contacts. This leads to no sneak paths, and to no loss of paths. (Check this.) Similarly, points 4 and 5 are connected to point 1 via $\bar{x}_3$-contacts which we can replace by a single $\bar{x}_3$-contact (lower dotted line). Rearranging the resulting figure, we obtain Figure 1.20.2(B). This circuit is equivalent to the circuit of Figure 1.19.1(C) although, geometrically, these two bridges are distinct. The two circuits are equally economical.

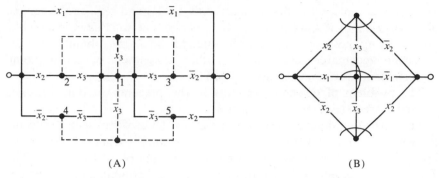

(A)   (B)

Dual approach to design of circuit of Figure 1.19.1
Figure 1.20.2

1.21 Don't-Care Combinations

In practice, it often occurs that while a function is to take on the value
1 at some combinations and the value 0 at others, there remain certain
combinations at which the function may assume either value without
altering the usefulness of the circuit for the purpose for which it is designed.
Such combinations are called **don't-care combinations.** In the function
table, the function value is listed as "d" for such combinations. In designing the circuit, we then assign to each d the value 0 or the value 1, in
such a way that the resulting function is as simple as possible. Different
assignments of values to the d's may well result in different but equally
simple functions. There is no cause for concern when this occurs. The
only requirement is that every such function assume the value 1 where
required and the value 0 where required.

By way of example, consider Table 1.21.1.

Table 1.21.1

x_1	x_2	x_3	h
0	0	0	0
0	0	1	d
0	1	0	d
0	1	1	1
1	0	0	0
1	0	1	d
1	1	0	d
1	1	1	1

Here, if we replace the first and third d's by 1's and replace the second and fourth d's by 0's, we obtain $h_1 = x_3$ as one function that is acceptable. By reversing these assignments of values to the d's, we obtain $h_2 = x_2$ as a second acceptable function. Any other assignment of values would result in a more complicated expression for h.

The problem of designing circuits in the presence of don't-cares is treated more extensively in Chapter 4.

To illustrate a different use of don't-cares, let us once again determine for what functions h we have $f \vee h = g \vee h$ and for what functions k we have $fk = gk$, where f and g are given functions of $x_1, x_2, \ldots, x_n$. The Tables 1.21.2A and 1.21.2B show the possible combinations of values of $f \vee h$, $g \vee h$, fk, gk. The starred lines are excluded by the hypotheses $f \vee h = g \vee h$ and $fk = gk$. That is, for no combinations of values of the x's do these combinations of values of f, g, h and f, g, k occur.

Table 1.21.2A   **Table 1.21.2B**

f	g	h	$f \vee h$	$g \vee h$
0	0	0	0	0
0	0	1	1	1
*0	1	0	0	1
0	1	1	1	1
*1	0	0	1	0
1	0	1	1	1
1	1	0	1	1
1	1	1	1	1

f	g	k	fk	gk
0	0	0	0	0
0	0	1	0	0
0	1	0	0	0
*0	1	1	0	1
1	0	0	0	0
*1	0	1	1	0
1	1	0	0	0
1	1	1	1	1

The relationships among the functions f, g, h, k, when $f \vee h = g \vee h$ and $fk = gk$ are now revealed by the condensations of the first three columns of Tables 1.21.2A and 1.21.2B which are shown in Tables 1.21.3 A and 1.21.3B. These condensations are made possible by the omission of the starred lines, which are excluded by the hypotheses. The condensed tables define, in terms of f and g, all functions h and k that satisfy the given equations.

Table 1.21.3A   **Table 1.21.3B**

f	g	h
0	0	d
0	1	1
1	0	1
1	1	d

f	g	k
0	0	d
0	1	0
1	0	0
1	1	d

The don't-cares in Tables 1.21.3A and 1.21.3B arise from the bracketed pairs of rows in Tables 1.21.2A and 1.21.2B. For the associated pairs of values of f and g, the values of h and k may be either 0 or 1. Let us think carefully about the nature of these don't-cares. There may be *many combinations of values of the n circuit variables* for which f and g both assume the value 0. *At each such combination,* each of h and k may assume either the value 0 or the value 1. The same conclusion holds for all combinations at which both f and g assume the value 1. That is, in Tables 1.21.3A and 1.21.3B, the d's may represent 0's for some combinations of values of the x_j's, and may represent 1's for others. In every such case, however, the values of $f \vee h$ and $g \vee h$ will be equal, as will the values of fk and gk, as may be checked directly.

From Table 1.21.3A, we now see that if h assumes the value 0 at all the don't-care combinations, then $h = f\bar{g} \vee \bar{f}g$. Otherwise $h > f\bar{g} \vee \bar{f}g$. That is, for exactly those functions h such that $h \geqslant f\bar{g} \vee \bar{f}g$, we have $f \vee h = g \vee h$. Similarly, from Table 1.21.3B, we see that if k has the the value 1 at all the don't-care combinations, then $k = fg \vee \bar{f}\bar{g}$. Otherwise $k < fg \vee \bar{f}\bar{g}$. That is, for exactly those functions k such that $k \leqslant fg \vee \bar{f}\bar{g}$, we have $fk = gk$.

1.22   Further Examples of Circuit Simplification

From preceding examples, it is clear that one method of synthesizing a two-terminal relay contact network is this:

1. Determine the requirements the circuit is to satisfy.
2. Express the requirements algebraically in the form of a switching function, either directly or with the aid of a complete tabulation of the function.
3. Simplify the switching function as much as possible, using the various identities as they apply, and any "don't care" conditions which may exist.
4. Draw the circuit and see what further simplifications can be made.

We now illustrate this technique with some additional examples. In a number of these examples, it is shown how one may transform a series-parallel circuit into a bridge circuit by inspection. An ever-present risk in this process is the introduction of paths through the circuit which should not exist, **sneak paths,** as they are called. This problem is illustrated in these examples, as is a method which is at times effective in removing the sneak paths without losing all the gains of a proposed simplification. The examples show also that the final simplification is often a matter of inspection rather than algebra.

EXAMPLE 1.   Consider the function defined by Table 1.22.1.

Table 1.22.1

w	x	y	z	f
0	0	1	1	1
0	1	1	1	1
1	1	1	1	1
1	1	1	0	1
1	0	1	0	1
0	0	1	0	1

All other
combinations: 0

We have

$$f = \bar{w}\bar{x}yz \vee \bar{w}xyz \vee wxyz \vee wxy\bar{z} \vee w\bar{x}y\bar{z} \vee \bar{w}\bar{x}y\bar{z}.$$

Factoring terms by pairs and using the fact that $a \vee \bar{a} = 1$, we obtain next

$$f = \bar{w}yz \vee wxy \vee \bar{x}y\bar{z}$$

or

$$f = y(\bar{w}z \vee wx \vee \bar{x}\bar{z}).$$

The corresponding circuit is shown in Figure 1.22.1. Since the w and $\bar{w}$-contacts, as well as the x and $\bar{x}$-contacts, are coterminal, they may be combined into transfer contacts in each case. The final result has

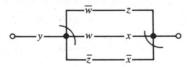

Circuit resulting from obvious factorization

Figure 1.22.1

twelve springs: three for each transfer contact, two for each of the remaining contacts.

This circuit admits of a simpler realization. Let us write first

$$f = y(\bar{w}\bar{x}z \vee \bar{w}xz \vee w\bar{x}z \vee w\bar{x}\bar{z} \vee wx\bar{z} \vee \bar{w}\bar{x}\bar{z}).$$

Recall that $a \lor a = a$ here, so that *any term may be combined with other terms as often as may be desired.* Then, combining terms as indicated, we have

$$f = y(wx \lor \bar{w}\bar{x} \lor xz \lor \bar{x}\bar{z})$$

or, finally,

$$f = y[x(w \lor z) \lor \bar{x}(\bar{w} \lor \bar{z})].$$

The corresponding circuit is shown in Figure 1.22.2. Since x and $\bar{x}$, w

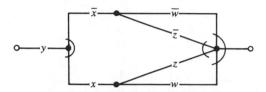

Simplification of preceding circuit
Figure 1.22.2

and $\bar{w}$, z and $\bar{z}$ all are coterminal pairs, three transfers may be used, as shown in Figure 1.22.3. This form of the circuit requires only eleven springs.

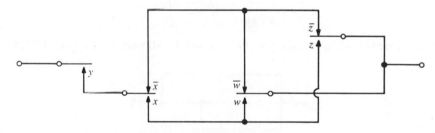

Contact equivalent of preceding diagram
Figure 1.22.3

EXAMPLE 2.   A make-contact on a relay X controls the closure of a path in a network (Figure 1.22.4). The power supply to X is in turn controlled by three keys, a, b, c. X is to be operated when any two of

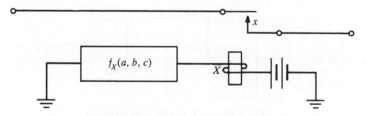

Schematic diagram of a control network
Figure 1.22.4

the three keys are operated but is to be released under all other conditions. Design the circuit for the control of X.

The table of combinations for the function f_X which has the value 1 when the lead to X is grounded is as shown in Table 1.22.2.

Table 1.22.2

a	b	c	f_X
0	0	0	0
0	0	1	0
0	1	0	0
0	1	1	1
1	0	0	0
1	0	1	1
1	1	0	1
1	1	1	0

The function f_X is therefore given by

$$f_X = \bar{a}bc \lor a\bar{b}c \lor ab\bar{c}$$
$$= (\bar{a}b \lor a\bar{b})c \lor ab\bar{c}.$$

The corresponding series-parallel circuit is shown in Figure 1.22.5.

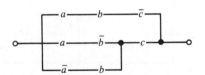

Series-parallel form of control circuit

Figure 1.22.5.

The question now arises, "Can any contacts be combined so as to simplify the circuit?" The obvious thing is to try to combine the two a-contacts as shown in Figure 1.22.6. That is, the upper a-contact is to

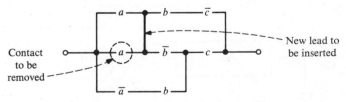

Simplification of preceding circuit
Figure 1.22.6

do the work of both, and the lower one is to be removed. A check of the eight combinations shows that the circuit is still closed only when exactly two of the three keys are operated. The circuit may be redrawn as shown in Figure 1.22.7. Employing three transfers as indicated, we obtain a final form with eleven springs. Why can't *four* transfers be used?

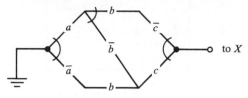

Final form of control circuit
Figure 1.22.7

This example shows that the algebra we have developed so far is not adequate for all simplifications. An algebraic tool that is useful in the design of bridge circuits such as this will be found in references [4], [5], [9]. The problem of designing bridge circuits by inspection is illustrated further with two more examples.

EXAMPLE 3.   In a railway signaling circuit, a make-contact on a relay X is to be *open* if any one of four keys is closed. Otherwise, the contact on X is to be closed. Design the circuit for the control of the relay.

We may write the function f_X, which is 0 when X is not operated, from the statement of the problem:

$$f_X = (\bar{a} \vee b \vee c \vee d)(a \vee \bar{b} \vee c \vee d)(a \vee b \vee \bar{c} \vee d)(a \vee b \vee c \vee \bar{d}).$$

Expanding, we finally obtain

$$\begin{aligned} f_X &= ab \vee ac \vee ad \vee bc \vee bd \vee cd \vee \bar{a}\bar{b}\bar{c}\bar{d} \\ &= a(b \vee c \vee d) \vee b(c \vee d) \vee cd \vee \bar{a}\bar{b}\bar{c}\bar{d}. \end{aligned}$$

On the basis of this factorization of f_X, the simplest series-parallel form seems to be that of Figure 1.22.8.

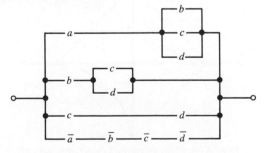

Series-parallel form of signaling circuit
Figure 1.22.8

In an attempt to combine contacts here we might proceed as shown in Figure 1.22.9. The idea is to make a pair $c \lor d$ do double duty and then

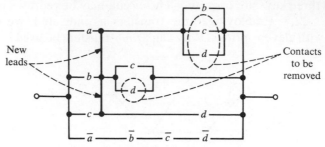

Simplification of preceding circuit
Figure 1.22.9

make a contact d do double duty. Unfortunately, the circuit is now closed when b(or c) alone is operated. That is, this proposed simplification introduces what are called "sneak paths" through the circuit. These paths could be blocked by means of back contacts, as shown in Figure 1.22.10. On a net basis, we have not saved much. We have one

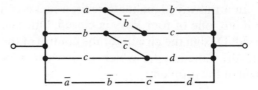

Bridge form of signaling circuit
Figure 1.22.10

contact less, and we have introduced the possibility of employing transfers where we could not before. On the other hand, there seems to be no obvious way to simplify this result further. Nevertheless, there is a simpler realization (Fig. 1.22.11), which may be obtained by the methods

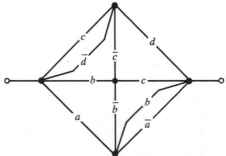

Alternative bridge form of preceding circuit

Figure 1.22.11

developed in references [4], [5]. Another approach is found in reference [9]. How many transfers are possible in Figure 1.22.11?

EXAMPLE 4.   As a final example, consider the function

$$f = \bar{x}\bar{y}zw \lor xyzw \lor xy\bar{z}\bar{w}$$

or

$$f = xy(zw \lor \bar{z}\bar{w}) \lor \bar{x}\bar{y}zw.$$

The corresponding series-parallel circuit is shown in Figure 1.22.12 along with a proposed simplification. Here the proposed elimination of the series

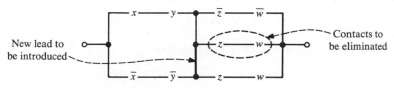

Alterations resulting in a sneak path
Figure 1.22.12

pair zw results in a sneak path $\bar{x}\bar{y}\bar{z}\bar{w}$. This is the only sneak path, and it may be blocked by restoring a z-contact in the bridge element, as shown in Figure 1.22.13.

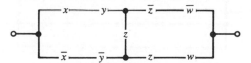

Proper reduction of preceding circuit
Figure 1.22.13

The process of constructing bridge circuits by inspection becomes very difficult for circuits of any complexity. Additional examples of simplification by inspection may be found in references [6] and [7].

1.23 Exercises

1.   Design the best possible circuits corresponding to the tables of combinations in Figure 1.23.1.

x	y	z	f		x	y	z	g
0	0	1	1		1	0	0	0
0	1	1	1	(b)	1	0	1	0
1	0	1	1		0	0	1	0

(a) at left; (b) in middle.

($f_j = 0$ otherwise)   ($g_j = 1$ otherwise)

w	x	y	z	h
1	1	0	0	1
0	1	1	0	1
0	1	0	0	1

(c)

($h_j = 0$ otherwise)

w	x	y	z	k
0	0	1	1	0
1	0	0	1	0
1	1	0	0	0

(d)

($k_j = 1$ otherwise)

Figure 1.23.1

2. Design a circuit realizing the switching function

$$f = xy(z \lor w) \lor [(\bar{x} \lor \bar{y}) \lor \bar{z}\bar{w}].$$

3. Design a circuit realizing the function

$$f = abc \lor \bar{a}\bar{b}c \lor \bar{a}b\bar{c} \lor a\bar{b}\bar{c}$$

by employing just four transfer contacts.

4. Simplify the network of Figure 1.23.2 to a form having eighteen springs or less.

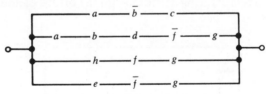

Circuit to be simplified
Figure 1.23.2

5. Write switching functions for the two networks shown in Figure 1.23.3 and contrast their behavior. This shows how a change of form

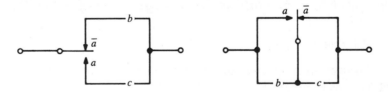

Circuits to be compared
Figure 1.23.3

can eliminate the hazard of an interrupted connection while a path is being shifted from one contact of a transfer to another. The path bc in the second circuit can hold the connection until it has been shifted from $\bar{b}\bar{a}$ to ac. Recall (S–12b) here.

6. Simplify the circuit of Figure 1.23.4 to a form having thirteen springs or less.

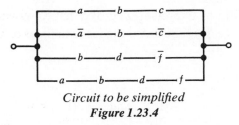

Circuit to be simplified

Figure 1.23.4

7. A single light is to be controlled by three switches so that if any one switch is thrown, the condition of the light (on or off) will change. Each switch has an *up* position (1) and a *down* position (0). Assume the light is to be on when all three switches are in the up position. Design the control circuit and describe the kinds of switches needed.

8. Design the simplest possible circuits corresponding to Tables 1.23.1A and 1.23.1B.

Table 1.23.1A				
x_1	x_2	x_3	x_4	f
0	0	1	1	1
1	0	0	1	1
1	1	0	0	1
0	1	0	1	1
1	0	1	0	1
0	1	1	0	1

($f_j = 1$ otherwise)

Table 1.23.1B				
x_1	x_2	x_3	x_4	f
1	0	1	0	0
0	0	1	0	0
0	1	1	0	0
0	1	0	0	0

($f_j = 0$ otherwise)

9. Rework Exercise 1 after complementing all *function* values.

10. Write the analog of Table 1.17.1 for $n = 4$.

11. Obtain both the disjunctive and conjunctive normal forms of these Boolean functions:

(a) $f = \overline{(x_1 \vee \bar{x}_2)x_3} \cdot (x_1 \vee \bar{x}_2 \vee x_3)$, $(n = 3)$
(b) $g = x_1\bar{x}_2 \vee x_2\bar{x}_3 \vee x_3\bar{x}_1$, $(n = 4)$
(c) $h = (x_1 \vee \bar{x}_2)x_3\bar{x}_4$, $(n = 4)$
(d) $k = x_1x_2 \vee x_1x_3 \vee x_1x_4 \vee x_2x_3 \vee x_2x_4 \vee x_3x_4$, $(n = 4)$

Then represent each function by a table of values.

12. Prove that if $f \geqslant g$, there exist functions h and k such that $f = g \lor h$ and $g = fk$. Determine all such h and k in normal form.

13. With the aid of Exercise 12, prove that for given f and g, $fh = gh$ if and only if $h \leqslant fg \lor \bar{f}\bar{g}$. See also the last examples of Sections 1.14 and 1.19.

*14. Prove that

$$\overset{2^n-1}{\underset{j=0}{\bigvee}} p_j = 1 \qquad \text{and} \qquad \overset{2^n-1}{\underset{j=0}{\prod}} u_j = 0.$$

*15. Let p_i and p_j denote arbitrary complete products and let u_i and u_j denote arbitrary complete unions. Show that $p_i p_j = 0$ if $i \neq j$ and $u_i \lor u_j = 1$ if $i \neq j$. Use these results to obtain simple formulas for fg and $f \lor g$ where

$$f = \overset{2^n-1}{\underset{i=0}{\bigvee}} f_i p_i = \overset{2^n-1}{\underset{i=0}{\prod}} (f_i \lor u_i)$$

and

$$g = \overset{2^n-1}{\underset{i=0}{\bigvee}} g_i p_i = \overset{2^n-1}{\underset{i=0}{\prod}} (g_1 \lor u_i).$$

*16. Prove that

(a)   if $f = \overset{2^n-1}{\underset{j=0}{\bigvee}} f_j p_j$, then $\bar{f} = \overset{2^n-1}{\underset{j=0}{\bigvee}} \bar{f_j} p_j$,

(b) $u_j = \bar{p}_j$, and hence that

(c) $f = \overset{2^n-1}{\underset{j=0}{\prod}} (f_j \lor u_j)$,

(d) $\bar{f} = \overset{2^n-1}{\underset{j=0}{\prod}} (\bar{f_j} \lor u_j).$

*17. Prove that if f and g are arbitrary switching functions of n variables and $\phi(y_1, y_2)$ is any switching function of two variables, then

$$\phi(f, g) = \overset{2^n-1}{\underset{j=0}{\bigvee}} \phi(f_j, g_j) p_j = \overset{2^n-1}{\underset{j=0}{\prod}} (\phi(f_j, g_j) \lor u_j).$$

Generalize.

*18. Prove that

$$f = \overset{2^n-1}{\underset{j=0}{\bigvee}} f(e_1, e_2, \ldots, e_n) p_j = \overset{2^n-1}{\underset{j=0}{\prod}} (f(e_1, e_2, \ldots, e_n) \lor u_j),$$

where $j_{\text{dec}} = e_1 e_2 \ldots e_{n\text{bin}}$.

19. (a) Given the disjunctive normal form,

$$f = \bar{x}_1\bar{x}_2\bar{x}_3 \lor \bar{x}_1\bar{x}_2x_3 \lor x_1x_2\bar{x}_3,$$

write the conjunctive normal form for f.

(b) Given the conjunctive normal form,

$$g = (\bar{x}_1 \lor \bar{x}_2 \lor \bar{x}_3)(\bar{x}_1 \lor \bar{x}_2 \lor x_3)(x_1 \lor x_2 \lor \bar{x}_3),$$

write the disjunctive normal form for g.

Give a verbal rule for going from disjunctive normal form to conjunctive normal form, and vice versa.

20. Prove that

$$f(x_1, x_2, \ldots, x_n) = x_1 f(1, x_2, \ldots, x_n) \lor \bar{x}_1 f(0, x_2, \ldots, x_n).$$

Then apply the same principle to $f(1, x_2, \ldots, x_n)$ and to $f(0, x_2, \ldots, x_n)$, and prove

$$f(x_1, x_2, \ldots, x_n) = x_1 x_2 f(1, 1, x_3, \ldots, x_n) \lor x_1\bar{x}_2 f(1, 0, x_3, \ldots, x_n)$$
$$\lor \bar{x}_1 x_2 f(0, 1, x_3, \ldots, x_n) \lor \bar{x}_1\bar{x}_2 f(0, 0, x_3, \ldots, x_n).$$

What result now follows by induction?

21. Prove that

$$f(x_1, x_2, \ldots, x_n) = [x_1 \lor f(0, x_2, \ldots, x_n)][\bar{x}_1 \lor f(1, x_2, \ldots, x_n)]$$

Continuing as in Exercise 20, what result follows by induction?

22. Find the simplest circuits corresponding to Tables 1.23.2A and 1.23.2B.

Table 1.23.2A			
x_1	x_2	x_3	f
0	0	0	d
0	0	1	d
0	1	0	0
0	1	1	1
1	0	0	1
1	0	1	d
1	1	0	d
1	1	1	1

Table 1.23.2B				
x_1	x_2	x_3	x_4	g
1	0	0	0	1
0	1	0	0	1
0	0	1	0	1
0	0	0	1	1
0	0	0	0	0

(All others, don't care).

23. Suppose the operation and release of contacts a, $\bar{a}$; b, $\bar{b}$; c, $\bar{c}$ are always timed as shown in Figure 1.23.5. Show how the circuits in Figure 1.23.6 can be simplified.

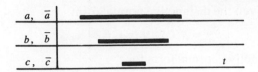

Relative timing of relay actions
Figure 1.23.5

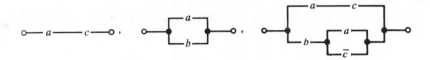

Circuits to be simplified
Figure 1.23.6

What rows of the table defining a switching function $f(a, b, c)$ are excluded in consequence of the timing? What are the resulting don't-care products?

Write switching functions for the three circuits in disjunctive normal form. Then show that by adjoining or deleting suitable don't-care terms, the simplifications made by inspection can also be made algebraically.

1.24   Other Problems

We have been dealing up to this point exclusively with two-terminal circuits. Frequently, however, more terminals are required. We might, for example, need to design a circuit which establishes prescribed connections between terminals $t_1, t_2, \ldots, t_p$ for specified combinations of values of the variables $x_1, x_2, \ldots, x_n$, the corresponding contacts being operated respectively by coils $X_1, X_2, \ldots, X_n$, whose control is independent of the circuit in question. A circuit of this kind may be represented as in Figure 1.24.1. As before, the box is presumed to contain all the contacts of the circuit, these being operated solely by the electromagnets $X_1, X_2, \ldots, X_n$, which are controlled from outside the box. Such circuits are again called **combinational circuits.**

The variables $x_1, x_2, \ldots, x_n$ of a multiterminal combinational circuit are called the **inputs** of the circuit. Any combination of values of these variables is called an **input combination.** The set of functions f_{ij} of $x_1, x_2, \ldots, x_n$, which are 1 for exactly those states of the input such that t_i and t_j are connected, may be called the **outputs** of the circuit. (We define $f_{ii} = 1$ for all i since any terminal may be regarded as always connected to itself.) Any particular set of values of these functions will be called an **output**

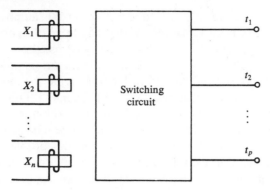

Generalized combinational switching circuit
Figure 1.24.1

combination. Thus *a combinational circuit is one in which the output combination ultimately depends only on the input combination.* All the two-terminal circuits previously discussed are special cases of this more general class of circuits. The problems to be stated below apply in large measure to multiterminal combinational circuits as well as to the two-terminal kind.

Many problems arise naturally out of the preceding discussion. The most obvious ones relate to the issue of economical design:

1. Is there a general way of designing a contact network satisfying given requirements and employing a *minimum* number of contacts?
2. Is there a general way of reducing a switching function to a form corresponding to the minimum *series-parallel* realization?
3. Is there a general way of designing a minimum circuit when there are certain input combinations which never occur in the use of the circuit?
4. Is there a general way of determining whether the minimum-contact realization of a given switching function is of series-parallel or of bridge type?

We could state other such mathematical problems, but these serve to illustrate the very practical type of question which may be asked. Not only is a minimal or near-minimal circuit neater and apt to be more reliable in operation, but also, when duplicates of the same circuit are used hundreds of times in an installation, the elimination of a few contacts from each may result in substantial savings. There is thus an economic motivation as well as an intellectual one for solving these minimization problems, all of which are still open as of this writing.

There are also problems of an entirely different nature involved in the theory of switching. Certain of these arise in the design of large switching systems. The complexities encountered in the application of the methods discussed here increase at a rate depending on the number $2^{(2^n)}$, where n is the number of circuit variables, so that any hope of rigorous minimization rapidly disappears. In fact, for large systems, the real question is, *"What types of basic switching circuits should be employed, and how should these be interconnected,* in order to provide the most economical systems possible to perform the given functions?" This is a problem which is in large measure still unsolved and which will require keen mathematical thinking for its solution. Long since a basic problem in the construction of telephone switching systems, the problem has become important in other connections as well. The digital computer and the automatic factory provide striking examples. An important point is that conclusions valid for systems based on relay circuitry may be invalid for systems based on electronic circuitry, and vice versa, because of fundamental differences in the components employed.

1.25   References

1.   C. E. Shannon, "A Symbolic Analysis of Relay and Switching Circuits," *Trans. Amer. Inst. Elec. Eng.,* **57,** 1938, pp. 713–23.

2.   C. E. Shannon, "The Synthesis of Two-Terminal Switching Circuits," *Bell System Tech. J.,* **28,** 1949, pp. 59–98.

3.   J. Riordan and C. Shannon, "The Number of Two-Terminal Series-Parallel Networks," *J. Math. Phys.,* **21,** 1942, pp. 83–93.

4.   F. E. Hohn and L. R. Schissler, "Boolean Matrices and the Design of Combinational Relay Switching Circuits," *Bell System Tech. J.,* **34,** 1955, pp. 177–202.

5.   F. E. Hohn, "A Matrix Method for the Design of Relay Circuits," *I.R.E. Trans. Circuit Theory,* **CT–2,** 1955, pp. 154–61.

6.   W. Keister, A. Ritchie, S. H. Washburn, *The Design of Switching Circuits.* New York: Van Nostrand, 1951, chapters 4, 5, and 6.

7.   S. H. Caldwell, *Switching Circuits and Logical Design.* New York: John Wiley, 1958, chapters 3 and 4.

8.   R. Higonnet and R. Grea, *Logical Design of Electrical Circuits.* New York: McGraw-Hill, 1959, chapters 2 and 4.

9.   R. E. Miller, "Formal Analysis and Synthesis of Bilateral Networks," *I.R.E. Trans.,* **EC–7,** 1958, pp. 231–44.

10.   G. Birkhoff and S. MacLane, *A Survey of Modern Algebra* (Third Edition). New York: Macmillan, 1965, chapter XI.

2

The Algebra of the Subsets of a Set

2.1   The Concept of a Set

The notion of a **set** or **class** or simply a collection of objects is generally regarded as the most fundamental concept of mathematics. It is also a familiar concept, as expressions like "a set of books," "a flock of sheep," "a covey of quail," "a collection of stamps," and so on, attest. The objects of a set are called its **members** or its **elements.**

In many cases, the simplest way to define a set is to list all of its elements, for example, "the set consisting of the positive integers 2, 3, 5, 7." To decide whether or not a given object belongs to the set in question, it is sufficient to examine the list.

A set may also be defined by some property or combination of properties by which we may test whether or not a given object belongs to the set. That is, the members of the set all exhibit all the properties in question, but this is not true of any objects not in the set. Thus, the set whose elements are 2, 3, 5, 7 may be defined as "the set of all prime numbers less than 10."

When there are infinitely many members of a set, which is true in the case of the set of *all* prime numbers, it is impossible to list all the members of the set. However, the phrase "the set of all prime numbers" defines the set completely. On the other hand, the set consisting of the North Star, the name Cleopatra, and the number 13 cannot readily be defined in any other way than by listing its three elements, for it is hard to produce any property or combination of properties, other than the property of belonging to the given list, that will characterize precisely these three elements.

When a set is defined by a property, the property may often be formu-
lated with the aid of what is called an **open sentence,** namely, the result
of deleting each instance of certain nouns or names from a sentence and
inserting symbols for variables in their places. For example, consider the
open sentence "x is an asynchronous, digital computing machine,"
where the variable symbol x may be replaced by the name of any object
whatsoever. If, for some specific name, this becomes a true sentence, the
corresponding object belongs to the set of asynchronous digital computing
machines. If the sentence is false, the object does not belong to the
class. As another example, the open sentence, "x is white and x is a
rose," defines a certain set of flowers. In order to decide whether or not
such statements are true for given replacements of the variable symbols,
we must be able to determine whether or not the defining properties
(of being asynchronous, a digital computing machine, white, a rose, and
so on) are actually possessed by the object in question. At times, this
problem is nontrivial, for example, when biological classifications are
being made.

It is interesting to observe that the elements of a set may themselves
be sets. For example, we can list the measures of the three angles of a
triangle in the form (a, b, c) where $a + b + c = 180$. Let us denote the
set of all such ordered triples by A. Then each member of A is an ordered
triple of positive real numbers and a given triple of positive real numbers
belongs to A if and only if the sum of the three numbers is 180. Thus the
triple $(10, 15, 155)$ is a member of A, but it is also a set whose members
are $10, 15$, and 155.

The customary symbol for the property of belonging to (being a
member of) a set is "$\in$". Thus, we express the fact that an element a
belongs to a set A by writing $a \in A$. If the element b does *not* belong to
A, we write $b \notin A$.

The expression "the set consisting of" is customarily denoted by
braces. Thus $\{2, 3, 5, 7\}$ denotes the set consisting of the integers $2, 3, 5$,
and 7. The defining property of a set may also be put into braces in the
manner of the following examples:

1. $\{(a, b, c) \mid a, b, c \text{ real}; a + b + c = 180\}$ denotes "the set of all
    ordered triples, (a, b, c) of real numbers whose sum is 180." (The
    vertical bar in this notation conveys the meaning "such that" and
    the braces mean "the set of all.")

2. $\{(x, y) \mid y = x^2; x, y \text{ real}\}$, denotes "the set of all ordered pairs (x, y)
    of real numbers such that $y = x^2$."

3. $\{x \mid x \text{ prime}, x < 10\}$ denotes "the set of all numbers x such that x is
    a prime number less than 10," that is, the set $\{2, 3, 5, 7\}$ which was
    mentioned earlier.

It is possible for different properties to define the same set. Thus "the set of all integral multiples of the smallest prime" and "the set of all differences of two odd integers" are in fact the same set, namely the set of all even integers. We shall regard the defining properties as **equivalent** in a case like this.

Regardless of what properties are used to define them, we regard two sets as **equal** (written "=") if and only if they contain exactly the same elements.

When a property is such that there are no elements possessing it, we call it a **null property** and we say it defines the **null set** or the **zero set** or the **empty set.** Since any two empty sets contain exactly the same elements (namely, none at all) any two empty sets, however defined, are to be regarded as equal. Hence we refer to *the* empty set rather than to *an* empty set. In the algebra of sets, the concept of the empty set plays a role analogous to that played by the function 0 in the algebra of switching functions, or by the number 0 in the algebra of complex numbers.

If we inquire whether or not the elements of a given set possess some *additional* property, we are led to the concept of a subset of a given set. When all the elements of a set A are also elements of a set B, then we say that A is a **subset** of B and that B is a **superset** of A. We represent the relationship by writing $A \subseteq B$ which may be read, "A is a subset of B," or, "A **is contained in** B." It is convenient to regard a set as a subset of itself, which is in agreement with the definition. The empty set is a subset of every set, again by the definition. An especially important case is that in which A is a *nonempty* subset of B which is *distinct* from B so that B contains at least one element that does not belong to A. Then A is called a **proper subset** of B. For example, since one of the residents of the village in which I live has an unfriendly dog, I can assert that, as of this writing, "The set of friendly dogs in Philo, Illinois, is a proper subset of the set of dogs in Philo, Illinois." If A is a proper subset of B, we write $A \subset B$. (In some books $\subset$ is used in the sense in which we use $\subseteq$ here.)

2.2   Operations on Sets

Suppose we wish to consider exclusively the subsets of some fixed superset S. We then call S the **universal set** or the **universe of discourse** and denote it by the symbol "U." The empty set we denote by the symbol "$\varnothing$." Proper subsets of U will be denoted by capital letters $A, B, \dots$.

It is convenient to represent the universal set pictorially by a rectangular, plane region and to represent its proper subsets by oval or otherwise conveniently shaped regions within the rectangle. Such a diagram

is called a **Venn diagram.** Venn diagrams help us to visualize the fundamental notions concerning sets, but since many sets are not plane regions,
such diagrams do *not* provide proofs of theorems about sets in general.
They can, however, yield counterexamples to prove statements false.

The **complement** $\bar{A}$ of a set A contained in U is the set of all elements
of U which do *not* belong to A. The **union** $A \cup B$ of two subsets A and
B of U is that subset of U which consists precisely of those elements
which belong to A or to B or to both. The **intersection** $A \cap B$ of A and B
is the subset of U which consists of all elements belonging simultaneously
to both A and B. These concepts are illustrated by the shaded regions in
Figure 2.2.1. For convenience, the symbols $\cup$ and $\cap$ are often read
"cup" and "cap," respectively.

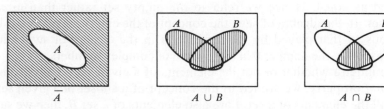

$$\bar{A} \qquad\qquad\qquad A \cup B \qquad\qquad\qquad A \cap B$$

Venn diagrams illustrating complement, union, intersection
Figure 2.2.1

To illustrate further the concept of the complement, let U denote the
set of all possible paths from terminal t_1 to terminal t_2 in a relay switching
network. At a given instant in time, let A denote the set of these paths
which are closed. Since every path must be open or closed, $\bar{A}$ represents
at that same instant the set of all open paths from t_1 to t_2.

Let U denote the set of all living humans, A denote the subset of all
people who are sailors, and B denote the subset of all people who have
been shipwrecked. Then $A \cup B$ represents the set of all living people
who are sailors or who have been shipwrecked or both, and $A \cap B$
represents the set of all living sailors who have been shipwrecked.
These examples should be interpreted on the Venn diagrams in Figure
2.2.1.

More complicated combinations may also be represented by Venn
diagrams, as is suggested by Figure 2.2.2. In this case, the set D is
indicated as having no elements in common with B or C. Hence we have
$B \cap D = C \cap D = \varnothing$ in this case. When the intersection of two sets is
the empty set, they are said to be **disjoint.**

As the definition and the preceding examples emphasize, the union is
analogous to the connective *or:* that an element is in $A \cup B$ means
that the element is in A *or* in B *or* in both. Similarly, intersection is analogous to the connective *and:* that an element is in $A \cap B$ means that it is

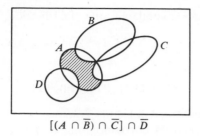

$$[(A \cap \bar{B}) \cap \bar{C}] \cap \bar{D}$$

A more complicated intersection
Figure 2.2.2

in both *A and B*. Thus the expression $((A \cap \bar{B}) \cap \bar{C}) \cap \bar{D}$ means those elements in *A* and outside each of *B*, *C*, and *D*.

As a further illustration of these concepts, observe that in the case of switching functions of three variables, the eight possible combinations of values of these variables may be represented as the vertices of a cube (Figure 2.2.3). Let us treat this set of eight vertices as the universal set *U*.

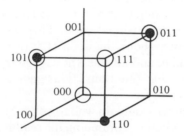

Three-dimensional unit cube
Figure 2.2.3

Then a given switching function may be represented as a subset of *U*, namely as the set of those vertices corresponding to the combinations at which the function assumes the value 1, for as soon as these combinations are given, the function is uniquely determined. For example, the function

$$f = x_1\bar{x}_2x_3 \lor \bar{x}_1x_2x_3 \lor x_1x_2\bar{x}_3$$

corresponds to the set of vertices V_f where

$$V_f = \{101, 011, 110\}.$$

These vertices are marked extra heavily in Figure 2.2.3. The complement $\bar{f}$ is represented by the remaining vertices of the cube, that is, by $\bar{V}_f$. Thus

$$V_{\bar{f}} = \bar{V}_f = \{000, 001, 010, 100, 111\}.$$

Let us consider, as a second example, the function

$$g = x_1\bar{x}_2x_3 \vee \bar{x}_1x_2x_3 \vee \bar{x}_1\bar{x}_2\bar{x}_3 \vee x_1x_2x_3.$$

Then

$$V_g = \{101, 011, 000, 111\}.$$

These vertices are encircled in Figure 2.2.3.

Now the set of vertices corresponding to $f \vee g$ is easily seen to be $V_f \cup V_g$; that is,

$$V_{f \vee g} = V_f \cup V_g = \{101, 011, 110, 000, 111\},$$

and the set of vertices corresponding to fg is found to be

$$V_{fg} = V_f \cap V_g = \{101, 011\}.$$

The three rules illustrated in these examples: $V_{\bar{f}} = \bar{V}_f$, $V_{f \vee g} = V_f \cup V_g$, $V_{fg} = V_f \cap V_g$, hold for arbitrary switching functions f and g of three variables.

The geometrical interpretation and the three rules extend to higher dimensions. A switching function of n variables corresponds to a subset of the vertices of an n-dimensional cube. This is a useful interpretation since so much is known about the geometry (especially the symmetry properties) of the n-cube, and all this knowledge may be brought to bear on the study of switching functions. This fact is used extensively in research in switching theory.

At this point, the reader would do well to solve Exercises 1, 2, 4, 6, 7, 8, 9, 10, 12, of Section 2.8 before continuing his reading of this chapter.

2.3   Basic Theorems Concerning Equality and Inclusion

Since the equation $A = B$ means that the sets A and B are in fact the same set, we have at once that

1.   if $A = B$, then for all sets C, $A \cup C = B \cup C$ and $A \cap C = B \cap C$,
2.   if $A = B$ and $C = D$, then $A \cup C = B \cup D$ and $A \cap C = B \cap D$,
3.   if $A = B$, then $\bar{A} = \bar{B}$, and conversely,

for in each equation both members actually represent the same set. That is, *one can join equals to equals, intersect equals with equals, and complement equals to get equals.*

On the other hand, from an equation $A \cup C = B \cup C$ or $A \cap C = B \cap C$, it does not necessarily follow that $A = B$. For example, let

$$A = \{1, 2, 3\}, \quad B = \{1, 2, 4\}, \quad C = \{3, 4, 5\}, \quad D = \{1, 2, 5\}.$$

Then $A \cup C = B \cup C = \{1, 2, 3, 4, 5\}$, but $A \neq B$. Also, $A \cap D = B \cap D$, but again $A \neq B$. The implication of these examples is that *there are no general cancellation laws for union and intersection.*

Let us examine next the properties of the inclusion relation. Since $\varnothing$ contains no elements, so that it is correct to say that every element of the empty set $\varnothing$ is an element of every set A, and since every element of a subset A of U is an element of U, we have the **universal bounds property:** For all subsets A of a universal set U,

(SS–1) $\varnothing \subseteq A \subseteq U.$

Since every set A is a subset of itself, we have the **reflexive property:**

(SS–2) $A \subseteq A.$

If every element of A belongs to B and every element of B belongs to A, then A and B contain precisely the same elements. This is formalized as the **antisymmetric property:**

(SS–3)   If $A \subseteq B$ and $B \subseteq A$,   then $A = B$.

The antisymmetric property is often used to prove that two sets are equal: We only have to show that each set is a subset of the other in order to prove that they are in fact the same set.

If every element of A belongs to B and every element of B belongs to C, then every element of A belongs to C. This is known as the **transitive property:**

(SS–4)   If $A \subseteq B$ and $B \subseteq C$,   then $A \subseteq C$.

The next two laws make up the **consistency principle:**

(SS–5a) $A \subseteq B$ if and only if $A \cup B = B$.
(SS–5b) $A \subseteq B$ if and only if $A \cap B = A$.

To prove the first of these, note simply that if every element of A is also an element of B, then the set $A \cup B$ contains all elements of B but contains no elements not in B. Hence $A \cup B = B$. Conversely, if $A \cup B = B$, then the union of A and B contains no elements not in B, so that every element of A must belong to B. Hence $A \subseteq B$.

In the case of (SS–5b), if every element of A belongs to B, then the set of elements common to A and B is just A. That is, $A \cap B = A$. Conversely, if $A \cap B = A$, then the set of elements common to A and B is just A, so that $A \subseteq B$.

These tests for inclusion are clarified by a Venn diagram (Figure 2.3.1).

Later we obtain other laws concerning the inclusion relation. The laws just established suffice for our present needs.

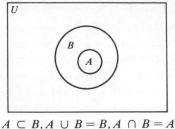

$$A \subseteq B, A \cup B = B, A \cap B = A$$

Venn diagram illustrating
the equivalent conditions
Figure 2.3.1

2.4   Basic Theorems Concerning Union and Intersection

We note first that the **commutative laws** of union and intersection hold for all subsets A and B of U, that is,

(SS–6a) $$A \cup B = B \cup A,$$

and

(SS–6b) $$A \cap B = B \cap A,$$

since, by the definitions of $\cup$ and $\cap$, in each equation both members contain exactly the same elements.

Next, let $A \cup B \cup C$ and $A \cap B \cap C$ respectively denote the set of elements belonging to at least one of A, B, and C (the union of A, B, and C), and the set of elements belonging simultaneously to all three of A, B, and C (the intersection of A, B, and C). Then, for all subsets A, B, C, of U, we have the **associative laws** for union and intersection:

(SS–7a) $A \cup B \cup C = (A \cup B) \cup C = A \cup (B \cup C),$
(SS–7b) $A \cap B \cap C = (A \cap B) \cap C = A \cap (B \cap C).$

Indeed, every element of $A \cup B \cup C$ belongs to $(A \cup B) \cup C$ since it belongs to at least one of A, B, C. Similarly, every element of $(A \cup B) \cup C$ belongs to at least one of $A \cup B$ and C, hence to at least one of A, B, C and hence to $A \cup B \cup C$. Therefore, $A \cup B \cup C \subseteq (A \cup B) \cup C$ and $(A \cup B) \cup C \subseteq A \cup B \cup C$. Hence, by (SS–3), $A \cup B \cup C = (A \cup B) \cup C$. The remaining equalities are proved in a similar fashion and are left to the reader.

Now consider the elements of $A \cap (B \cup C)$. They belong to A and to at least one of B and C, that is, they belong to $A \cap B$ or to $A \cap C$ or to both. Therefore, $A \cap (B \cup C) \subseteq (A \cap B) \cup (A \cap C)$. Conversely, every element of $(A \cap B) \cup (A \cap C)$ belongs to at least one of $A \cap B$ and $A \cap C$, hence to A and to at least one of B and C. That is, it belongs to A and to $B \cup C$, namely to $A \cap (B \cup C)$. Thus $(A \cap B) \cup (A \cap C)$ $\subseteq A \cap (B \cup C)$. Now applying (SS–3), we conclude the first of the two **distributive laws:** For all subsets A, B, and C of U,

(SS–8a) $\qquad\qquad A \cap (B \cup C) = (A \cap B) \cup (A \cap C),$
(SS–8b) $\qquad\qquad A \cup (B \cap C) = (A \cup B) \cap (A \cup C).$

The second of these may be proved in a closely analogous manner. The details are left to the reader as an exercise.

It is helpful to illustrate the distributive laws with Venn diagrams (Figure 2.4.1).

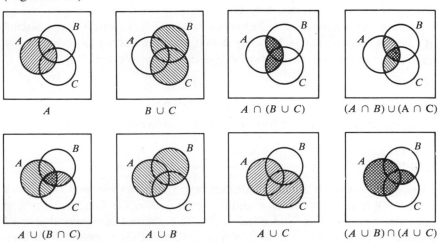

$$A \qquad\qquad B \cup C \qquad\qquad A \cap (B \cup C) \qquad\qquad (A \cap B) \cup (A \cap C)$$

$$A \cup (B \cap C) \qquad\qquad A \cup B \qquad\qquad A \cup C \qquad\qquad (A \cup B) \cap (A \cup C)$$

Venn diagrams of the distributive laws
Figure 2.4.1

Next we have the **idempotent laws,** which hold for every subset A of U:

(SS–9a) $\qquad\qquad\qquad\qquad A \cup A = A,$
(SS–9b) $\qquad\qquad\qquad\qquad A \cap A = A.$

These follow immediately from the definitions of union and intersection. These laws account for the absence of multiples and powers in the algebra of the subsets of a universal set.

Similarly, the definitions of $\cup$, $\cap$, $\varnothing$, and U yield at once the **laws of operation with $\varnothing$ and U:** For every subset A of U,

(SS–10a) $\qquad\qquad\qquad\qquad A \cup \varnothing = A,$
(SS–10b) $\qquad\qquad\qquad\qquad A \cap U = A,$
(SS–11a) $\qquad\qquad\qquad\qquad A \cup U = U$
(SS–11b) $\qquad\qquad\qquad\qquad A \cap \varnothing = \varnothing,$
(SS–11c) $\qquad\qquad\qquad\qquad \overline{\varnothing} = U,$
(SS–11d) $\qquad\qquad\qquad\qquad \overline{U} = \varnothing.$

Indeed, in each instance it is immediate that the equated sets have precisely the same elements.

Notice that in the first two of these laws, $\varnothing$ acts as 0 does in addition: $a + 0 = a$, while U acts as 1 does in multiplication: $a \cdot 1 = a$. That is, $\varnothing$ is an *identity element with respect to union* while U is an *identity element with respect to intersection*.

In the second pair of these laws, $\varnothing$ acts as 0 does in multiplication: $a \cdot 0 = 0$. There is, however, no contrasting arithmetic counterpart for the role of U in the union operation, unless one wishes to write $a + \infty = \infty$. We say that U and $\varnothing$ are **dominant elements** with respect to the operations union and intersection, respectively.

Since every element of U belongs to A or to $\bar{A}$, where A is any subset of U, and since A and $\bar{A}$ have by definition no elements in common, we have next the **laws of complementarity:** For any subset A of U,

(SS–12a) $$A \cup \bar{A} = U,$$
(SS–12b) $$A \cap \bar{A} = \varnothing.$$

DeMorgan's laws are the following: For all subsets A and B of U,

(SS–13a) $$\overline{A \cup B} = \bar{A} \cap \bar{B},$$
(SS–13b) $$\overline{A \cap B} = \bar{A} \cup \bar{B}.$$

Consider the first of these. It simply says that if an element of U does not belong to at least one of A and B, then it does not belong to A *and* also does not belong to B, and conversely. The second law says that if an element does not belong to both A and B, then it fails to belong to at least one of them, and conversely. It is helpful to learn verbal forms of these laws: *The complement of a union is the intersection of the separate complements* and *the complement of an intersection is the union of the separate complements*.

We conclude this initial list of laws with the **law of involution:**

(SS–14) $$\text{For all } A \subseteq U, \quad \overline{(\bar{A})} = A.$$

This simply says that every element of U, which does not belong to the complement of A, belongs to A itself.

At this point the reader would do well to solve Exercises 5, 11, 14, 15, 16, 23 through 28, 34, 36, 37, of Section 2.8.

2.5   The Algebra of the Subsets of U as a Boolean Algebra

In Section 1.15, we defined a Boolean algebra as a set B for which are defined relations "=" and "≤" (here $\subseteq$), three operations "$\vee$," "$\cdot$," and "$\bar{\ }$," (here $\cup$, $\cap$, and $\bar{\ }$), which contains two distinguished elements 0 and 1, (here $\varnothing$ and U), and which satisfies certain basic laws. With the changes in notation indicated here, these same laws hold for the set of subsets of a universal set, as the first four sections of this chapter reveal. That is, *the algebra of the subsets of a universal set is a Boolean algebra,* just as were the set $\{0, 1\}$ and the set of switching functions of n variables studied in Chapter 1.

2.6   The Principle of Duality, Some Useful Identities

We now have a list of laws long enough so that we can manipulate expressions in a manner similar to that of ordinary algebra and thereby prove some interesting and useful identities in a purely formal fashion. For example, we have the **absorption laws.** For all subsets A and B of U,

(SS–15a) $$A \cup (A \cap B) = A$$

and

(SS–15b) $$A \cap (A \cup B) = A.$$

The first of these may be proved thus:

$$
\begin{aligned}
A \cup (A \cap B) &= (A \cap U) \cup (A \cap B), && \text{by (SS–10b)} \\
&= A \cap (U \cup B), && \text{by (SS–8a)} \\
&= A \cap U, && \text{by (SS–6a, 11a)} \\
&= A. && \text{by (SS–10b)}
\end{aligned}
$$

The second may be proved similarly:

$$
\begin{aligned}
A \cap (A \cup B) &= (A \cup \varnothing) \cap (A \cup B), && \text{by (SS–10a)} \\
&= A \cup (\varnothing \cap B), && \text{by (SS–8b)} \\
&= A \cup \varnothing, && \text{by (SS–6b, 11b)} \\
&= A. && \text{by (SS–10a)}
\end{aligned}
$$

The proof of (SS–15b), simple though it is, is actually unnecessary. The reason lies in the nature of laws (SS–6) through (SS–14). Notice that these laws, except (SS–14), occur in pairs and that each law of one pair is obtainable from the other by

1. the interchange of union and intersection, and
2. the interchange of $\varnothing$ and U.

The complement symbol remains untouched. This situation is described by saying that the laws appear in **dual pairs.** Even (SS-14) meets the test in a fashion, for it involves neither union nor intersection, neither $\varnothing$ nor U. When the prescribed interchanges are made, (SS–14) therefore remains unaltered. This is described by saying that (SS–14) is **self-dual.**

The importance of duality is this: Suppose we can prove a theorem by an application of certain of the laws (SS–6) through (SS–14). Then if at each step we use the dual laws instead, the conclusion must be a theorem dual to the one we proved at first. That is, for every theorem we prove, we know at once that the dual theorem is also correct, no additional proof being necessary. This doubling of the effectiveness of proofs is known as the **principle of duality**. Since (SS–15b) is the dual theorem of (SS–15a), the proof of (SS–15a) therefore suffices to imply also (SS–15b), without further consideration. Notice that the above proofs of (SS–15a) and (SS–15b) employ dual steps throughout.

From (SS–15a) we might expect offhand that $A \cup (A \cap B) = A = A \cup \emptyset$ ought to imply $A \cap B = \emptyset$. However, in many cases $A \cap B \neq \emptyset$. Hence, as was pointed out earlier, *we cannot ordinarily cancel in the case of the union operation*. In the same way, $A \cap (A \cup B) = A = A \cap U$ might lead us to conclude offhand that $A \cup B = U$, but again, simple examples will show that ordinarily $A \cup B \neq U$. Thus *we cannot ordinarily cancel in the case of the intersection operation* either.

Another useful identity and its dual are

(SS–16a) $A \cup (\bar{A} \cap B) = A \cup B$

and

(SS–16b) $A \cap (\bar{A} \cup B) = A \cap B.$

The proof of (SS–16a) proceeds as follows:

$$
\begin{aligned}
A \cup (\bar{A} \cap B) &= (A \cup \bar{A}) \cap (A \cup B), &&\text{by (SS–8b)}\\
&= U \cap (A \cup B), &&\text{by (SS–12a)}\\
&= (A \cup B) \cap U, &&\text{by (SS–6b)}\\
&= A \cup B. &&\text{by (SS–10b)}
\end{aligned}
$$

By the principle of duality, it is unnecessary to prove (SS–16b) separately.

A final dual pair of useful identities is

(SS–17a) $(A \cup B) \cap (\bar{A} \cup C) \cap (B \cup C) = (A \cup B) \cap (\bar{A} \cup C)$

and

(SS–17b) $(A \cap B) \cup (\bar{A} \cap C) \cup (B \cap C) = (A \cap B) \cup (\bar{A} \cap C).$

The proof of (SS–17a) proceeds thus:

$$
\begin{aligned}
(A \cup B) \cap (\bar{A} \cup C) \cap (B \cup C) &= (A \cup B) \cap (\bar{A} \cup C) \cap ((A \cap \bar{A})\\
&\quad \cup B \cup C) &&\text{by (SS–10a)}\\
&= (A \cup B) \cap (\bar{A} \cup C) \cap\\
&\quad (A \cup B \cup C) \cap (\bar{A} \cup B \cup C), &&\text{by (SS–8b)}\\
&= (A \cup B) \cap (A \cup B \cup C) \cap\\
&\quad (\bar{A} \cup C) \cap (\bar{A} \cup B \cup C), &&\text{by (SS–6b)}\\
&= (A \cup B) \cap (\bar{A} \cup C). &&\text{by (SS–15b)}
\end{aligned}
$$

Here only the principal reasons have been given. A number of small steps have been omitted. The reader would do well to identify these. In the last step, (SS–15b) was used twice. The identity (SS–17b) follows by the principle of duality.

The laws (SS–13) and (SS–14) permit the effective computation of complements. For example

$$\overline{(\bar{A} \cap B) \cup (A \cap \bar{B})} = \overline{(\bar{A} \cap B)} \cap \overline{(A \cap \bar{B})} \qquad \text{by (SS–13a)}$$
$$= (A \cup \bar{B}) \cap (\bar{A} \cup B), \qquad \text{by (SS–13b), (SS–14)}$$

or, if we wish to continue,

$$= (A \cap \bar{A}) \cup (A \cap B) \cup (\bar{B} \cap \bar{A}) \cup (\bar{B} \cap B),$$
$$= (A \cap B) \cup (\bar{A} \cap \bar{B}).$$

Again, the reader should supply detailed reasons for these last two steps.

Now if $A = B$, then $\bar{A} = \bar{B}$. Hence, by (SS–14) and the preceding argument, we have also proved the formula:

$$\overline{(A \cap B) \cup (\bar{A} \cap \bar{B})} = (\bar{A} \cap B) \cup (A \cap \bar{B}).$$

Finally, let us illustrate the manipulations that are possible here by expressing $(A \cap \bar{B}) \cup (\bar{A} \cap B)$ as an intersection of unions. We have, by (SS–12b) and (SS–10a),

$$(A \cap \bar{B}) \cup (\bar{A} \cap B) = (A \cap \bar{A}) \cup (A \cap \bar{B}) \cup (\bar{A} \cap B) \cup (\bar{B} \cap B)$$
$$= [A \cap (\bar{A} \cup \bar{B})] \cup [B \cap (\bar{A} \cup \bar{B})]$$
$$= (A \cup B) \cap (\bar{A} \cup \bar{B}).$$

Here we have repeatedly used the commutative, associative, and distributive laws. The last expression may be reduced by (SS–13b) to the form $(A \cup B) \cap \overline{(A \cap B)}$. This illustrates the fact that an expression representing a particular subset of the universal set is not unique but may assume a variety of distinct but equivalent forms.

2.7 Further Properties of the Inclusion Relation

From the definition of intersection, we have

(SS–18) $A \cap B \subseteq A$ and $A \cap B \subseteq B$.

From the first of these, by (SS–5a), we have

$$A \cup (A \cap B) = A,$$

so that we have a new and shorter proof of (SS–15a).

Similarly, from the definition of union,

(SS–19) $A \subseteq A \cup B$ and $B \subseteq A \cup B.$

From the first of these we have, by (SS–5b),

$$A \cap (A \cup B) = A,$$

which is the identity (SS–15b).

These two results are made intuitively clear by a glance at a Venn diagram (Figure 2.7.1(A)).

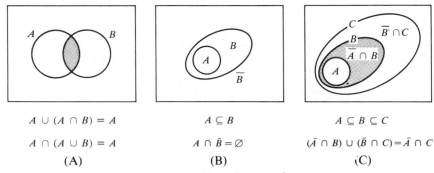

$A \cup (A \cap B) = A$	$A \subseteq B$	$A \subseteq B \subseteq C$
$A \cap (A \cup B) = A$	$A \cap \bar{B} = \varnothing$	$(\bar{A} \cap B) \cup (\bar{B} \cap C) = \bar{A} \cap C$
(A)	(B)	(C)

Properties of the inclusion relation
Figure 2.7.1

Next we prove the useful result:

(SS–20) *If* $A \subseteq B$, *then, for all* C, $A \cup C \subseteq B \cup C$ *and* $A \cap C \subseteq B \cap C.$

Since $A \subseteq B$, we have $A \cup B = B$, by (SS–5a). Joining equals to equals, we obtain $(A \cup B) \cup C = B \cup C$. Therefore, since $C \cup C = C$, by using the commutative and associative laws, we have $(A \cup C) \cup (B \cup C) = (B \cup C)$. Hence, by (SS–5a) again, $A \cup C \subseteq B \cup C.$

From $A \subseteq B$, we have $A \cap B = A$, by (SS–5b). Intersecting equals with equals, we have $(A \cap B) \cap C = A \cap C$. Since $C \cap C = C$, by using the commutative and associative laws, we obtain $(A \cap C) \cap (B \cap C) = A \cap C$. Hence, by (SS–5b), $A \cap C \subseteq B \cap C.$

Another important result that is easily proved formally is this:

(SS–21) $A \subseteq B$ *if and only if* $A \cap \bar{B} = \varnothing.$

This result expresses the equivalence of an inclusion and an equality, just as do (SS–5a) and (SS–5b).

To prove the theorem, assume first that $A \subseteq B$. Then, by (SS–5b), $A = A \cap B$. Intersecting both members with $\bar{B}$, we have

$$A \cap \bar{B} = (A \cap B) \cap \bar{B} = A \cap (B \cap \bar{B}) = A \cap \varnothing = \varnothing.$$

Conversely, assume $A \cap \bar{B} = \varnothing$. Then we have the equations,

$$A = A \cap U = A \cap (B \cup \bar{B}) = (A \cap B) \cup (A \cap \bar{B}) = (A \cap B) \cup \varnothing =$$
$$A \cap B.$$

Hence $A \subseteq B$, by (SS–5b). This theorem is illustrated in Figure 2.7.1(B). As a final example, we prove:

> *If* $A \subseteq B \subseteq C$, *then* $(\bar{A} \cap B) \cup (\bar{B} \cap C) = \bar{A} \cap C$.

This result is illustrated in Figure 2.7.1(C).

From $A \subseteq B$, we have $A \cap B = A$. Hence $\overline{A \cap B} = \bar{A}$; that is, $\bar{A} \cup \bar{B} = \bar{A}$. Also, from $B \subseteq C$, we have $B \cap C = B$. Hence

$$
\begin{aligned}
(\bar{A} \cap B) \cup (\bar{B} \cap C) &= [\bar{A} \cap (B \cap C)] \cup (\bar{B} \cap C) && \text{(substitution for } B) \\
&= [(\bar{A} \cap B) \cap C] \cup (\bar{B} \cap C) \\
&= [(\bar{A} \cap B) \cup \bar{B}] \cap C && \text{by (SS–8a)} \\
&= (\bar{A} \cup \bar{B}) \cap C && \text{by (SS–16a)} \\
&= \bar{A} \cap C && \text{(substitution for } \bar{A} \cup \bar{B}).
\end{aligned}
$$

The theorems and examples of Sections 2.6 and 2.7 illustrate some types of manipulations and arguments that are useful and natural in the algebra of the subsets of a set. The following exercises provide the reader an opportunity to master the preceding techniques and to develop others of his own.

2.8   Exercises

1.   Give an example of an interesting set that is most conveniently defined by listing all its members. Then give an example of a set that cannot be defined by listing all its members.

2.   Give an example of a set whose elements are sets.

3.   Define the empty set by means of properties in two different ways.

4.   Give an example of nonempty sets which are equal although defined by different properties.

5.   Is the belonging relation ($\in$) reflexive? symmetric? transitive?

6.   (a)   Give an example showing that one can have $a \in A$ and $A \in \mathscr{A}$ without having $a \in \mathscr{A}$. Can all three hold true at once?
   (b)   Contrast the meanings of the statements

$$a \in A; \qquad \{a\} \subseteq A.$$

Is it ever legitimate to write $\{a\} \in A$?

7. Are the sets $\varnothing$ and $\{\varnothing\}$ equal? Why? Are they different from $\big\{\{\varnothing\}\big\}$? How many distinct sets can one construct in this way?

8.   Identify these sets: $\{A \mid A \neq A\}$, $\{A \mid A = B, B \text{ fixed}\}$, $\{x \mid x \in A\}$.

9.   What are the union and the intersection of the infinite sets $\{1, 2, 4, 6, \dots, 2(n - 1), \dots\}$ and $\{1, 3, 6, 9, \dots, 3(n - 1), \dots\}$?

10.   Let N denote the set of all positive integers. Let $A = \{2n \mid n \in N\}$ and $B = \{3n \mid n \in N\}$. Determine which of the following are true statements:

$$A = B, \qquad A \cap B = \varnothing,$$
$$A \subseteq B, \qquad A \cup B = \{6n \mid n \in N\},$$
$$B \subseteq A, \qquad A \cap B = \{6n \mid n \in N\},$$
$$A \cup B = \big\{6n + k - 6 \mid n \in N \text{ and } k \in \{0,2,3,4\}\big\}.$$

11.   Give an example of two sets A and B such that $A \not\subseteq \bar{B}$, $B \not\subseteq \bar{A}$, and $A \neq B$ are all true. (A Venn diagram will suffice.)

12.   Draw a Venn diagram showing that one can have $A \cup C = B \cup C$ with $A \neq B$. Draw another showing that one can have $A \cap D = B \cap D$ with $A \neq B$.

13.   Many of the laws of set algebra given in preceding sections do not require the use of the assumption that the sets involved are subsets of some specifically identified universal set. Which laws are these? (One example is the law $A \cup B = B \cup A$ since one can form the union without naming a specific universal set U, and for given A and B, infinitely many choices for U are possible.)

14.   What common fact (expressed in terms of set operations) holds for the sets A, B, C, illustrated in the Venn diagrams of Figure 2.8.1?

   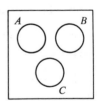

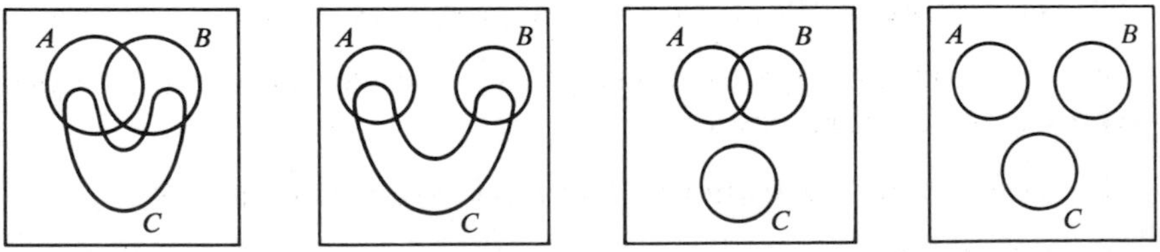

Sets satisfying a common relation
Figure 2.8.1

Same question for the diagrams of Figure 2.8.2.

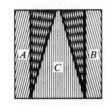 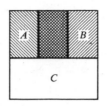 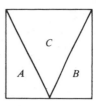

Sets satisfying another common relation
Figure 2.8.2

15.   Given that $A \cap B \cap C \neq \varnothing$, draw Venn diagrams illustrating the various relationships that can exist among A, B, C, with respect to intersection and inclusion.

16.   Draw Venn diagrams illustrating these conditions:

(a) $A \cup B \subset A \cup C$ but $B \not\subset C$,
(b) $A \cap B \subset A \cap C$ but $B \not\subset C$.

Now illustrate the same relationships with specific finite sets A, B, C, of real numbers.

17.   Prove that for arbitrary subsets of a universal set U:

(a) $[A \cup (B \cap \bar{C})] \cap (B \cup C) = (A \cup \bar{C}) \cap (B \cup C)$,
(b) $(A \cap \bar{B} \cap C) \cup (\bar{A} \cap B \cap D)$
$$= [(A \cap C) \cup (B \cap D)] \cap (\bar{A} \cup \bar{B})$$
$$= (A \cup B) \cap [(A \cap D) \cup (\bar{B} \cap C)],$$
(c) $(A \cap B) \cup (B \cap C) \cup (C \cap A)$
$$= (A \cup B) \cap (B \cup C) \cap (C \cup A),$$
(d) $\overline{[(A \cap C) \cup (B \cap \bar{C})]} = (\bar{A} \cap C) \cup (\bar{B} \cap \bar{C})$,
(e) $\overline{A \cup B} = \bar{A} \cap \bar{B}; \overline{A \cap B} = \bar{A} \cup \bar{B}$,
(f) $A \cap B \cap (\bar{A} \cup B) = A \cap B \cap (A \cup B)$
$$= A \cap B \cap (A \cup \bar{B}) = A \cap B,$$
(g) $(A \cap B \cap C) \cup (\bar{B} \cap C) \cup \bar{C} = A \cup \bar{B} \cup \bar{C}$,
(h) $(A \cap \bar{B}) \cup (\bar{A} \cap B \cap C) = (A \cap \bar{B}) \cup (\bar{A} \cap C)$.

18.   Simplify each expression:

(a) $(A \cap B) \cup (\bar{A} \cap B) \cup (A \cap \bar{B}) \cup (\bar{A} \cap \bar{B})$,
(b) $(A \cap B \cap \bar{C}) \cup (A \cap \bar{B} \cap \bar{C}) \cup (A \cap \bar{B} \cap C)$,
(c) $\overline{[\overline{A \cup B} \cap (A \cup C) \cap \overline{B \cap C}]} \cup \bar{C}$,
(d) $(A \cap B) \cup \overline{B \cap (\bar{A} \cup C)}$,
(e) $A \cap (A \cup \bar{\bar{B}})$.

19.   Prove that for all subsets A, B, C of a universal set $U, (A \cup B) \cap C \subseteq A \cup (B \cap C)$. Illustrate with a Venn diagram.

*20. Prove each of the following, where A, B, C, are subsets of a universal set U:

(a) If $A \cup B = \emptyset$, then $A = \emptyset$ and $B = \emptyset$.

(b) If $A \cap B = U$, then $A = U$ and $B = U$.

(c) If there exists a set C such that $A \cup C = B \cup C$ and $A \cap C = B \cap C$, then $A = B$.

(d) If $A \cap \bar{B} = \emptyset$ and $B \cap \bar{C} = \emptyset$, then $A \cap \bar{C} = \emptyset$.

(e) If $A \cup B = B$ and $\bar{A} \cap B = \emptyset$, then $A = B$.

(f) If $A \cup B = U$ and $A \cap B = \emptyset$, then $B = \bar{A}$.

(g) If $(A \cap C) \cup (B \cap \bar{C}) = \emptyset$, then $A \cap B = \emptyset$.

(h) If $(A \cap C) \cup (B \cap \bar{C}) = U$, then $A \cup B = U, B \cup C = U$, and $A \cup \bar{C} = U$.

(i) If $A \cap B = A$ and $B \cup C = C$, then $A \cap \bar{C} = \emptyset$.

(j) If $A \subseteq B$ and $B \subseteq C$, then $A \cup B \cup C = C$.

(k) If $A \cap B = A$ and $B \cup C = B$, then $(A \cup C) \cap B = A \cup C$.

(l) If $A \cap \bar{B} = \emptyset$ and $A \neq \emptyset$, then $B \neq \emptyset$.

(m) If $A \cap \bar{B} = \emptyset$ and $A \cap B = \emptyset$, then $A = \emptyset$.

(n) $A = \emptyset$ if and only if $(A \cap \bar{B}) \cup (\bar{A} \cap B) = B$ for some $B \subseteq U$.

*21. Prove each of the following, where A, B, C, D are arbitrary but fixed subsets of a universal set:

(a) $A \cap B \subseteq A \subseteq A \cup B$.

(b) If $A \subseteq B$ and $C \subseteq D$, then $A \cup C \subseteq B \cup D$ and $A \cap C \subseteq B \cap D$.

(c) If $A \subseteq B$ and $C \subseteq B$, then $A \cup C \subseteq B$ and $A \cap C \subseteq B$.

(d) If $A \cup B \subseteq C$, then $A \subseteq C$ and $B \subseteq C$.

(e) If $A \subseteq B$ and $A \subseteq C$, then $A \subseteq B \cap C$ and $A \subseteq B \cup C$.

(f) $A \subseteq B$ if and only if $\bar{A} \cup B = U$.

(g) $A \cap B \subseteq (A \cap C) \cup (B \cap \bar{C}) \subseteq A \cup B$.

(h) $A \subseteq B$ if and only if $\bar{B} \subseteq \bar{A}$.

(i) If $A \supseteq B \supseteq C$, then $(A \cap \bar{B}) \cup (B \cap \bar{C}) = A \cap \bar{C}$.

(j) If $A \subseteq \bar{A}$, then $A = \emptyset$ and if $\bar{A} \subseteq A$, then $A = U$.

(k) If $A \subseteq B$ and $\bar{A} \subseteq B$ for some A, then $B = U$.

22. The **symmetric difference** of two sets A and B is denoted by $A \oplus B$ and is defined by the formula

$$A \oplus B = (\bar{A} \cap B) \cup (A \cap \bar{B}).$$

Illustrate $A \oplus B$ and $(A \oplus B) \oplus C$ with Venn diagrams. Then prove

(a) $A \oplus B = B \oplus A$; $(A \oplus B) \oplus B = A$ (these explain the name),

(b) $A \oplus (B \oplus C) = (A \oplus B) \oplus C$,

(c) $A \cap (B \oplus C) = (A \cap B) \oplus (A \cap C)$,

(d) $A \cup B = A \oplus B \oplus AB$,
(e) $A \oplus A = \emptyset$,
(f) $A \oplus \emptyset = A$,
(g) $A \oplus U = \bar{A}$,
(h) $A \oplus \bar{A} = U$.
(i)   If $A \oplus B = C$, then $B = A \oplus C$.
(j) $A \oplus B = A \cup B$ if and only if $A \cap B = \emptyset$.

*23.   Prove that for arbitrary subsets A_i, $i = 1, 2, \ldots, n$, of a universal set U and for every positive integer n,

(a) $\overline{\bigcap_{i=1}^{n} A_i} = \bigcup_{i=1}^{n} \bar{A}_i$,   (b) $\overline{\bigcup_{i=1}^{n} A_i} = \bigcap_{i=1}^{n} \bar{A}_i$.

Note that these are generalized DeMorgan laws.

*24.   Prove that for arbitrary sets A and B_i, $i = 1, 2, \ldots, n$, and for each positive integer n,

(a) $A \cap \left(\bigcup_{i=1}^{n} B_i \right) = \bigcup_{i=1}^{n} (A \cap B_i)$,   (b) $A \cup \left(\bigcap_{i=1}^{n} B_i \right) = \bigcap_{i=1}^{n} (A \cup B_i)$.

Note that these are generalized distributive laws.

25.   What is wrong with this "proof"?

"Theorem":   *For all A, B, which are subsets of U,*

(a) $A \cap B = B$.

   "PROOF":   We have

(b) $\bar{A} = \bar{A}$.

Uniting corresponding members of (a) and (b), we obtain

$$\bar{A} \cup (A \cap B) = \bar{A} \cup B.$$

By the distributive law,

$$(\bar{A} \cup A) \cap (\bar{A} \cup B) = \bar{A} \cup B$$

so

$$U \cap (\bar{A} \cup B) = \bar{A} \cup B$$

or

$$\bar{A} \cup B = \bar{A} \cup B.$$

Hence

$$A \cap B = B.$$

26.   Prove *in detail* that for all sets A, B, C, D,

(a) $(A \cap B) \cap (C \cap D) = (A \cap C) \cap (D \cap B)$,
(b) $A \cap (B \cap C \cap D) = (A \cap B) \cap (C \cap D)$.

*27.   Prove that for all subsets A, B, C, of a universal set U,

   (a) $A \subseteq B$ if and only if $A \cup C \subseteq B \cup C$ for *all* C.
   (b) $A \subseteq B$ if and only if $A \cap C \subseteq B \cap C$ for *all* C.

28.   Prove that if $A \cup X = A \cup B$ and $A \cap X = \varnothing$, then $X = \bar{A} \cap B$.

29.   Define

$$Y_1 = X_1,$$
$$Y_2 = X_1 \cup (\bar{X}_1 \cap X_2),$$
$$Y_3 = X_1 \cup (\bar{X}_1 \cap X_2) \cup (\bar{X}_1 \cap \bar{X}_2 \cap X_3),$$

$$\cdot$$
$$\cdot$$
$$\cdot$$

$$Y_n = X_1 \cup (\bar{X}_1 \cap X_2) \cup \cdots \cup (\bar{X}_1 \cup \bar{X}_2 \cap \cdots \cap \bar{X}_{n-1} \cap X_n)$$

Prove by induction that for all positive integers n,

$$Y_n = X_1 \cup X_2 \cup \cdots \cup X_n.$$

Note that this is a generalization of (SS–16a) and that it permits the representation of $\bigcup_{j=1}^{n} X_j$ as a union of disjoint sets. Dualize.

30.   Referring to the definition of "$\oplus$" in Exercise 22, prove

   (a) $\bigcup_{i=1}^{n} A_i \oplus \bigcup_{i=1}^{n} B_i \subseteq \bigcup_{i=1}^{n} (A_i \oplus B_i),$

   (b) $\sum_{i=1}^{n} A_i = \sum_{i=1}^{n} \bar{A}_i$ (*n* even),

   (c) $\sum_{i=1}^{n} A_i = \sum_{i=1}^{n} \bar{A}_i$ (*n* odd).

Here Σ refers to the operation $\oplus$. Exercise 22(g) will help with (b) and (c).

31.   Let subsets A and B of U be plane regions enclosed by simple closed curves, and let the curves themselves be parts of the regions. In Figure 2.8.3 (A), (B), what parts of the boundaries of A and B, in

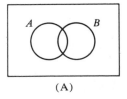
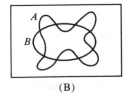

(A)   (B)

Sets for computation of symmetric difference
Figure 2.8.3

particular the points where the boundaries intersect, belong to $A \oplus B$? Can you devise a general rule?

32. (a) Given that $A \oplus B \subseteq C$, prove that $A \subseteq B \cup C$.
    (b) Give an example to show that $A \oplus B \subseteq C$ does *not* imply $A \subseteq B \oplus C$.
    (c) Simplify $(A \oplus B \oplus C) \cap (A \cup B) \cap (B \cup C) \cap (C \cup A)$.

33. Given that x is an element of U and that $A_1, A_2, \ldots, A_n$ are subsets of U, under what condition will x be an element of $A_1 \oplus A_2 \oplus \cdots \oplus A_n$?

34. Given that $A_j \subseteq B_j, j = 1, 2, \ldots, n$, prove that

$$\bigcup_{j=1}^{n} A_j \subseteq \bigcup_{j=1}^{n} B_j \quad \text{and} \quad \bigcap_{j=1}^{n} A_j \subseteq \bigcap_{j=1}^{n} B_j.$$

Do these conclusions extend to infinite sequences of sets?

35. Show that it is proper to define the dual of $A \subseteq B$ to be $A \supseteq B$; that is, $B \subseteq A$. Then state and also prove directly the dual of (SS–21), Section 2.7.

36. Prove that if $j_1, j_2, \ldots, j_n$ is a permutation of $1, 2, \ldots, n$,

$$\bigcup_{i=1}^{n} A_i = \bigcup_{p=1}^{k} A_{j_p} \cup \left(\bigcup_{p=k+1}^{n} A_{j_p} \right).$$

37. Prove that

$$\bigcup_{j=1}^{n} (A_j \cup B_j) = \left(\bigcup_{j=1}^{n} A_j \right) \cup \left(\bigcup_{j=1}^{n} B_j \right).$$

38. Prove (SS–8b) directly.

39. Prove that the principle of duality is a consequence of DeMorgan's laws, the law of involution, and the facts that $\emptyset = U$, $\bar{U} = \emptyset$. (For example, for all subsets A and B of U, $A \cup B = B \cup A$. But $\bar{A}$ and $\bar{B}$ are subsets of U. Hence $\bar{A} \cup \bar{B} = \bar{B} \cup \bar{A}$. By DeMorgan, $A \cap B = B \cap A$. Then by the law of involution, $A \cap B = B \cap A$, and similarly for all other dual pairs of laws.)

2.9 Partitioning of the Universal Set

Let X_1 denote an arbitrary subset of the universal set U. Then

$$X_1 \cup \bar{X}_1 = U.$$

If X_1 and X_2 are arbitrary subsets of U, the identities we have established show also that

$$(\bar{X}_1 \cap \bar{X}_2) \cup (\bar{X}_1 \cap X_2) \cup (X_1 \cap \bar{X}_2) \cup (X_1 \cap X_2) = U$$

and, in the case of three arbitrary subsets of U,

$$(\bar{X}_1 \cap \bar{X}_2 \cap \bar{X}_3) \cup (\bar{X}_1 \cap \bar{X}_2 \cap X_3) \cup (\bar{X}_1 \cap X_2 \cap \bar{X}_3) \cup (\bar{X}_1 \cap X_2 \cap X_3)$$
$$\cup (X_1 \cap \bar{X}_2 \cap \bar{X}_3) \cup (X_1 \cap \bar{X}_2 \cap X_3) \cup (X_1 \cap X_2 \cap \bar{X}_3) \cup$$
$$(X_1 \cap X_2 \cap X_3) = U.$$

Let us adopt a notation similar to that of Chapter 1. Let the **complete intersections** I_j of $X_1, X_2, \ldots, X_n$ be defined thus:

$$I_j = X_1^{e_1} \cap X_2^{e_2} \cap \cdots \cap X_n^{e_n},$$

where

$$j_{\text{dec}} = e_1 e_2, \ldots, e_{n_{\text{bin}}}; \qquad j = 0, 1, \ldots, 2^n - 1.$$

Then these three decompositions of U are illustrated by the Venn diagrams of Figure 2.9.1.

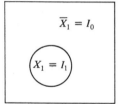
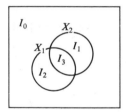
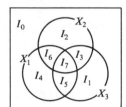

Complete intersections of sets
Figure 2.9.1

It is not hard to prove by induction that, for arbitrary subsets X_1, X_2, $\ldots, X_n$ of U,

$$\bigcup_{j=0}^{2^n-1} I_j = U,$$

and also that in every case

$$I_j \cap I_k = \varnothing, \qquad j \neq k.$$

That is,

The n arbitrary subsets $X_1, X_2, \ldots, X_n$ of U subdivide U into 2^n mutually disjoint subsets.

Similarly, we have

$$X_1 \cap \bar{X}_1 = \varnothing$$

and, in the case of two variables X_1, X_2, we have

$$(X_1 \cup X_2) \cap (X_1 \cup \bar{X}_2) \cap (\bar{X}_1 \cup X_2) \cap (\bar{X}_1 \cup \bar{X}_2) = \emptyset.$$

If we define **complete unions** thus:

$$U_i = X_1^{e_1} \cup X_2^{e_2} \cup \cdots \cup X_n^{e_n},$$

where again

$$i_{\text{dec}} = \bar{e}_1 \bar{e}_2 \cdots \bar{e}_{n_{\text{bin}}}; \qquad i = 0, 1, \ldots, 2^n - 1,$$

we have, by induction,

$$\bigcap_{i=0}^{2^n-1} U_i = \emptyset.$$

It is important to observe that each complete intersection assumes the value U for exactly one assignment of $\emptyset$'s and U's as values to the X_i's, and that a complete union assumes the value $\emptyset$ for exactly one assignment of $\emptyset$'s and U's as values to the X_i's. If values *other* than $\emptyset$'s and U's are assigned to the X_i's, the resulting value of a complete union or intersection may be $\emptyset$, U, or another subset of U.

2.10   Subsets of Finite Sets

Most of the sets of concern in switching theory are subsets of finite sets, as is illustrated in Section 2.2. To pursue this matter further, consider a set S with just two elements, a and b. Its subsets, starting with the empty set, are

$$\emptyset, \quad \{a\}, \quad \{b\}, \quad \{a, b\},$$

where the braces, as explained before, mean "the set consisting of the elements represented by the symbols enclosed." If we interpret the symbol $\tilde{a}$ to mean the rejection of the element a, and similarly for b, in the formation of subsets, then these four subsets may be represented respectively as

$$\{\tilde{a}, \tilde{b}\}, \quad \{a, \tilde{b}\}, \quad \{\tilde{a}, b\}, \quad \{a, b\}.$$

Similarly, the set $\{a, b, c\}$ has the eight subsets:

$$\{\tilde{a}, \tilde{b}, \tilde{c}\}, \quad \{\tilde{a}, \tilde{b}, c\}, \quad \{\tilde{a}, b, \tilde{c}\}, \quad \{\tilde{a}, b, c\},$$
$$\{a, \tilde{b}, \tilde{c}\}, \quad \{a, \tilde{b}, c\}, \quad \{a, b, \tilde{c}\}, \quad \{a, b, c\}.$$

In general, if a set S contains n elements, then in the formation of a subset we have two choices as we look at each element: we either reject or accept the element for membership in the subset. Hence there are $2 \cdot 2 \cdot \cdots \cdot 2 = 2^n$ choices altogether, that is, we have the result:

A finite set S of n elements has exactly 2^n subsets.

Moreover, by preceding sections, these 2^n subsets form a Boolean algebra with respect to the definitions of $=$, $\subseteq$, $\varnothing$, U, $\cup$, $\cap$, and $^{-}$ employed here.

That a finite set has 2^n subsets may also be seen by totaling the number of subsets with *no* elements, with *one* element, ..., with *n* elements:

$$\binom{n}{0} + \binom{n}{1} + \binom{n}{2} + \cdots + \binom{n}{n} = (1 + 1)^n = 2^n$$

by the formula for the binomial expansion.

Many of the things we have already studied in this book involve subsets of finite sets. For example, starting with *n* switching variables $x_1, x_2, \ldots, x_n$, we can form a set U of 3^n distinct products of the form $x_{i_1}^{e_1} x_{i_2}^{e_2} \cdots x_{i_k}^{e_k}$, $k \leq n$, since in the formation of such a product each variable is rejected, accepted as it stands, or accepted in complemented form. If all the variables are rejected, the product is, by definition, 1. These 3^n products are called the **fundamental products** determined by the *n* variables. The 2^n *complete* products $x_1^{e_1} x_2^{e_2} \cdots x_n^{e_n}$ are a particularly useful subset of the set U. Another useful subset of U consists of the 2^n distinct products which are free of complements, that is, all products of the form $x_{i_1} x_{i_2} \cdots x_{i_k}$, $k \leq n$. Again, if *all* the variables are rejected, the product is, by definition, 1. Still another useful subset of products is the set $x_1, \bar{x}_1 x_2, \bar{x}_1 \bar{x}_2 x_3, \ldots, \bar{x}_1 \bar{x}_2 \cdots \bar{x}_{n-1} x_n$.

As a different kind of example, let S be a set of n properties $a_1, a_2, \ldots, a_n$ which define *n* distinct subsets $A_1, A_2, \ldots, A_n$ of a possibly infinite universal set U. As we have seen in Section 2.9, these *n* subsets of U partition U into 2^n disjoint subsets, one for each complete intersection:

$$I_j = A_1^{e_1} \cap A_2^{e_2} \cap \cdots \cap A_n^{e_n}, \qquad j = 0, 1, \ldots, 2^n - 1.$$

Thus we have one subset of U for each of the 2^n sets of properties

$$\{a_1^{e_1}, a_2^{e_2}, \ldots, a_n^{e_n}\}, \qquad e_j = 0 \text{ or } 1,$$

where a_j^1 means a_j and where a_j^0 means the denial of property a_j, that is, that the property a_j does *not* hold. Thus, each of the 2^n possible sets of properties or denials of properties in S leads to a subset I_j, which may be empty, nonempty but finite, or infinite, depending on circumstances.

To illustrate the preceding example concretely, let a_j be the property, "relay X_j is operated," so that a_j^0 implies that X_j is *not* operated. Let each relay X_j be equipped with 2^{j-1} transfer contacts as shown in Figure 2.10.1 for the case $n = 3$. Such a switching circuit is called a **relay tree**.

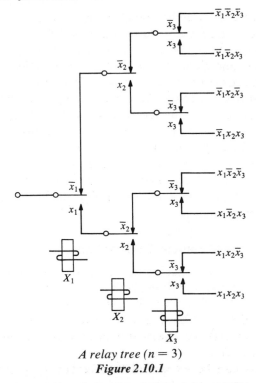

A relay tree (n = 3)

Figure 2.10.1

Then to each subset $\{a_1^{e_1}, a_2^{e_2}, \ldots, a_n^{e_n}\}$ of S there corresponds exactly one of the 2^n switching functions realized by the relay tree.

Now, consider any switching function of two variables x_1 and x_2. We can check each of the combinations of x_1 and x_2 to determine whether or not the value of f is 1 there. Then a circuit realizing f may be obtained by connecting the outputs of a relay tree corresponding to the combinations at which f assumes the value 1 to a common terminal and, of course, deleting the unnecessary contacts. For example, if f assumes the value 1 at the combinations 00 and 11, we have the circuit shown in Figure 2.10.2.

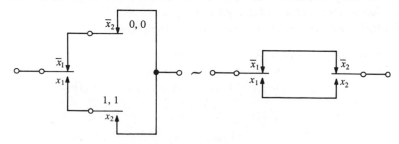

Example of design using a relay tree

Figure 2.10.2

The products which are the switching functions associated with the terminals of a relay tree are what we have called complete products of the variables in question. Hence, in this case, $f = \bar{x}_1\bar{x}_2 \lor x_1x_2$. This is at times a very uneconomical way of realizing a function f, since it may well require unnecessarily many contacts. However, the idea is useful nonetheless, and many circuits have been designed by beginning with a relay tree. For details, see the references given for Chapter 1. The idea also has useful analogues in other parts of switching theory.

Realizing a switching function in this way—that is, by connecting to an appropriate subset of the output terminals of a relay tree—amounts to a direct realization of its disjunctive normal form: the terminals to which we connect are those corresponding to the complete products appearing in the normal form.

2.11   Normal Forms of Boolean Set Functions

Let $X_1, X_2, \ldots, X_n$ be variables denoting subsets of a universal set U. Any function f of these variables, built up by a finite number of uses of the operations $\cup$, $\cap$, and $^-$ will be called a **Boolean set function.** Two Boolean set functions will be said to be **equal** if and only if they assume the same value (a set) for every substitution of subsets of U for the variables $X_1, X_2, \ldots, X_n$.

Such functions can be expanded into certain normal forms, just as are switching functions of n binary variables. For example, if $n = 3$, we have, with the aid of various rules developed earlier,

$$
\begin{aligned}
\overline{X_1 \cup X_2} \cup (\bar{X}_1 \cap X_3) &= (\bar{X}_1 \cap \bar{X}_2) \cup (\bar{X}_1 \cap X_3) \\
&= [\bar{X}_1 \cap \bar{X}_2 \cap (X_3 \cup \bar{X}_3)] \\
&\qquad\qquad \cup [\bar{X}_1 \cap (X_2 \cup \bar{X}_2) \cap X_3] \\
&= (\bar{X}_1 \cap \bar{X}_2 \cap \bar{X}_3) \cup (\bar{X}_1 \cap \bar{X}_2 \cap X_3) \\
&\qquad\qquad \cup (\bar{X}_1 \cap X_2 \cap X_3) \\
&= I_0 \cup I_1 \cup I_3.
\end{aligned}
$$

Thus we have expanded the given set function into *disjunctive normal form,* that is, into a union of complete intersections.

Similarly, we can obtain a *conjunctive normal form:*

$$
\begin{aligned}
\overline{X_1 \cup X_2} \cup (\bar{X}_1 \cap X_3) &= (\bar{X}_1 \cap \bar{X}_2) \cup (\bar{X}_1 \cap X_3) \\
&= \bar{X}_1 \cap (\bar{X}_2 \cup X_3) \\
&= [\bar{X}_1 \cup (X_2 \cap \bar{X}_2) \cup (X_3 \cap \bar{X}_3)] \\
&\qquad \cap [(X_1 \cap \bar{X}_1) \cup \bar{X}_2 \cup X_3] \\
&= (\bar{X}_1 \cup X_2 \cup X_3) \cap (\bar{X}_1 \cup \bar{X}_2 \cup X_3) \\
&\qquad \cap (\bar{X}_1 \cup X_2 \cup \bar{X}_3) \cap (\bar{X}_1 \cup \bar{X}_2 \cup \bar{X}_3) \\
&\qquad\qquad \cap (X_1 \cup \bar{X}_2 \cup X_3) \\
&= U_2 \cap U_4 \cap U_5 \cap U_6 \cap U_7.
\end{aligned}
$$

These two examples illustrate the fact that, given any Boolean set function f of the variables $X_1, X_2, \ldots, X_n$, by exactly the same procedures used for switching functions, we can expand f into **disjunctive and conjunctive normal forms**—that is, into unions and intersections of complete intersections and unions, respectively. Moreover, for a given function, these expansions must be unique, since otherwise there would be an assignment of $\varnothing$'s and U's as values to the X_i's such that one expansion would assume the value $\varnothing$, whereas another would assume the value U. That is, we have the

Theorem: *Every Boolean set function* $f(X_1, X_2, \ldots, X_n)$ *of arbitrary subsets of a universal set U has a unique disjunctive normal form:*

$$f(X_1, X_2, \ldots, X_n) = \bigcup_{j=0}^{2^n-1} (f_j \cap I_j)$$

in which f_j *is U or* $\varnothing$ *according as* I_j *does or does not appear in the expansion. The function f also has a unique conjunctive normal form:*

$$f(X_1, X_2, \ldots, X_n) = \bigcap_{j=0}^{2^n-1} (f_j \cup U_j)$$

where f_j *is* $\varnothing$ *or U according as* U_j *does or does not appear in the expansion.*

Since the normal forms are *unique*, two Boolean set functions are equal if and only if they have the same disjunctive (or conjunctive) normal form. This shows that *there are exactly* 2^{2^n} *distinct Boolean functions of n variable subsets* $X_1, X_2, \ldots, X_n$ *of a universal set U.* On the other hand, two normal forms are equal if and only if they contain exactly the same complete intersections I_j (or complete unions U_j); that is, because of the special character of the I_j's (and of the U_j's) they are equal if and only if they assume the value U (or $\varnothing$) for exactly the same sequences of n $\varnothing$'s and U's. We therefore have what is known as the

Verification Theorem: *Two Boolean set functions f and g of the variables* $X_1, X_2, \ldots, X_n$ *whose common domain is the set of all subsets of a universal set U are identically equal if and only if they assume equal values for each of the* 2^n *assignments of* $\varnothing$'s *and U's as values to the variables* $X_1, X_2, \ldots, X_n$.

By way of illustration, let us prove that if X_1, X_2, X_3 are arbitrary subsets of a universal set U, and if

$$f(X_1, X_2, X_3) = (X_1 \cup X_2) \cap (X_2 \cup X_3) \cap (X_3 \cup X_1)$$

and

$$g(X_1, X_2, X_3) = (X_1 \cap X_2) \cup (X_2 \cap X_3) \cup (X_3 \cap X_1),$$

then

$$f = g.$$

The proof is provided by Table 2.11.1, in view of the verification theorem.

Table 2.11.1

X_1	X_2	X_3	$X_1 \cup X_2$	$X_2 \cup X_3$	$X_3 \cup X_1$	f	$X_1 \cap X_2$	$X_2 \cap X_3$	$X_3 \cap X_1$	g
$\varnothing$	$\varnothing$	$\varnothing$	$\varnothing$	$\varnothing$	$\varnothing$	$\varnothing$	$\varnothing$	$\varnothing$	$\varnothing$	$\varnothing$
$\varnothing$	$\varnothing$	U	$\varnothing$	U	U	$\varnothing$	$\varnothing$	$\varnothing$	$\varnothing$	$\varnothing$
$\varnothing$	U	$\varnothing$	U	U	$\varnothing$	$\varnothing$	$\varnothing$	$\varnothing$	$\varnothing$	$\varnothing$
$\varnothing$	U	U	U	U	U	U	$\varnothing$	U	$\varnothing$	U
U	$\varnothing$	$\varnothing$	U	$\varnothing$	U	$\varnothing$	$\varnothing$	$\varnothing$	$\varnothing$	$\varnothing$
U	$\varnothing$	U	U	U	U	U	$\varnothing$	$\varnothing$	U	U
U	U	$\varnothing$	U	U	U	U	U	$\varnothing$	$\varnothing$	U
U	U	U	U	U	U	U	U	U	U	U

The power of the verification theorem, as illustrated by this example, should be well noted. Strictly speaking, two set functions f and g of $X_1, X_2, \ldots, X_n$ are equal if and only if they have the same value for *every* possible assignment of values to the X_j's, including assignments which are not $\varnothing$ or U. The verification theorem says that it is necessary to consider only $\varnothing$ and U as possible values of the X_j's in testing two functions for equality.

This is similar to the fact that in the algebra of complex numbers, two polynomials of degree n in the variable x are identical if and only if they have the same value for all values of x. However, in order to prove that they are equal at all values of x, it suffices to prove they are equal at only $n + 1$ distinct values of x.

2.12   Boolean Algebras of Set Functions

It is not hard to see that the 2^{2^n} Boolean set functions of $X_1, X_2, \ldots, X_n$ discussed in the preceding section constitute a Boolean algebra. Indeed, equality has just been defined and a test for it has been established. The functions $\varnothing = \bigcap_{j=0}^{2^n-1} U_j$ and $U = \bigcup_{j=0}^{2^n-1} I_j$ belong to the set. The function $\bar{f}$ may be defined as the union of those I_j's not appearing in the disjunctive normal form of f, for then, for every assignment of values to $X_1, X_2, \ldots, X_n$, f and $\bar{f}$ will have complementary sets as values because the I_j's are mutually disjoint. Similarly $f \cup g$ may properly be defined as the union of all I_j's belonging to one or the other or both of the disjunctive normal forms of f and g. Also, $f \cap g$ may be defined as the union of all those I_j's belonging to both of the disjunctive normal forms of f and g. Thus this set of functions is closed with respect to the operations $\cup$, $\cap$, $^-$. We can also define $f \subseteq g$ if and only if every I_j in the disjunctive normal form of f appears also in the disjunctive normal form of g, for then and only then, no matter what values are assigned to the X_i's, the value of f will be a subset of the corresponding value of g. Again, this is because the I_j's are disjoint sets. It is now a routine matter to establish that all the laws of a Boolean algebra (Section 1.15) are satisfied by the class of Boolean set functions, so that once again we have an example of a Boolean algebra. The remaining details are left as an exercise for the reader.

This algebra of Boolean set functions of $X_1, X_2, \ldots, X_n$ bears the same relation to the class of subsets of the universal set U as does the algebra of switching functions of $x_1, x_2, \ldots, x_n$ to the Boolean algebra of two values $\{0, 1\}$. This points up an important difference between these two algebras: a switching variable, and a switching function, may assume, in any given case, only one of *two* values, 0 or 1. In the algebra of Boolean set functions, any subsets of U may be assigned as values to the variables and may appear as function values. For example, the function defined by $f(X_1, X_2, \ldots, X_n) = X_1$ may assume as its value any subset A of the universal set that we choose to assign as the value of X_1. If the universal set contains infinitely many elements, the variables $X_1, X_2, \ldots, X_n$ have the infinite class of subsets of U as their common domain, and a given set function f may have an infinite class of sets as its range. Thus the Boolean algebra of the subsets of a universal set is a vastly more general algebra than is the algebra of switching functions (even though the formal structure is the same). It is because of this increase in generality that the verification theorem, which permits checking set identities only at the 2^n combinations of $\varnothing$'s and U's, is seen to be a very striking and useful result.

2.13   Fields of Subsets and the Stone Representation Theorem

Let U denote an arbitrary universal set, and let $\mathscr{F}$ denote an arbitrary, nonempty family of subsets of U. For example, $\mathscr{F}$ might denote the set of all subsets of U, or the set of n subsets $A_1, A_2, \ldots, A_n$, or the set of 3^n distinct fundamental intersections $U, A_{i_1}^{e_1} \cap A_{i_2}^{e_2} \cap \cdots \cap A_{i_k}^{e_k}, k \leqslant n$; and so on.

Consider now the formation of $\bar{A}, A \cup B$, and $A \cap B$, where A and B are any two sets belonging to $\mathscr{F}$. These are all subsets of U, but they are not necessarily subsets in $\mathscr{F}$. In the event that for all sets A, B

belonging to $\mathscr{F}$, the sets $\bar{A}, A \cup B$, and $A \cap B$ also belong to $\mathscr{F}$, we call $\mathscr{F}$ a **field of subsets** of U. The most familiar example of such a field is the set of all subsets of U. The next most familiar example is the set of values of the 2^{2^n} Boolean functions of n fixed subsets $A_1, A_2, \ldots, A_n$ of U. We have readily the following

Theorem: *Every field $\mathscr{F}$ of subsets of a universal set U is a Boolean algebra.*

Indeed, $\mathscr{F}$ contains some set $A \subseteq U$. Hence $\mathscr{F}$ contains also $\bar{A}$, $A \cap \bar{A} = \varnothing$, and $A \cup \bar{A} = U$. All the laws of the Boolean algebra of subsets of U hold for the sets of $\mathscr{F}$ since they are subsets of U. Moreover, the application of these laws never produces sets that do not belong to $\mathscr{F}$. These facts, taken together, prove the theorem.

The importance of the concept of a field of subsets of a universal set U is indicated by the following result, which is one form of the

Stone Representation Theorem: *Every Boolean algebra may be represented as the algebra of a field of subsets of a suitable universal set. In particular every finite Boolean algebra may be represented as the field of all subsets of a finite set* [7].

The proof of the theorem is beyond us here. However, the theorem shows that every theorem about the Boolean algebras of fields of subsets of a universal set holds in essence in *all* Boolean algebras, the only difference being a notational one resulting from the particular representation given to the elements of the algebra in question.

The Stone Representation Theorem just quoted is one indication of why the theory of sets has become the dominant aspect of modern mathematics: No matter what mathematics one studies, it can be interpreted as a study of the properties of certain types of sets.

2.14   Exercises

1.   What subsets of the set $\{1,2,3,4,5,6\}$ constitute the smallest field of subsets containing $A_1 = \{2,3,4\}$ and $A_2 = \{4,5\}$?

2.   Expand the Boolean set function defined by

$$f(X_1, X_2, X_3, X_4) = X_1 \oplus X_2 \oplus X_3 \oplus X_4$$

into each of the two normal forms.

3.   Complete the proof that the set of all functions defined by

$$f(X_1, X_2, \ldots, X_n) = \bigcup_{j=0}^{2^n-1} (f_j \cap I_j),$$

where each f_j is $\varnothing$ or U, is a Boolean algebra.

4.   List the sixteen Boolean set functions of two variables X_1 and X_2 in simplified form.

5.   Use the verification theorem to prove the identity

$$(A \oplus B \oplus C) \cap [(A \cap B) \cup (B \cap C) \cup (C \cap A)] = A \cap B \cap C.$$

6.   Given that $\mathscr{F}$ is a field of subsets of U and that A is any fixed subset of U which does not belong to $\mathscr{F}$, does the family of all sets

$$\{\bar{A}, A \cap X, \bar{A} \cap X, A \cup X, \bar{A} \cup X \,|\, X \in \mathscr{F}\}$$

constitute a field of sets?

7.   Prove that a nonempty family $\mathscr{F}$ of subsets of U is a field of subsets if and only if, for all A, B of $\mathscr{F}$, $\bar{A}$ and $A \cap B$ also belong to $\mathscr{F}$. Show that the condition that $\bar{A}$ and $A \cup B$ always belong to $\mathscr{F}$ also is sufficient to guarantee that $\mathscr{F}$ is a field. Prove the same for $\bar{A}$ and $A \oplus B$. Does the condition that $A \,|\, B = \bar{A} \cup \bar{B}$ always belong to $\mathscr{F}$ suffice to guarantee that $\mathscr{F}$ is a field?

8.   Are there any subsets of the Boolean algebra of all set functions of n variables that are also Boolean algebras? What subsets of the set of all fundamental intersections of n sets (Section 2.13) constitute Boolean algebras?

9.   Consider the class of all functions $f(x)$ with the set of all real numbers as their common domain and such that for each real number x_0, $f(x_0) = 0$ or $f(x_0) = 1$, where the function values 0 and 1 are the Boolean 0 and 1. Define equality, $\bar{f}$, $f \vee g$, fg, $f \leqslant g$, the function 0, and the function 1. Then show that this class of functions constitutes a Boolean algebra with respect to your definitions.

10.   Let P_f denote the set of all complete products in the disjunctive normal form of the switching function f and let U_f denote the set of all complete unions in the conjunctive normal form of f. Prove the following:

(a)   For given f, $fg = 0$ if and only if $P_g \subseteq P_{\bar{f}}$. Also, $fg = 0$ if and only if $U_g \supseteq U_{\bar{f}}$.

(b)   For given f, $f \vee h = 1$ if and only if $P_h \supseteq P_{\bar{f}}$. Also, $f \vee h = 1$ if and only if $U_h \subseteq U_{\bar{f}}$.

(c)   For given f and g such that $f \geqslant g$, $f = g \vee h$ if and only if $P_f \supseteq P_h \supseteq P_f \cap P_{\bar{g}}$ and $g = fk$ if and only if $U_g \supseteq U_k \supseteq U_g \cap U_{\bar{f}}$.

2.15   References

1.   A. Ambrose and M. Lazerowitz, *Fundamentals of Symbolic Logic, Revised*. New York: Holt, Rinehart and Winston, 1962.

This is a very readable and useful treatment of many of the topics that are introduced in Chapters 2 and 3.

2. A. A. Bennett and C. A. Bayliss, *An Introduction to Formal Logic*. Englewood Cliffs, N.J.: Prentice–Hall, 1939.

This book contains an unusually clear and interesting discussion of the algebra of classes as well as good exercise material.

3. Lewis Carroll, *Complete Works*. New York: Modern Library, 1929, pp. 1242 ff.

Here will be found many clever and challenging exercises in logic and the algebra of the classes. This should be in your library for "cultural" reasons.

4. P. Suppes, *Introduction to Logic*. Princeton: Van Nostrand, 1957.

An excellent introductory book. Part II, on elementary intuitive set theory, is particularly helpful.

5. P. Halmos, *Naive Set Theory*. Princeton: Van Nostrand, 1960.

A basic book for every mathematician.

6. P. Suppes, *Axiomatic Set Theory*. Princeton: Van Nostrand, 1960.

This is a mature treatment of high expository quality.

7. G. Birkhoff, *Lattice Theory*. New York: American Mathematical Society, 1948.

Chapter 10 of this book contains the Stone Representation theorem quoted above.

3

Logic and Logic Circuits

3.1 Propositions and Propositional Functions

In the process of communication, we make use of many simple declarative sentences, such as

"Two plus two is four."
"Twee en twee is vier."
"$10 + 10 = 100$."
"It is false that two plus two is not four." *yes*
"The normally open contact on this relay is closed."
"This clock says five minutes before ten."
"This lead has not been pulsed during the last five nanoseconds."
"John loves Louise."
"For all real numbers $x, x^2 + 1 > 0$."
"There exists a real number x such that $x^2 + 1 = 0$."

Sometimes different sentences, such as the first four above, have the same meaning. The meaning conveyed by such a sentence, apart from the actual words used, apart from the language in which it is expressed, and apart from any subjective significance such a sentence may have for speaker or listener, will be called a **proposition,** *provided* the meaning conveyed by the sentence can properly be classified as true or false. Its truth or falsity may not be apparent from the sentence itself, as the example "$10 + 10 = 100$" is intended to suggest. As another example, "The sum of the angles of a triangle equals the sum of two right angles" is true in Euclidean geometry but not in non-Euclidean geometries.

103

A proposition may be believed, doubted, or disbelieved, and a large fraction of human energy is expended in efforts to convince people that certain propositions are to be believed or are not to be believed. Sentences such as those we listed are often stated in such a way as to convey the further information that the writer or speaker believes the proposition defined by the sentence. Whether or not this is the case is usually discernible from context or tone of voice. Preceding sentences in this paragraph illustrate the point.

Some sentences represent true propositions; for example, "There exist real numbers x and y such that $x + y = 5$." Others represent false propositions; for example, "For all real numbers x and y, $x + y = 5$." Still other sentences represent propositions that are true, or false, but for lack of knowledge of the relevant facts, we may not be able to decide which; for example, "It rained July 4, 1776, in Timbuctoo," or, more significantly, "The number of pairs of prime numbers differing by two is infinite."

Finally, there are sentences that do not define propositions; for example, "The sentence you are now reading is false." One concludes that if the sentence is indeed false, then it must be true, and that if it is true, then it must be false. It is thus inherently impossible to decide the issue of truth or falsity here, so that the sentence does not define a proposition.

Many well-known riddles exploit the problem of undecidability. An example is the story of the ancient philosopher who had lost favor with his emperor. The emperor said to him, "Wise man, you may make one last statement. If it is true, I shall have you hanged. If it is false, I shall have you thrown into boiling oil." The philosopher replied, "I will be thrown into boiling oil." In what follows, we avoid the emperor's resulting dilemma by excluding from consideration all sentences leading to this kind of undecidability.

Another—but more useful—kind of sentence that does not represent a proposition is illustrated by

$$``x + y = 5,"$$

where x and y are variables representing arbitrary complex numbers. Here the meaning of the sentence is not of such nature that it is possible to answer the question, "Is this true or false?" (Contrast this sentence with the two related sentences used in an earlier paragraph.) The given sentence yields a proposition, however, when we replace x and y by specific numbers. Thus, "$3 + 8 = 5$" defines a (false) proposition.

We call the sentence "$x + y = 5$" an **open sentence** or a **propositional form** since replacement of the symbols x and y by any specific pair of complex numbers always results in a unique proposition. We also say that this form defines or represents a **propositional function,** that is, a function whose "values" are propositions. If w and z are also variables whose domain is the set of complex numbers, then the sentence "$w + z = 5$" must be regarded as defining *the same propositional function* as does "$x + y = 5$," since "$w + z = 5$" determines precisely the same associations of propositions to ordered pairs of complex numbers as does "$x + y = 5$." In fact, the symbols used as variables here are introduced only as a convenience and are arbitrary. The function could also have been represented verbally, or even by a notation like "$(\ ) + [\ ] = 5$." Here one is to insert an arbitrarily chosen complex number in the parentheses and then insert an arbitrarily chosen complex number in the brackets. The fact that the parentheses and brackets are different is intended to imply that the choices are to be made independently of each other.

The preceding example suggests a general definition: Consider an expression $P(x_1, x_2, \ldots, x_n)$ which depends on variables $x_1, x_2, \ldots, x_n$ whose **allowable values** are arbitrary members of some specific set or sets of objects (such as the set of real numbers, a specific group of people, a certain collection of propositions, and so on). When such an expression defines a unique proposition for any substitution of allowable values of the variables, it will be called a **propositional form** and will be said to represent a **propositional function** P. The propositional function itself is the set of all ordered pairs whose first member is any n-tuple $(\xi_1, \xi_2, \ldots, \xi_n)$ of allowable values of the variables and whose second member is the proposition defined by $P(\xi_1, \xi_2, \ldots, \xi_n)$. The sets from which the values of $x_1, x_2, \ldots, x_n$ are to be chosen are called the **domains** of the respective variables. The set of all propositions defined by substitution of values for the x's in $P(x_1, x_2, \ldots, x_n)$ is called the **range** of the function P. The set of all ordered n-tuples of allowable substitutions $(\xi_1, \xi_2, \ldots, \xi_n)$ is called the **domain** of P. The proposition $P(\xi_1, \xi_2, \ldots, \xi_n)$ is called the **value** of the function P at the combination of values $(\xi_1, \xi_2, \ldots, \xi_n)$ of the variables.

The most familiar functions of elementary mathematics have numbers as values and their variables have sets of numbers as their domains. However, in both pure and applied mathematics, there are many important functions whose values are not numbers, or whose variables do not have sets of numbers as their domains, or both. Most of this book illustrates the point.

The totality of ordered n-tuples $(\xi_1, \xi_2, \ldots, \xi_n)$ for which $P(\xi_1, \xi_2, \ldots, \xi_n)$ defines a *true* proposition will be said to constitute the **truth set** S of the propositional function P. For example, the truth set of the propositional function defined by "The circuit whose switching function is $y_1 \bar{y}_2 \vee y_3$ is closed for the combination of values (x_1, x_2, x_3)" is the set of combinations $\{(0, 0, 1), (0, 1, 1), (1, 0, 0), (1, 0, 1), (1, 1, 1)\}$.

As another example, if the variables x and y have the real numbers as their domain, the truth set of $P(x,y)$: $x + y = 5$ is infinite. If x and y

have the positive integers as their domain, the truth set of $P(x, y)$ consists of the four ordered pairs $(1, 4)$, $(2, 3)$, $(3, 2)$, $(4, 1)$. This emphasizes the fact that *a propositional form alone does not define a propositional function: the domains of the variables must also be specified.*

In the definition of a propositional function, we have introduced symbols for variables whose domains are certain sets. As in the case of the example, "$x + y = 5$," if only the symbols representing these variables are changed, the function which is defined by the form remains the same. As a further example, if x, y, z, w, each may represent an arbitrary born and living human male, the forms "x is the father of y" and "z is the father of w" each represent the same propositional function at a given point in time.

There is a propositional function which is of particular conceptual importance. This is the **identity function** $I_j{}^n$ defined by $I_j{}^n(x_1, x_2, ..., x_n) = x_j$ where j is fixed, $1 \leqslant j \leqslant n$, where the domain of x_j is some set of propositions, and where the range of $I_j{}^n$ is the same set as the domain of x_j. The equal sign here means simply that for each allowable set of values $(\xi_1, \xi_2, ..., \xi_n)$, the function value $I_j{}^n(\xi_1, \xi_2, ..., \xi_n)$ and the value ξ_j are, by definition, the same proposition. This function is analogous to the real identity function defined by $f(x) = x$ where the domain of x and the range of f are both the set of real numbers.

Often a single, specific proposition P is of concern rather than a family of propositions. However, *we may still regard P as a propositional function of any convenient set of variables.* We simply agree that P represents a **constant propositional function** in this case. This is analogous to regarding a constant number k as a function of one or more numerical variables. If we write $f(x) = k$, then for each value assigned to x from its domain, the unique value k is the corresponding value of f.

The idea involved here may be generalized. For example, we may regard each of $P(x_1, x_2)$ and $Q(x_3, x_4)$ as a function of x_1, x_2, x_3, x_4 if that is useful. The values of x_3 and x_4 simply do not happen to affect the value of P and those of x_1 and x_2 do not affect the value of Q. One does this sort of thing in other contexts also. Thus, in analytic geometry, the graph of

$$f(x, y) = x^2$$

is a parabolic cylinder parallel to the y-axis and the graph of

$$g(x, y) = y^2$$

is a parabolic cylinder parallel to the x-axis. Recognition of the missing variable is in each case essential for the geometrical representation, but a value assigned to that variable has no effect on the value of the function in question.

Given two propositional functions, represented by the forms $G(x_1, x_2, \ldots, x_n)$ and $H(x_1, x_2, \ldots, x_n)$ and having a common domain D, and given any ordered n-tuple $(\xi_1, \xi_2, \ldots, \xi_n)$ belonging to D, we shall call the propositions defined by $G(\xi_1, \xi_2, \ldots, \xi_n)$ and $H(\xi_1, \xi_2, \ldots, \xi_n)$ **corresponding values** of the propositional functions represented by the given forms.

The notations $P(x_1, x_2, \ldots, x_n)$, $(\xi_1, \xi_2, \ldots, \xi_n)$, and $P(\xi_1, \xi_2, \ldots, \xi_n)$ are cumbersome to read and write. Hence, in what follows, we shall follow standard practice and abbreviate them to $P(x)$, ξ, and $P(\xi)$ when no misunderstanding regarding the number of variables can occur.

Also, instead of the more precise expression, "the propositional function defined by $P(x)$," we shall at times use the shorter and more familiar phrase, "the propositional function $P(x)$." Similarly, we replace "the proposition defined by $P(\xi)$" by "the proposition $P(\xi)$."

3.2 Quantifiers, Free and Bound Variables

It is often necessary in mathematics to define propositions or propositional functions with the aid of what are known as **quantifiers,** that is, with expressions that relate to the question, "How many?" One of these is the **existential quantifier,** denoted by "$\exists$," which is read "there exists an," or "for some." (Here "some" means "at least one.") For example, if the domain of x is the set of real numbers R, the formula

$$\exists\, x \in R \ni x^2 - 1 > 0$$

may be read, "there exists an x belonging to R such that $x^2 - 1 > 0$," or "For some real number x, $x^2 - 1 > 0$." The sentence defines a unique, true proposition. The symbol "$\in$" means "belonging to" or "belong(s) to," as fits grammatically, and the symbol "$\ni$" means "such that."

The **uniqueness quantifier,** "there exists a *unique*," is conveniently represented by the symbol "$\exists!$." For example, employing the same domain for x as in the previous example, the formula

$$\exists!\, x \in R \ni x - 1 = 0$$

may be read, "There exists a unique real number x such that $x - 1 = 0$."

Finally, we introduce the **universal quantifier,** "for all," or, "for every," or, "for each," denoted by "$\forall$." Continuing as above,

$$\forall\, x \in R, \quad x^2 + 1 > 0$$

may be read, "For all real numbers x, $x^2 + 1 > 0$," or "For every real number x, $x^2 + 1 > 0$."

At times, more than one quantifier appears in a sentence. For example, if x, y, z have the set N of positive integers as their common domain, the proposition

$$\forall\, x \in N, \quad \forall\, y \in N, \quad \exists\, z \in N \ni x^2 + y^2 = z^2$$

may be read, "For each x and for each y in N, there exists a positive integer z such that $x^2 + y^2 = z^2$." (The proposition is false.)

The reader will note that, in the preceding examples, symbols for "variables" appear, but that the sentences in question represent propositions rather than propositional forms. In each case, every variable present is deprived of the ability to yield a variety of propositions by a quantifier, so that, in these examples, variables simply serve the purpose of permitting the economical statement of propositions. The same is true of the variable t in "$\int_0^1 t\, dt = 1/2$" and of the variable n in $\sum\limits_{n=1}^{5} (2n - 1) = 25$. A variable that is used in the statement of a proposition (or of a propositional form) and is deprived of arbitrariness by a quantifier or by an operator (whether explicitly or implicitly employed) is often called a **dummy variable** or a **bound variable.**

In a propositional form, on the other hand, there are variables the replacement of which yields a specific proposition. Such variables are called **free variables.** For example, in the propositional form "$x^2 + y^2 = 25$," x and y are free variables. Both free and bound variables may appear in the same propositional form. In "$\int_0^x t\, dt = x^2/2$," the variable x is free and the variable t is bound. In the form, "The switching function defined by $y_1\bar{y}_2 \lor y_3$ assumes the value 1 for the combination (x_1, x_2, x_3)," the variables y_1, y_2, y_3 are bound variables serving only to define the switching function in question. The free variables are x_1, x_2, x_3.

In this book it should always be clear from the context whether a variable is bound or free, even though no formal notation is used to distinguish the two usages. In fact, this limited and informal excursion into the calculus of propositional functions will require very little use of bound variables whereas a more complete treatment would use them extensively.

In conclusion, we agree that the expression "propositional functions $P, Q, \ldots$, of a common set of variables" will always refer to a common set of *free* variables.

3.3   Three Basic Logical Operations

In our use of propositional functions, we often combine them or operate on them in various ways by what are known as **logical operations** in order to form new propositional functions. The resulting functions are called **logical functions** of the original ones.

Let P, Q, R denote propositional functions of a common set of variables $x_1, x_2, \ldots, x_n$. In particular, P, Q, R may denote fixed propositions, that is, they may denote constant functions. They may also denote instances of the identity function, each with an appropriate set of propositions as its domain. In this last case, if we want independent variables to enter explicitly, we can consider P, Q, R each a function of x_1, x_2, x_3 with $P(x_1, x_2, x_3) = x_1$, $Q(x_1, x_2, x_3) = x_2$, $R(x_1, x_2, x_3) = x_3$. Ordinarily, however, there is no need to introduce the variables x_1, x_2, x_3 in this way; the symbols P, Q, R suffice for our needs.

A simple way to obtain a new function from a given one is to form its **negation** (or **denial** or **contradiction**). The negation of P is denoted here by $\bar{P}$, which may be read, "not P." For every value P_0 of P, the corresponding value of $\bar{P}$ is a proposition $\bar{P}_0$ which is false if P_0 is true and true if P_0 is false. For example, the negation of "The circuit whose switching function is $x_1(x_2 \vee \bar{x}_2) \vee \bar{x}_1(x_2 \vee \bar{x}_2)$ is closed" is, "The circuit whose switching function is $x_1(x_2 \vee \bar{x}_2) \vee \bar{x}_1(x_2 \vee \bar{x}_2)$ is *not* closed (that is, is open)." Note that here we have a proposition and its negation. The proposition is true. Its negation is false.

As a second example, consider the propositional function and its negation represented respectively by "$x + y = 5$" and "$x + y \neq 5$," where the common domain of the variables is the set of complex numbers. If we substitute 2 for x and 3 for y, we obtain two propositions of which the first is true and the second is false. If we substitute $2 + i$ for x and $3 - 2i$ for y, we obtain two propositions of which the first is false and the second is true. Indeed, for any substitution of complex numbers for x and y, exactly one of the resulting propositions is true.

An important aspect of negation is the fact that it operates on only one propositional function in order to produce another. This is described by calling negation a **unary operation.** On the other hand, operations which combine two functions are called **binary operations** or **binary connectives.** Examples of binary operations follow at once.

From two propositional functions P and Q we may form a third known as their **disjunction** (or **alternation** or **logical sum**). It is denoted by $P \vee Q$ and yields, for each assignment ξ of allowable values to the variables, the proposition $(P \vee Q)\,(\xi)$, that is, "$P(\xi)$ or $Q(\xi)$ or both," more briefly, "$P(\xi)$ or $Q(\xi)$," the "or both" being tacitly understood. This connective is often called the **inclusive-or.** If P represents the proposition, "The program is faulty" and if Q represents the proposition, "The computer is out of order," then $P \vee Q$ represents the proposition, "The program is faulty *or* the computer is out of order (or both)." As another example, consider the functions $P \colon x + y = 5$ and $Q \colon x - y = 7$. Then $P \vee Q$ is the function represented by the form, "$x + y = 5$ or $x - y = 7$." The substitutions $(1, 4)$, $(5, -2)$, $(6, -1)$ for (x, y) in $P \vee Q$ each yield a true proposition, because at least one of the component propositions is true. The substitution $(1, 1)$ for (x, y) yields a false value for $P \vee Q$ because neither component is true.

Given two propositional functions P and Q, we can also form their **conjunction** (or **logical product**). This logical function is denoted here by the symbol PQ (or $P \cdot Q$ for emphasis) and yields, for each assignment ξ of values to the variables, the proposition (PQ) (ξ), that is, "$P(\xi)$ and $Q(\xi)$." The first example of the preceding paragraph now yields the proposition, "The program is faulty *and* the computer is out of order." The second example yields the form "$x + y = 5$ *and* $x - y = 7$," which has a true proposition as its value only for the substitution $(6, -1)$.

The logical product is also commonly denoted by the sumbol $P \wedge Q$, a notation which is highly desirable from the point of view of symmetry. We use the notation PQ to facilitate application of these sections to the theory of logic circuits, where the product notation is standard.

The truth set of the propositional function defined by "$x + y = 5$ *or* $x - y = 7$," x and y real, may be represented as the set of all points on either or both of two lines which are the graphs of $x + y = 5$ and $x - y = 7$, respectively (Fig. 3.3.1). On the other hand, the truth set of the function defined by "$x + y = 5$ *and* $x - y = 7$" has as its graph the single point $(6, -1)$ which is the intersection of the two lines just mentioned.

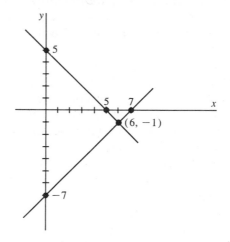

Graphs of given truth sets
Figure 3.3.1

The truth sets of P, Q, $\bar{P}$, $P \vee Q$, and PQ are related in a simple and natural way. Let the universal set U be the set of allowable substitutions, $\{(\xi_1, \xi_2, \ldots, \xi_n)\}$, for the variables of which P and Q are functions. Let S_P and S_Q denote the subsets of U which are the truth sets of P and Q, respectively. Then, from the definitions of negation, disjunction, and conjunction, it follows that the truth sets of $\bar{P}$, $P \vee Q$, and PQ are respectively given by

$$(3.3.1) \qquad S_{\bar{P}} = \bar{S}_P, \qquad S_{P \vee Q} = S_P \cup S_Q, \qquad S_{PQ} = S_P \cap S_Q.$$

These observations may be illustrated by an anlysis of Figure 3.3.1. Details are left to the reader.

3.4   Truth Values and Truth Functions

The **truth value** of a true proposition is "true" and that of a false proposition is "false." To simplify computations, we introduce symbols for truth values as follows: A true proposition has truth value "1" and a false proposition has truth value "0." (These symbols 1 and 0 are to be regarded as convenient marks, not as integers.) Correspondingly, with each propositional function P of n variables, we associate a **truth function** p of these same variables defined by the condition that for each assignment ξ of allowable values to those variables, $p(\xi)$ is the truth value of $P(\xi)$. The truth value of $\bar{P}(\xi)$ will be denoted by $\bar{p}(\xi)$, that of $(P \vee Q)(\xi)$ by $(p \vee q)(\xi)$ and that of $(PQ)(\xi)$ by $(pq)(\xi)$. It will presently be made clear how values of these three truth functions are to be computed from the values $p(\xi)$ and $q(\xi)$.

By way of illustration, the truth value of "2 is a prime number" is 1 and the truth value of "There are infinitely many even primes" is 0. Let P denote the propositional function, "The switching function defined by $y_1\bar{y}_2 \vee \bar{y}_1y_2$ assumes the value 1 for the combination (x_1, x_2)." Then P is a function of x_1 and x_2, and the truth values of the four propositions resulting from specific assignments of values to x_1 and x_2 are as shown in Table 3.4.1.

Table 3.4.1

ξ_1	ξ_2	$p(\xi)$
0	0	0
0	1	1
1	0	1
1	1	0

Note that the symbols 0 and 1 are used in two senses in this table. On the left they are the 0 and 1 of switching algebra. On the right they denote truth values of propositions. The truth values in this instance happen to be formally the same as the corresponding values of the given switching function. Thus by interpreting function values as truth values, we can employ $x_1\bar{x}_2 \vee \bar{x}_1x_2$ as the truth function of P. (See Section 3.11.)

Now let P denote any propositional function and let $\bar{P}$ denote its negation. Then, in every case, $P(\xi_1, \xi_2, \ldots, \xi_n)$ and $\bar{P}(\xi_1, \xi_2, \ldots, \xi_n)$ have opposite truth values, as is shown in Table 3.4.2A.

Table 3.4.2A   **Table 3.4.2B**

$p(\xi)$	$\bar{p}(\xi)$		$p(\xi)$	$\bar{p}(\xi)$
0	1		0	1
1	0		1	0

We next *define* the negations or complements of 0 and 1 thus:

(3.4.1) $\bar{0} = 1, \qquad \bar{1} = 0,$

after which the **negation** or **complement** of the truth function p is defined by Table 3.4.2B. In every case,

$$\bar{p}(\xi) = \overline{p(\xi)};$$

that is, *the truth function of the negation of a propositional function is the negation of its truth function.* Hence both may be denoted by the same symbol $\bar{p}$.

Again, consider the possible combinations of truth values of $P(\xi)$, $Q(\xi)$, and $(P \lor Q)(\xi)$. Since $(P \lor Q)(\xi)$ is true if at least one of $P(\xi)$ and $Q(\xi)$ is true, we obtain the possible combinations of truth values shown in the first three columns of Table 3.4.3. (Such a table of possible truth values of a propositional function is called a **truth table.**)

Table 3.4.3

$p(\xi)$	$q(\xi)$	$(p \lor q)(\xi)$	$p(\xi) \lor q(\xi)$
0	0	0	0
0	1	1	1
1	0	1	1
1	1	1	1

The entries of the third column of Table 3.4.3 can be obtained formally as the disjunctions of the corresponding entries of the first two columns, provided we define

(3.4.2) $0 \lor 0 = 0, \qquad 0 \lor 1 = 1 \lor 0 = 1 \lor 1 = 1.$

These definitions enable us next to compute the values $p(\xi) \lor q(\xi)$ (fourth column of Table 3.4.3), which we define to be the values of the

disjunction of the truth functions p and q. With these definitions, we have, in every case,

$$(p \lor q)(\xi) = p(\xi) \lor q(\xi),$$

so that *the truth function of the disjunction of two propositional functions of the same set of variables is the disjunction of their respective truth functions.*

Hence both may be denoted by the same symbol $p \lor q$.

In similar fashion, the conjunction PQ yields column 3 of Table 3.4.4 because $(PQ)(\xi)$ is true if and only if $P(\xi)$ and $Q(\xi)$ are both true.

Table 3.4.4

$p(\xi)$	$q(\xi)$	$(pq)(\xi)$	$p(\xi) \cdot q(\xi)$
0	0	0	0
0	1	0	0
1	0	0	0
1	1	1	1

Now the entries in the third column of Table 3.4.4 can be obtained formally as the conjunctions of the corresponding entries in the first two columns provided we define

$$0 \cdot 0 = 0 \cdot 1 = 1 \cdot 0 = 0, \qquad 1 \cdot 1 = 1.$$

These definitions enable us next to compute the values $p(\xi) \cdot q(\xi)$ (fourth column of Table 3.4.4), which we define to be the values of the **conjunction** of the truth functions p and q. With these definitions, we have in every case

$$(3.4.3) \qquad (pq)(\xi) = p(\xi) \cdot q(\xi),$$

so that *the truth function of the conjunction of two propositional functions is the conjunction of their respective truth functions.*

Hence, both may be denoted by the same symbol pq.

Using the equality sign to denote identity, we may summarize these results as follows: If $M = \bar{P}, R = P \lor Q, S = PQ$, then $m = \bar{p}, r = p \lor q$, $s = pq$. We can now prove by mathematical induction the general

Theorem: *The truth function of any logical function of propositional functions $P, Q,\ldots,$ built up by a finite number of successive applications of the operations $^-$, $\lor$, and $\cdot$, is the same logical function of the truth functions $p, q,\ldots$.*

Indeed, by the three preceding theorems, the present theorem holds for all logical functions involving only *one* use of the named operations; that is, for $\bar{P}, P \lor Q$, and PQ.

Now suppose k represents any integer such that the theorem holds for all logical functions involving $1, 2, \ldots, k$ uses of the operations $^-$, $\vee$, and $\cdot$. Let G denote any logical function of P, $Q, \ldots$, involving $k + 1$ uses of the operations $^-$, $\vee$, and $\cdot$. We assume that sufficient notation is employed in writing the function G so that the order in which these operations are used to construct G is fully clear. Then, according as $^-$, $\vee$, or $\cdot$ is the last operation employed, G must have one of the forms $G = \bar{R}$, $G = R \vee S$, or $G = RS$, where R, S represent logical functions of P, $Q, \ldots$, employing k or fewer operations. Then, applying the induction hypothesis first to R and S, and thereafter to G as a function involving *one* operation, we conclude that $g = \bar{r}$, $g = r \vee s$, or $g = rs$, where r and s are the same logical functions of p, $q, \ldots$, as R and S are of P, $Q, \ldots$. Hence g is the same logical function of p, $q, \ldots$, as G is of P, $Q, \ldots$.

Since the theorem holds for $k = 1$ and for $k + 1$ if it holds for k, it therefore holds for all positive integers, and the proof is complete.

This theorem is useful in the definition of further binary connectives and in the development of an algebra of propositional functions.

3.5   Equivalence of Propositional Functions

Two propositional functions P and Q, of the variables $x_1, x_2, \ldots, x_n$ are said to be **equivalent** if and only if $P(\xi)$ and $Q(\xi)$ are either both true or both false, that is, have equal truth values, for every allowable n-tuple of values $\xi = (\xi_1, \xi_2, \ldots, \xi_n)$. When this is the case, we write "$P \Leftrightarrow Q$." For example, the functions of one variable,

$$2x - 3 = 0 \qquad \text{and} \qquad 4x - 6 = 0,$$

where the domain of x is the set of complex numbers, are equivalent:

$$(2x - 3 = 0) \Leftrightarrow (4x - 6 = 0).$$

So are the functions of x_1 and x_2, "The switching function $y_1 \bar{y}_2 \vee \bar{y}_1 y_2$ has the value 1 for the combination (x_1, x_2)," and "The switching function $y_1 y_2 \vee \bar{y}_1 \bar{y}_2$ has the value 0 for the combination (x_1, x_2)."

It is immediate from the definition that $P \Leftrightarrow Q$ if and only if $p(\xi) = q(\xi)$ for every allowable set of values ξ, that is, $P \Leftrightarrow Q$ *if and only if the truth functions p and q are identically equal,* which we write "$p = q$."

In mathematical contexts, "$P \Leftrightarrow Q$" is also read "P if and only if Q" and "P is a necessary and sufficient condition for Q."

Particular cases of equivalence are those of two propositions with the same truth value. For example:

1.   [The switching function $y_1\bar{y}_2 \vee \bar{y}_1y_2$ has the value 1 for the combination $(1,0)$] $\Leftrightarrow$ [The switching function $y_1y_2 \vee \bar{y}_1\bar{y}_2$ has the value 0 for the combination $(1,0)$],
2. $(2 + 2 = 4) \Leftrightarrow$ [For all complex numbers x, $x^2 - 1 = (x - 1)(x + 1)$],
3. $(2 + 2 = 22) \Leftrightarrow$ [For some real numbers x, $x^2 + 1 \leqslant 0$].

Note that the variables appearing in (1), (2), (3) above are all bound variables so that only propositions are involved.

The examples of the preceding paragraph emphasize the fact that *equivalence of propositional functions and of propositions is equivalence with respect to truth value only*, not equivalence with respect to meaning.

Frequently two propositional functions yield equivalent propositions for some assignments of values to the variables, but not for others. A simple example is this:

$$P: \ (2x - 3 < 0)$$
$$\text{(x real).}$$
$$Q: \ (2x + 3 > 0)$$

For all values ξ such that $-\frac{3}{2} < \xi < \frac{3}{2}$, $P(\xi) \Leftrightarrow Q(\xi)$. For all other assignments ξ, $P(\xi)$ and $Q(\xi)$ have opposite truth values. Thus, if the domain of x is defined to be the open interval $-\frac{3}{2} < x < \frac{3}{2}$, then the relation "$P \Leftrightarrow Q$" holds. By contrast, for the domain $-\infty < x < \infty$, the relation "$P \Leftrightarrow Q$" does not hold. This example emphasizes the fact that it is often essential to specify fully the domain of each of the variables involved in a propositional function: Certain types of conclusions cannot be drawn unless this is done. At other times, the domains of certain variables need not be known for important conclusions to be drawn. This fact is illustrated in the next paragraph.

It follows at once from the definition that equivalence of propositional functions as just defined has these three properties:

1.   The reflexive property: $P \Leftrightarrow P$.
2.   The symmetric property: If $P \Leftrightarrow Q$, then $Q \Leftrightarrow P$.
3.   The transitive property: If $P \Leftrightarrow Q$ and $Q \Leftrightarrow R$, then $P \Leftrightarrow R$.

That is, the equivalence of propositional functions is an example of what is called *an equivalence relation*.

3.6   The Tautology and the Inconsistency

Let P be an arbitrary propositional function of $x_1, x_2, \ldots, x_n$. What is then the nature of the function $P \vee \bar{P}$? For every assignment ξ of allowable values to the variables, one of the propositions $P(\xi)$, $\bar{P}(\xi)$ is true. It follows that $P(\xi) \vee \bar{P}(\xi)$ is always true. This is represented in terms of truth values in Table 3.6.1.

Table 3.6.1

p	$\bar{p}$	$p \vee \bar{p}$
0	1	1
1	0	1

(Note that the headings in Table 3.6.1 have been abbreviated: p and $\bar{p}$ replace $p(\xi)$ and $\bar{p}(\xi)$, respectively. This should cause no confusion and will be continued in what follows.)

Every propositional function which, like $P \vee \bar{P}$, yields a true proposition for every allowable assignment of values to the variables, is called a **tautology.** In particular, every true proposition is a tautology. Another example is the function $(PQ) \vee (\bar{P} \vee \bar{Q})$. The proof that this is indeed a tautology appears in Table 3.6.2. The first two columns of the table represent all possible combinations of values of $p(\xi)$ and $q(\xi)$. The remaining columns are computed successively with the aid of the last theorem of Section 3.4.

Table 3.6.2

p q	pq	$\bar{p}$ $\bar{q}$	$\bar{p} \vee \bar{q}$	$(pq) \vee (\bar{p} \vee \bar{q})$
0 0	0	1 1	1	1
0 1	0	1 0	1	1
1 0	0	0 1	1	1
1 1	1	0 0	0	1

Table 3.6.2 can be considerably abbreviated, as is shown in Table 3.6.3. The saving occurs in the headings, which involve no unnecessary repetitions of symbols.

Table 3.6.3

$(p \cdot q) \vee (\bar{p} \vee \bar{q})$

0 0	0	1	1	1	1
0 0	1	1	1	1	0
1 0	0	1	0	1	1
1 1	1	1	0	0	0

Here columns 1 and 3 list all possible pairs of truth values $p(\xi)$ and $q(\xi)$. Column 2 lists the corresponding truth values $(pq)(\xi) = p(\xi) \cdot q(\xi)$. Columns 5 and 7 list the truth values $\bar{p}(\xi)$ and $\bar{q}(\xi)$, and column 6 lists the truth values $(\bar{p} \vee \bar{q})(\xi) = \bar{p}(\xi) \vee \bar{q}(\xi)$. Finally, column 4 lists the disjunctions of corresponding entries of columns 2 and 6, namely the values of $((pq) \vee (\bar{p} \vee \bar{q}))(\xi)$. Since column 4 contains only 1's, it follows that $(PQ) \vee (\bar{P} \vee \bar{Q})$ is a tautology. In a table of this latter kind, a column of truth values appears under each *literal symbol* p, q,..., and a column of truth values also appears for each *operation*. (Hence the dot to represent the operation *and*.) Complicated uses of negation can make this kind of table awkward to write unless another notation is used. The notation $\sim p$ in place of p solves the problem and is in common use.

In the two examples just given, the simplest situation is that in which P and Q are identity functions whose common domain is some set of propositions. On the other hand, if each of P and Q is a function of variables $x_1, x_2, \ldots, x_n$, then both the number of variables and the nature of their domains are irrelevant to the conclusion that $P \vee P$ and $(PQ) \vee (\bar{P} \vee \bar{Q})$ are tautologies. In each instance, for specific P and Q, it is entirely possible that a given combination of truth values never occurs for any allowable assignment of values ξ. The tables show, however, that no matter what combinations of truth values occur, $(P \vee \bar{P})(\xi)$ and $((PQ) \vee (\bar{P} \vee \bar{Q}))(\xi)$ are always true propositions. It is for this reason that the number and the domains of the variables $x_1, x_2, \ldots, x_n$ are irrelevant in these cases.

It follows from the definition of equivalence (Section 3.5) that all tautological functions of a given set of variables are equivalent. That is, as far as truth values are concerned, all such tautologies are indistinguishable. Their common property of always yielding a true proposition is abstracted as a function T such that $t(\xi) = 1$ for all ξ. This function is called **the tautology.** Every tautology is equivalent to T:

$$(2 + 2 = 4) \Leftrightarrow T,$$
$$(P \vee \bar{P}) \Leftrightarrow T,$$
$$(PQ) \vee (\bar{P} \vee \bar{Q}) \Leftrightarrow T,$$
$$(2\int_{li}^{x} t \, dt = x^2) \Leftrightarrow T,$$

and so on. The tautology T is analogous to the cardinal number 1 which abstracts the common property of all sets containing a single element. It is also analogous to the real unit function $u(x) = 1$, which can be represented in many different forms:

$$u(x) = \frac{6-4}{2},$$

$$u(x) = \frac{1}{2} \cdot \frac{2^x}{2^{x-1}},$$

$$u(x) = 2 + (x-1)(x+1) - x^2,$$

and so on. There are also, of course, unit functions of 2, 3,..., variables.

Next, for a given function P of x_1, x_2,..., x_n, let us inquire into the nature of the function $P\bar{P}$, whose truth values are calculated in Table 3.6.4. For all allowable assignments of values ξ, the proposition $P(\xi)\bar{P}(\xi)$

Table 3.6.4

p	$\bar{p}$	$p\bar{p}$
0	1	0
1	0	0

is false because one of $P(\xi)$ and $\bar{P}(\xi)$ is false. Any propositional function which, like $P\bar{P}$, yields false propositions for all allowable assignments of values to the variables is called **an inconsistency.** In particular, every false proposition is an inconsistency. Another example is $(\bar{P}\bar{Q})(P \vee Q)$ (see Table 3.6.5). Here we first fill in columns 5 and 7 in the usual way,

Table 3.6.5

$(\bar{p} \cdot \bar{q})$			$\cdot$	$(p \vee q)$		
1	1	1	0	0	0	0
1	0	0	0	0	1	1
0	0	1	0	1	1	0
0	0	0	0	1	1	1

then column 6 by disjunction. Next come columns 1 and 3, the negations of the entries in columns 5 and 7, respectively. These next yield column 2 by conjunction. Finally, the conjunction of the entries of columns 2 and 6 yields the entries of column 4. The fact that these latter values are all 0's shows that the given function is an inconsistency.

In this example, the simplest situation is again that in which P and Q are both identity functions whose common domain is some set of propositions. However, P and Q may represent arbitrary propositional functions of a common set of variables x_1, x_2,..., x_n, in which case both the number of these variables and their domains are irrelevant to the conclusion that $(\bar{P}\bar{Q})(P \vee Q)$ is an inconsistency.

It follows now, from the definition of the equivalence of propositional functions (Section 3.5), that all inconsistencies in a given set of variables are equivalent. The common property of all such inconsistencies is abstracted as a function F, **the inconsistency,** such that $f(\xi) = 0$ for all ξ. Every inconsistency is equivalent to F:

$$(\ln 5 - \ln 3 = \ln 2) \Leftrightarrow F,$$
$$P\bar{P} \Leftrightarrow F,$$
$$(\bar{P}\bar{Q})(P \vee Q) \Leftrightarrow F,$$
$$(2\int_0^x t \, dt = x^2 + 1) \Leftrightarrow F,$$

and so on. The function F is analogous to the real zero function $z(x) = 0$, which can be represented in many forms:

$$z(x) = 6 - 12/2,$$
$$z(x) = \frac{1}{2} - \frac{2^{x-1}}{2^x},$$
$$z(x) = x^2 - (x-1)(x+1) - 1,$$

and so on. (Again, there are also zero functions of 2, 3,..., variables.)

3.7 An Algebra of Propositional Functions

As we have pointed out in preceding paragraphs, in addition to the simple, logical functions $\bar{P}$, $P \vee Q$, and PQ, we are often concerned with more complicated functions, built up by use of these three operations. The nature and properties of such functions may be studied by the construction of truth tables, just as in the simpler cases. The tables provide a convenient method for determining the equivalence of functions and, at times, of effecting simplifications.

For example, if P and Q are propositional functions of the same set of variables, the equivalences

(3.7.1) $\overline{P \vee Q} \Leftrightarrow \bar{P}\bar{Q}, \qquad \overline{PQ} \Leftrightarrow \bar{P} \vee \bar{Q}$

follow from Table 3.7.1, with the aid of the last theorem of Section 3.4.

Table 3.7.1

p q	$\bar{p}$ $\bar{q}$	$p \vee q$	pq	$\overline{p \vee q}$	$\bar{p}\bar{q}$	$\overline{pq}$	$\bar{p} \vee \bar{q}$
0 0	1 1	0	0	1	1	1	1
0 1	1 0	1	0	0	0	1	1
1 0	0 1	1	0	0	0	1	1
1 1	0 0	1	1	0	0	0	0

Up to this point, parentheses have always been employed to make clear the order of operations. Let us agree, as in earlier chapters, that *and* precedes *or* so that, for example, $(PQ) \vee R$ may be written $PQ \vee R$

without ambiguity. When more complex expressions appear in this and later sections, parentheses will always be employed when needed to render expressions unambiguous. The bar for negation often removes the need for parentheses. Unless parentheses indicate otherwise, the sign "$\Leftrightarrow$" asserts the equivalence of all on its left to all on its right, in each case as far as the next "$\Leftrightarrow$" sign.

As another example of the use of truth tables, let us prove that

$$(P \vee QR)\overline{(PQ)R} \Leftrightarrow (\bar{P}Q \vee P\bar{Q})R \vee P\bar{R}.$$

The proof is given in Table 3.7.2, where for brevity we put $S_1 = (P \vee QR) \cdot \overline{(PQ)R}$ and $S_2 = (\bar{P}Q \vee P\bar{Q})R \vee P\bar{R}$. (As before, equality means identity: S_1 and S_2 are defined by these equations.) Again we use the last theorem of Section 3.4 and omit some minor steps. The reader should check all entries in Table 3.7.2 as an exercise.

Table 3.7.2

$p\ q\ r$	$p \vee qr$	$\overline{(pq)r}$	s_1	$\bar{p}q \vee p\bar{q}$	$(\bar{p}q \vee p\bar{q})r$	$p\bar{r}$	s_2
0 0 0	0	1	0	0	0	0	0
0 0 1	0	1	0	0	0	0	0
0 1 0	0	1	0	1	0	0	0
0 1 1	1	1	1	1	1	0	1
1 0 0	1	1	1	1	0	1	1
1 0 1	1	1	1	1	1	0	1
1 1 0	1	1	1	0	0	1	1
1 1 1	1	0	0	0	0	0	0

By the use of the basic definitions and truth tables, we may now establish the following equivalences in which P, Q, R represent arbitrary propositional functions of some fixed set of variables. In particular, P, Q, R may be identity functions so that the range and domain of each is some set of propositions.

We have first **the commutative laws:** For all P and Q,

(L–1a) $P \vee Q \Leftrightarrow Q \vee P,$

(L–1b) $PQ \Leftrightarrow QP.$

These follow at once from the definitions of *or* and of *and*: If at least one of $P(\xi)$ and $Q(\xi)$ is true, so is at least one of $Q(\xi)$ and $P(\xi)$, and conversely. Similarly, $P(\xi)$ and $Q(\xi)$ are both true if and only if $Q(\xi)$ and $P(\xi)$ are both true.

From a similar argument, or from a truth table, we conclude next **the associative laws:** For all $P, Q, R,$

(L–2a) $$(P \lor Q) \lor R \Leftrightarrow P \lor (Q \lor R),$$
(L–2b) $$(PQ)R \Leftrightarrow P(QR).$$

The reader may supply the details of the proof. Because of the associative laws, the expressions $P \lor Q \lor R$ and PQR are unambiguous. Moreover, $(P \lor Q \lor R)(\xi)$ is true if and only if at least one of $P(\xi)$, $Q(\xi)$, $R(\xi)$ is true, and $(PQR)(\xi)$ is true if and only if $P(\xi)$, $Q(\xi)$, $R(\xi)$ are all three true. *We can extend these observations to longer expressions,* grouping conjunctions and disjunctions in a manner entirely analogous to the manner in which one groups products and sums in the algebra of complex numbers. The proofs are by induction.

Next we have **the distributive laws:** For all P, Q, R,

(L–3a) $$P(Q \lor R) \Leftrightarrow PQ \lor PR,$$
(L–3b) $$P \lor QR \Leftrightarrow (P \lor Q)(P \lor R).$$

Here, truth tables provide simple proofs and are left to the reader to construct.

Consider the entries of Table 3.7.3 in the headings of which "0" and "1" denote the constant truth functions of F and T, respectively. From this table we have first **the idempotent laws:** For all P,

(L–4a) $$P \lor P \Leftrightarrow P,$$
(L–4b) $$PP \Leftrightarrow P.$$

Table 3.7.3

p	0	1	$p \lor p$	pp	$p \lor 0$	$p \cdot 1$	$p \cdot 0$	$p \lor 1$
0	0	1	0	0	0	0	0	1
1	0	1	1	1	1	1	0	1

The table also yields **the laws of operation with F and T,** which again hold for all P under consideration:

(L–5a) $$P \lor F \Leftrightarrow P,$$
(L–5b) $$PT \Leftrightarrow P,$$

from which F and T are seen to be **identity elements** for disjunction and conjunction respectively, and

(L–6a) $$PF \Leftrightarrow F,$$
(L–6b) $$P \lor T \Leftrightarrow T,$$

from which F and T are seen to be **dominant elements** for conjunction and disjunction, respectively.

From our earlier discussion of the tautology and the inconsistency, we have the **laws of complementarity:** For all P,

(L–7a) $$P \vee \bar{P} \Leftrightarrow T,$$
(L–7b) $$P\bar{P} \Leftrightarrow F.$$

In Table 3.7.1, at the beginning of this section, we have the proof of the tautologies known as **DeMorgan's laws:** For all P, Q,

(L–8a) $$\overline{P \vee Q} \Leftrightarrow \bar{P}\bar{Q},$$
(L–8b) $$\overline{PQ} \Leftrightarrow \bar{P} \vee \bar{Q}.$$

Finally, we have **the law of involution:** For all P,

(L–9) $$\overline{(\bar{P})} \Leftrightarrow P.$$

This derives from the fact that to deny that a proposition is false is to assert that it is true. The details of the arithmetic appear in Table 3.7.4.

Table 3.7.4

p	$\bar{p}$	$\overline{(\bar{p})}$
0	1	0
1	0	1

From (L–1) through (L–9), it is clear that we can manipulate *and-or-not* functions of propositional functions P, Q, $R,\ldots$, in precisely the same way we manipulate analogous expressions in switching theory and in set theory. For example, we have, for all P, Q, R,

$$(P \vee QR)\overline{PQR} \Leftrightarrow (P \vee QR)(\bar{P} \vee \bar{Q} \vee \bar{R})$$
$$\Leftrightarrow P\bar{Q} \vee P\bar{R} \vee \bar{P}QR$$
$$\Leftrightarrow P\bar{Q}R \vee P\bar{Q}\bar{R} \vee PQ\bar{R} \vee \bar{P}QR$$
$$\Leftrightarrow (P\bar{Q} \vee \bar{P}Q)R \vee P\bar{R}.$$

Here each use of L–1 through L–9 should be identified by the reader. We thus have an algebraic proof of the same equivalence established previously in Table 3.7.2. The next to the last line of the present proof also suggests (correctly) the existence of *disjunctive and conjunctive normal forms*, which may be obtained in the familiar manner and should be used as needed.

The exercises which follow provide practice in matters discussed so far in this chapter. The *principle of duality* holds here, and should be employed where it is appropriate. The statement of the quantifier "for all" is at times omitted, in accordance with standard mathematical usage, when that can cause no confusion. Finally, we remark that *if $P \Leftrightarrow Q$, P may be replaced by Q in any logical formula* without altering the truth value of that formula at any combination of allowable values of the variables. This fact is called **the substitution principle** and is a basic postulate in more rigorous treatments of this material.

3.8 Exercises

*1.   Again assuming P, Q, R, to be propositional functions of a fixed set of variables, prove these further equivalences, which are important and will be used in what follows: For all P, Q, R,

(L–10a) $P \vee PQ \Leftrightarrow P$,
(L–10b) $P(P \vee Q) \Leftrightarrow P$,
(L–11a) $P \vee \bar{P}Q \Leftrightarrow P \vee Q$,
(L–11b) $P(\bar{P} \vee Q) \Leftrightarrow PQ$,
(L–12a) $(P \vee Q)(\bar{P} \vee R)(Q \vee R) \Leftrightarrow (P \vee Q)(\bar{P} \vee R)$,
(L–12b) $PQ \vee \bar{P}R \vee QR \Leftrightarrow PQ \vee \bar{P}R$.

2.   Make a truth table for each of the following formulas. Are any of these tautologies?

(a) $\overline{P\bar{Q} \vee R} \vee (P\bar{R} \vee Q)$,
(b) $(PQ \vee R)\overline{(P \vee QR)}$,
(c) $(PQ \vee R)(P \vee R) \vee \overline{(PQ \vee R)}\overline{(P \vee R)}Q$.

Under what restrictions on the values of the truth functions p, q, r would these represent tautologies? (That is, what combinations of truth values must not occur if these formulas are to be tautologies?)

3.   If P is the propositional function defined by "$2x + 3y \geqslant 5$" and Q is the propositional function defined by "$3x - 2y \geqslant 1$," where x and y have the set of integers as their common domain, write expressions defining $\bar{P}$, $P \vee Q$, PQ, and $\bar{P} \vee Q$. Then construct a graph of the truth set of each function. Is the proposition $P \Leftrightarrow Q$ true? Why? For what pairs (ξ, η) is $P(\xi, \eta) \Leftrightarrow Q(\xi, \eta)$? (Describe this last set geometrically.)

4.   Assuming the domains of x, x_1, x_2 to be the set of real numbers, determine the truth set of each of the following:

(a) $\int_{x_1}^{x_2} t \, dt = \frac{x_2{}^2}{2}$,   (c) $\int_0^x t \, dt = -1$,

(b) $\int_0^x t \, dt = \frac{x}{2}$,   (d) $x^2 - x > \frac{3}{4}$,

(e) $x - i = \dfrac{1}{x + i}, (i = \sqrt{-1})$,   (f) $\dfrac{d}{dt}(t^2 + x) = 2t$.

5.   Invent two additional examples of tautology and two of incon-
·sistency,

  (a)   in the form of logical functions of $P, Q, R, \ldots$,
  (b)   in the form of mathematical formulas or statements,
  (c)   unrelated to logic or mathematics.

6.   Assuming that the domain of x is the set of complex numbers, are
any of the following propositional functions equivalent to T or to F? Can
any that are not tautologies be made tautologies by restricting the domain
of x to some nonempty set?

  (a) $x = 5$,   (d) $x = 100x$,
  (b) $x + x = 2x$,   (e) $x = 100 + x$,
  (c) $x + 3 = 3x$,   (f) $2x \leqslant x^2 + 1$.

7.   For what common domain are the following three propositional
functions equivalent?

  (a) $x^2 - x - 1 = 0$,

  (b) $\dfrac{x - 1}{x + 1} + 1 = 2(x - 1)$

  (c) $\dfrac{x}{x^2 - 1} = 1$.

8.   Illustrate with Venn diagrams the truth sets of

  (a) $P \vee Q$ and PQ,
  (b) $PQ \vee R$,
  (c) $P \vee \bar{P}Q$,
  (d) $(P \vee R)(Q \vee R)$.

(See the last paragraph of Section 3.3.)

9.   Identify the free and the bound variables in each of the following.
Also define the truth set when that is relevant, assuming the domain of
each variable to be the set R of real numbers:

  (a) $x^2 + y^2 \geqslant 2xy$,
  (b) $\forall\, x \in R, x^2 + y^2 \geqslant 2xy$,
  (c) $\forall\, x \in R, \forall\, y \in R, x^2 + y^2 \geqslant 2xy$,
  (d) $\exists\, x \in R \ni x^2 + 2x - 3 < 0$,
  (e) $\exists!\, x \in R \ni x^2 + 2x - 3 < 0$,
  (f) $\forall\, x \in R, x^2 + y > 0$.

10.   Represent graphically the truth sets of each of the following propositional functions of x and y, where x and y are real:

  (a) $P: x^2 + y^2 \leqslant 1$,
  (b) $Q: y^2 < 1$,
  (c) PQ,
  (d) $P \vee Q$.

*11.   Prove that

$$PQ \vee \bar{P}Q \vee P\bar{Q} \vee \bar{P}\bar{Q} \Leftrightarrow T.$$

Write the corresponding identity relating truth functions. Explain verbally what this equivalence means. Then generalize and also dualize.

12.   Express each of the functions of Exercise 2 in disjunctive normal form and in conjunctive normal form. Explain the use of a truth table to accomplish this.

13.   Illustrate graphically the truth set of PQR where P, Q, and R are defined thus, where x and y are real:

$$
\begin{aligned}
P: & \quad (x + 2y \geqslant 6), \\
Q: & \quad (2x + y \geqslant 6), \\
R: & \quad (x + y \leqslant 6).
\end{aligned}
$$

*14.   Prove that if $P = Q_1 Q_2 \cdots Q_r$, then P is a tautology if and only if each of $Q_1, Q_2, \ldots, Q_r$ is a tautology. Prove that if $P = Q_1 \vee Q_2 \vee \cdots \vee Q_r$, then P is a tautology if and only if at least one disjunction $Q_{i_1} \vee Q_{i_2} \vee \cdots \vee Q_{i_r}$, $1 \leqslant s \leqslant r$ is a tautology.

*15.   Prove the following equivalences:

  (a) $P \vee \prod\limits_{j=1}^{m} P_j \Leftrightarrow \prod\limits_{j=1}^{m} (P \vee P_j)$,

  (b) $P \cdot \bigvee\limits_{j=1}^{m} P_j \Leftrightarrow \bigvee\limits_{j=1}^{m} PP_j$,

  (c) $\overline{P_1 P_2 \cdots P_m} \Leftrightarrow \bar{P}_1 \vee \bar{P}_2 \vee \cdots \vee \bar{P}_m$,
  (d) $\overline{P_1 \vee P_2 \vee \cdots \vee P_m} \Leftrightarrow \bar{P}_1 \bar{P}_2 \cdots \bar{P}_m$.

16.   Prove that

  (a) $p_1 \bar{p}_2 \vee p_2 \bar{p}_1 = (p_1 \vee p_2) \, \overline{p_1 p_2}$,
  (b) $p_1 \bar{p}_2 \vee p_2 \bar{p}_3 \vee p_3 \bar{p}_1 = (p_1 \vee p_2 \vee p_3) \overline{p_1 p_2 p_3}$,
  (c) $p_1 \bar{p}_2 \vee p_2 \bar{p}_3 \vee p_3 \bar{p}_4 \vee p_4 \bar{p}_1 = (p_1 \vee p_2 \vee p_3 \vee p_4) \overline{p_1 p_2 p_3 p_4}$.

Find a system for reducing the left member to the right. Then generalize.

17.   Prove the following equivalences:

(a) $P\bar{Q}R \vee \bar{P}QS \Leftrightarrow (P \vee QS)(\bar{P} \vee \bar{Q}R),$
(b) $PQ \vee \bar{P}\bar{Q} \vee PR \Leftrightarrow PQ \vee \bar{P}\bar{Q} \vee \bar{Q}R,$
(c) $PQ \vee \bar{P}R \Leftrightarrow PQ \vee \bar{P}R \vee QRS.$

*18.   Let P, Q, R be propositional functions of the same set of variables. Prove that if $P \Leftrightarrow Q$, then $PR \Leftrightarrow QR$, $P \vee R \Leftrightarrow Q \vee R$, and $\bar{P} \Leftrightarrow \bar{Q}$. Show that in the first two cases the converse is not true; that is, give an example where $P \vee R \Leftrightarrow Q \vee R$ but not $P \Leftrightarrow Q$, and an example where $PR \Leftrightarrow QR$ but not $P \Leftrightarrow Q$. Prove that if $\bar{P} \Leftrightarrow \bar{Q}$ then $P \Leftrightarrow Q$.

19.   Consider the sentence $P:$ "Each variable of this statement P is a free variable."

(a)   Is P a proposition, a propositional function? Why?
(b)   Which are the variables of P? Are they free or bound?
(c)   Is P an inconsistency? A tautology?
(d)   Write the negation of P.

3.9   Other Logical Functions and Connectives

The operations *and, or, not* can be used to form a variety of logical functions of two propositional functions P and Q. Let S be any such function. Then we can make a truth table for s in the usual way (Table 3.9.1). Here, each of the four values s_j will be either 0 or 1.

Table 3.9.1

p	q	s
0	0	s_0
0	1	s_1
1	0	s_2
1	1	s_3

As a consequence, there are exactly sixteen inequivalent logical functions of P and Q and every logical function of P and Q must be equivalent to one of these. The sixteen possible combinations of truth values are listed in the *rows* of Table 3.9.2, along with simple expressions for corresponding logical functions $S_i(P, Q)$. Note that P and Q themselves are the functions S_3 and S_5 of the table, that F and T are the functions S_0 and S_{15}, respectively, and that $PQ = S_1$, $P \vee Q = S_7$, $\bar{P} = S_{12}$, and $\bar{Q} = S_{10}$. Thus the familiar binary logical functions all appear here, along with the two constant functions F and T and eight other logical functions, all of which explicitly involve P and Q. These functions lead to the definition of further connectives (binary operations) which are of particular importance and which are denoted by special symbols.

Table 3.9.2

i	s_0	s_1	s_2	s_3	$S_i(P, Q)$
0	0	0	0	0	F
1	0	0	0	1	PQ
2	0	0	1	0	$P\bar{Q}$
3	0	0	1	1	P
4	0	1	0	0	$\bar{P}Q$
5	0	1	0	1	Q
6	0	1	1	0	$P\bar{Q} \vee \bar{P}Q$
7	0	1	1	1	$P \vee Q$
8	1	0	0	0	$\bar{P}\bar{Q}$
9	1	0	0	1	$PQ \vee \bar{P}\bar{Q}$
10	1	0	1	0	$\bar{Q}$
11	1	0	1	1	$\bar{Q} \vee P$
12	1	1	0	0	$\bar{P}$
13	1	1	0	1	$\bar{P} \vee Q$
14	1	1	1	0	$\bar{P} \vee \bar{Q}$
15	1	1	1	1	T

Consider first the function $S_6 = P\bar{Q} \vee \bar{P}Q$. This is known as the **exclusive-or function,** since $(P\bar{Q} \vee \bar{P}Q)(\xi)$ is true if and only if $P(\xi)$ is true or $Q(\xi)$ is true, but *not both.* For example, if a man proposed to buy exactly one automobile, then his statement, "I will buy a Jaguar or I will buy a Corvette," would be an exclusive-or statement. In accord with earlier usage, we define a binary connective, the **exclusive-or operation,** and denote it by the symbol $\oplus$:

(3.9.1) $$P \oplus Q = P\bar{Q} \vee \bar{P}Q.$$

Note that this equation actually defines the binary operation $\oplus$ because it tells how to compute $P \oplus Q$ in every case.

The exclusive-or connective, also called the **ring sum,** is used frequently in circuit applications, as we shall see later. In this connection we often use the equivalence

$$P\bar{Q} \vee \bar{P}Q \Leftrightarrow (P \vee Q)\overline{PQ},$$

or the equality

$$p\bar{q} \vee \bar{p}q = (p \vee q)\overline{pq},$$

the correctness of which the reader should verify.

Next let us examine the function $S_{13} = \bar{P} \vee Q$, which states, for each allowable assignment ξ, "not $P(\xi)$, or $Q(\xi)$," that is, "if $P(\xi)$, then $Q(\xi)$." This is of course a proposition whose truth or falsity is subject to examination. When $P(\xi)$ is false, nothing is said about the truth value of $Q(\xi)$, but if $P(\xi)$ is true, $Q(\xi)$ is stated to be true also. To help make this clear, we abstract from Table 3.9.2 the truth table for $\bar{P} \vee Q$ (Table 3.9.3). Asserting $\bar{P} \vee Q$ amounts to asserting that the combination of values appearing in the third line of this table does not occur. The assertion may be true or false at any given ξ.

Table 3.9.3

p	q	$\bar{p} \vee q$
0	0	1
0	1	1
1	0	0
1	1	1

It is convenient at this point to introduce another binary connective, the **conditional,** which is denoted by the symbol "$\to$" and which is defined, for all P and Q, by the equation

(3.9.2) $$P \to Q = \bar{P} \vee Q.$$

The expression "$P \to Q$" is read, "If P, then Q."

An example illustrating a familiar manner of using the conditional is, "If this button is pressed, then the computer will stop," or

(3.9.3)   (This button is pressed) $\to$ (the computer will stop).

We have said nothing about the computer's stopping if the button is *not* pressed (the first two lines of the truth table above). Indeed, if the button is not pressed, the computer may continue to run, or it may well stop because a program is faulty, because of a power failure, or because it has finished its work. In no such case is the assertion (3.9.3) invalidated. On the other hand, the claim is that when the button *is* pressed, the computer will not continue to operate (last line of the truth table). Thus the only case in which the assertion (3.9.3) is false is that represented by the third line of the truth table. When the control button is functioning properly, this case does not occur, and (3.9.3) becomes a tautology. In this example, as is often the case, the ultimate variables, and their domains, are not easily defined.

Another example, involving a well-defined variable having a specified domain, is provided by the simple but often useful theorem, "If x is real, then $x^2 + x + 1 > 0$." In symbols,

(3.9.4) $(x \text{ is real}) \rightarrow (x^2 + x + 1 > 0)$.

Let the domain of x be the set of complex numbers. Then for some values ξ of x, the proposition "ξ is real" is false. For such values ξ, we may or may not have $\xi^2 + \xi + 1 > 0$. The theorem says nothing about that case. To prove the theorem, we observe that when ξ is real, $\xi^2 + \xi + 1 = (\xi + \frac{1}{2})^2 + \frac{3}{4}$, which is the sum of a non-negative number and a positive number and hence is positive. That is, the proof consists in showing that for P: $(x \text{ is real})$ and Q: $(x^2 + x + 1 > 0)$, the combination of truth values in the third line of Table 3.9.3 cannot occur — in short, we prove $\bar{P} \vee Q$ is a tautology.

This example illustrates the fact that in the proof of every mathematical statement of the form $P \rightarrow Q$, we demonstrate the impossibility of the situation: $P(\xi)$ true, $Q(\xi)$ false. Putting it another way, we show in effect that the truth set of P is a *subset* of the truth set of Q. The relation between P and Q that exists in this case is the **relation of implication,** and we say that P **implies** Q. To distinguish an established or hypothesized fact of implication from the conditional "if $\cdots$ then $\cdots$," we write

(3.9.5) $P \Rightarrow Q$

to mean "P implies Q." That is, *we write $P \Rightarrow Q$ and say "P implies Q" if and only if the conditional, $P \rightarrow Q$, is or is assumed to be a tautology.* Thus, continuing with the above example, we have

$$(x \text{ real}) \Rightarrow (x^2 + x + 1 > 0),$$

and the symbol is read "implies."

Two special cases of implication require comment. Let P and Q denote *specific propositions.* Then, by Table 3.9.3, if P is true, $P \Rightarrow Q$ if and only Q is true also. That is, by our definition, a true proposition implies every other true proposition, but it implies no false proposition. For example, (not every computer is digital) $\Rightarrow$ (7 is a prime number). This example illustrates the fact that even though $P \Rightarrow Q$, there may be no way to deduce Q from P. In this manner, implication as we have defined it appears to depart from colloquial usage.

Now suppose P is a false proposition. Then, again by Table 3.9.3, $P \Rightarrow Q$, no matter whether Q is true or false. For example, consider:

P: The switching function $y_1 y_2 y_3$ has the value 1 for every combination $(1, x_2, x_3)$,

Q: The switching function $y_1 y_2 y_3$ has the value 1 for the combination $(1, 0, 0)$,

R: The switching function $y_1 y_2 y_3$ has the value 1 for the combination $(1, 1, 1)$.

Here P and Q are false but R is true. Also $P \Rightarrow Q$ and $P \Rightarrow R$.

Notice that these last two implications appeal to one as being entirely legitimate. It is only when unrelated propositions enter, as in the preceding paragraph, that we begin to feel uncomfortable. However, even this sort of implication is more in accord with colloquial usage than one might think offhand. To illustrate, if I were convinced that another person were misrepresenting the facts, I might say to him, "If what you say is true, then I'm a grasshopper's left hind foot." (One false proposition implies another.) Again, my wife sometimes declares, "You *always* choose the wrong color tie for that shirt." On rare occasions, I do. On such an occasion, her false proposition implies a true one. Implications of this sort are, of course, ordinarily adduced only for illustration or for amusement and do not enter into serious argument. Hence their nonsensical character causes no problem. They are just by-products of a natural and useful definition, and they help to make speech interesting.

The conditional leads naturally to the connective called the **biconditional,** which we denote by "$\leftrightarrow$" and which is defined, for all P and Q, by the equation

$$(3.9.6) \qquad\qquad (P \leftrightarrow Q) = (P \to Q)(Q \to P).$$

This is read, "If P, then Q, and if Q, then P," or "P if and only if Q." From the definition of the conditional, we have $(P \to Q) = \bar{P} \vee Q$ and hence also $(Q \to P) = \bar{Q} \vee P$, so that, substituting and expanding, we have

$$(3.9.7) \qquad\qquad P \leftrightarrow Q \Leftrightarrow (\bar{P} \vee Q)(\bar{Q} \vee P) \Leftrightarrow PQ \vee \bar{P}\bar{Q}.$$

Thus the function $P \leftrightarrow Q$ is equivalent to the function S_9 of Table 3.9.2. Formula (3.9.7) (or row 9 of Table 3.9.2) shows that $(P \leftrightarrow Q)(\xi)$ is true if and only if $P(\xi)$ and $Q(\xi)$ are both true or both false, that is, if and only if $P(\xi)$ and $Q(\xi)$ have the same truth value. For example, the propositional function

$$(3.9.8) \qquad\qquad (x > 0) \leftrightarrow (1 - x^2 > 0) \qquad (x \text{ real})$$

yields true propositions for $0 < \xi < 1$, for then $\xi > 0$ and $1 - \xi^2 > 0$ are both true. It also yields true propositions for $\xi \leqslant -1$ for then the component propositions $\xi > 0$ and $1 - \xi^2 > 0$ are both false. For all other values ξ, the function (3.9.8) yields a false proposition since only one of the propositions $\xi > 0$ and $1 - \xi^2 > 0$ is then true.

A more significant kind of example is the following result from Euclidean geometry:

(Triangle ABC is equilateral) $\leftrightarrow$ (Triangle ABC is equiangular). Since this holds for *all* triangles ABC, the function in this case is a tautology. That is, the functions, "Triangle ABC is equilateral" and "Triangle ABC is equiangular" are equivalent functions. This example illustrates the connection between the biconditional and equivalence:

$$P \Leftrightarrow Q \text{ if and only if } P \leftrightarrow Q \text{ is a tautology.}$$

Indeed, in mathematics we frequently wish to establish the equivalence of two propositional functions P and Q, and we often do it by proving that the combinations of values $(1,0)$ and $(0,1)$ for $(p(\xi), q(\xi))$ cannot occur, that is, by proving that $P \Rightarrow Q$ and $Q \Rightarrow P$. Thus the proof of the theorem $P \Leftrightarrow Q$ is accomplished by the proof of two others which are mutually converse. If either of these is false, $P \Leftrightarrow Q$ is not true.

A final comment about the notations "$\rightarrow$," "$\Rightarrow$," "$\leftrightarrow$," and "$\Leftrightarrow$" is in order. We use each of "$\rightarrow$" and "$\leftrightarrow$" to construct new propositional functions of $x_1, x_2, \ldots, x_n$ from two others; thus "$\rightarrow$" and "$\leftrightarrow$" are logical connectives. On the other hand, we use "$\Rightarrow$" and "$\Leftrightarrow$" to designate relations that exist between two logical functions. Thus these are *not* logical connectives. Rather, we use them to state certain propositions *about* the functions with which we are working. At times, in a discussion, a relation $P \Leftrightarrow Q$ or $P \Rightarrow Q$ may, for purposes of argument, be assumed to hold. At other times, $P \Leftrightarrow Q$ or $P \Rightarrow Q$ may represent a proposition the truth of which is, or is to be, proved. We make no notational distinction between these usages since the context always makes the matter clear.

Two other connectives are of special interest. The first of these is associated with the function S_{14} in our table and is known as the **Scheffer stroke.** The name derives from the notation "$|$" used to represent this connective. We define, for all P and Q

$$(3.9.9) \qquad\qquad P \mid Q = \bar{P} \vee \bar{Q},$$

from which we have at once the often useful equivalence:

$$(3.9.10) \qquad\qquad P \mid Q \Leftrightarrow \overline{PQ}.$$

The interesting thing about the Scheffer stroke from the point of view of logic is that *all logical functions of P and Q can be expressed in terms of this one connective.* Indeed, we have

$$P \mid P \Leftrightarrow \overline{PP} \Leftrightarrow \bar{P},$$
$$(P \mid Q) \mid (P \mid Q) \Leftrightarrow \overline{PQ} \mid \overline{PQ} \Leftrightarrow PQ,$$
$$(P \mid P) \mid (Q \mid Q) \Leftrightarrow \bar{P} \mid \bar{Q} \Leftrightarrow (\bar{P}) \vee (\bar{Q}) \Leftrightarrow P \vee Q.$$

Thus, since all logical functions of two propositional functions can be expressed in terms of *not, and,* and *or,* they can all be expressed in terms of the stroke function.

The other connective of special interest is associated with the function S_8 of the table. It is known as **joint denial** and is sometimes denoted by a dagger "†" (the dagger function) and sometimes by an arrow "↓" (the Pierce arrow function). In this book we use a **double stroke,** "‖," and so define, for all P and Q,

(3.9.11) $$P \| Q = \bar{P}\bar{Q},$$

from which we have at once the often useful fact:

(3.9.12) $$P \| Q \Leftrightarrow \overline{P \vee Q}.$$

Here again we have a connective in terms of which all logical functions of two propositional functions can be expressed. The details are left to the reader.

The stroke and double stroke functions are of considerable practical use in the design of transistor logic circuits, as will appear later.

Note that the stroke function $P \mid Q$ claims, at each ξ, "*at least one* of $P(\xi)$, $Q(\xi)$ is false," whereas the double stroke function $P \| Q$ claims, at each ξ, "$P(\xi)$ and $Q(\xi)$ are *both* false." This explains the choice of notation here.

Table 3.9.2 shows that all sixteen logical functions of P and Q can be expressed in terms of the operations *or, and,* and *not.* (In fact, all may be expressed in terms of *or* and *not* only, or in terms of *and* and *not* only. See exercises which follow.) We may therefore conclude the following

Theorem: *Every logical function, employing a finite number of unary or binary operations, of propositional functions $P, Q, \ldots,$ is equivalent to a function involving only the operations $\vee, \cdot, and ^{-}$.*

Transforming other connectives into *and-or-not* expressions often helps in the transformation of a given function. For example,

$$(P \to Q)(P \to R) \Leftrightarrow (\bar{P} \vee Q)(\bar{P} \vee R)$$

$$\Leftrightarrow \bar{P} \vee QR.$$

Hence

$$(P \to Q)(P \to R) \Leftrightarrow (P \to QR).$$

This formula leads to a simple conclusion concerning implication. If one member of the formula is a tautology, then so is the other. Hence, P implies Q and P implies R if and only if P implies QR, that is, $(P \Rightarrow Q) \cdot (P \Rightarrow R) \Leftrightarrow (P \Rightarrow QR)$. Frequently formulas have similar specializations which are recognizable as familiar laws of reasoning. More will appear in following exercises.

One can also use the above procedure to establish that a given formula is a tautology. Thus

$$[(P \rightarrow Q) \oplus (Q \rightarrow P)] \leftrightarrow (P \oplus Q) \Leftrightarrow [(\bar{P} \vee Q) \oplus (\bar{Q} \vee P)] \leftrightarrow (P \oplus Q)$$
$$\Leftrightarrow [(\bar{P} \vee Q)\overline{(\bar{Q} \vee P)} \vee \overline{(\bar{P} \vee Q)}(\bar{Q} \vee P)] \leftrightarrow (P \oplus Q)$$
$$\Leftrightarrow [(\bar{P} \vee Q) \, Q\bar{P} \vee P\bar{Q}(\bar{Q} \vee P)] \leftrightarrow (P \oplus Q)$$
$$\Leftrightarrow (\bar{P}Q \vee P\bar{Q}) \leftrightarrow (P \oplus Q)$$
$$\Leftrightarrow (P \oplus Q) \leftrightarrow (P \oplus Q)$$
$$\Leftrightarrow T,$$

since $(X \leftrightarrow X) \Leftrightarrow T$ for all X. Alternatively, we could have proved

$$(P \rightarrow Q) \oplus (Q \rightarrow P) \Leftrightarrow P \oplus Q.$$

The reader should think carefully about what this says concerning truth values.

In Section 3.4, we defined truth functions, their complements, disjunctions, and conjunctions, and the corresponding operations on 0 and 1 in such a way that

$$\bar{p}(\xi) = \overline{p(\xi)}, \qquad (p \vee q)(\xi) = p(\xi) \vee q(\xi), \qquad (pq)(\xi) = p(\xi)q(\xi).$$

This procedure can be extended to other functions, if we wish to do so. For any binary connective $*$, we define $0 * 0$, $0 * 1$, $1 * 0$, and $1 * 1$ in such a way that if $p * q$ denotes the truth function of $P * Q$, then

$$(p * q)(\xi) = p(\xi) * q(\xi).$$

Table 3.9.4

$p \ \ q$	$(p \oplus q)(\xi)$	$(p \mid q)(\xi)$	$(p \parallel q)(\xi)$
0 0	0	1	1
0 1	1	1	0
1 0	1	1	0
1 1	0	0	0

For the exclusive-or, the Scheffer stroke, and the double stroke, these definitions are dictated by the truth values in Table 3.9.4, that is, we define

$$0 \oplus 0 = 0, \qquad 0 \oplus 1 = 1 \oplus 0 = 1, \qquad 1 \oplus 1 = 0,$$
$$0 \mid 0 = 0 \mid 1 = 1 \mid 0 = 1, \qquad 1 \mid 1 = 0,$$
$$0 \parallel 0 = 1, \qquad 0 \parallel 1 = 1 \parallel 0 = 1 \parallel 1 = 0,$$

so that, in every case,

$$(p \oplus q)(\xi) = p(\xi) \oplus q(\xi), \qquad (p \mid q)(\xi) = p(\xi) \mid q(\xi),$$
$$(p \parallel q)(\xi) = p(\xi) \parallel q(\xi).$$

These rules are useful in the design of certain types of transistor circuits.

The same procedure may be extended to the connectives "→" and "↔." With these definitions, we can now prove a generalization of the theorem at the end of Section 3.4:

Theorem: *The truth function of any logical function, built up by a finite number of uses of arbitrary unary or binary operations, of propositions $P, Q, \ldots$, is the same function of the corresponding truth functions $p, q, \ldots$.*

The method of proof is essentially the same as before, and we leave the details to the reader.

3.10   Boolean Algebras of Propositional Functions

Let P, Q, R denote arbitrary propositional functions of a fixed set of variables $x_1, x_2, \ldots, x_n$. The relations "⟺" and "⟹" between pairs of such functions exhibit properties corresponding respectively to those of "=" and "≤" in Chapter 1 and "=" and "⊆" in Chapter 2. For example, we have at once, from the definition, **the universal bounds property:** for all P,

(L–13) $F \Rightarrow P \Rightarrow T,$

and **the reflexive property:** for all P,

(L–14) $P \Rightarrow P.$

Also, if $P \Rightarrow Q$ and $Q \Rightarrow P$, then $P(\xi)$ and $Q(\xi)$ have the same truth value in every case, so that $P \Leftrightarrow Q$. We have thus **the antisymmetric property:**

(L–15)   If $P \Rightarrow Q$ and $Q \Rightarrow P$,   then $P \Leftrightarrow Q$.

The converse of (L–15) is also true. We can combine (L–15) and its converse in the equivalence,

$$(P \Rightarrow Q)(Q \Rightarrow P) \Leftrightarrow (P \Leftrightarrow Q),$$

which formulates the fact mentioned earlier that to prove P and Q equivalent, that is, to prove that "P if and only if Q" or "P is a necessary and sufficient condition for Q" is a tautology, we prove a theorem and its converse: P implies Q and Q implies P.

Now suppose $P \Rightarrow Q$ and $Q \Rightarrow R$. Then, whenever $P(\xi)$ is true, $Q(\xi)$ is true, and hence $R(\xi)$ is also true. Thus $P \rightarrow R$ is a tautology, so $P \Rightarrow R$. That is, we have **the transitive property:**

(L–16) $(P \Rightarrow Q)(Q \Rightarrow R) \Rightarrow (P \Rightarrow R).$

We have also

(L–17a) $(P \Rightarrow Q) \Leftrightarrow (PQ \Leftrightarrow P)$

and

(L–17b) $(P \Rightarrow Q) \Leftrightarrow (P \vee Q \Leftrightarrow Q).$

Indeed, suppose $P \Rightarrow Q$. Then, whenever $P(\xi)$ is true, $Q(\xi)$ is true, so $P(\xi)Q(\xi)$ is also true. If $P(\xi)$ is false, then $P(\xi)Q(\xi)$ is also false. Thus $P(\xi)Q(\xi)$ and $P(\xi)$ always have the same truth value, so that $PQ \Leftrightarrow P$. Conversely, suppose $PQ \Leftrightarrow P$. Then, if $P(\xi)$ is true, $P(\xi)Q(\xi)$ is also true, so that $Q(\xi)$ is necessarily true. Thus $P \Rightarrow Q$. This proves (L–17a). The proof of (L–17b) is similar and is left to the reader.

We now have a set $\mathscr{P}$ of objects, namely the set of propositional functions P of n variables $x_1, x_2, \ldots, x_n$; a set of operations " $\vee$," " $\cdot$," and "$^{-}$" defined on $\mathscr{P}$ and yielding elements of $\mathscr{P}$; the particular, distinct elements F and T of $\mathscr{P}$; and the relations $\Leftrightarrow$ and $\Rightarrow$ defined for pairs of elements of $\mathscr{P}$. If, in Section 1.15, we replace "=" by "$\Leftrightarrow$," "$\leqslant$" by "$\Rightarrow$," "0" by "F," and "1" by "T," our total set of objects, operations, and relations is seen to satisfy all the conditions in the definition of a Boolean algebra. That is, *the set $\mathscr{P}$ of all propositional functions of n given variables constitutes a Boolean algebra.*

Now let $\mathscr{L}$ be any nonempty subset of $\mathscr{P}$ which is closed with respect to the operations $\vee$, $\cdot$, and $^{-}$, that is, such that for all P and Q which belong to $\mathscr{L}$, $P \vee Q$, PQ, and $\bar{P}$ also belong to $\mathscr{L}$. Then $\mathscr{L}$ necessarily contains with a function P the functions $P\bar{P}$ or F and $P \vee \bar{P}$ or T. The subset $\mathscr{L}$ now may be seen to satisfy all the conditions for a Boolean algebra so that $\mathscr{L}$ constitutes a subalgebra of $\mathscr{P}$. A simple example is the set of sixteen essentially distinct propositions concerning the closure of two contacts a and b. This is a subalgebra $\mathscr{L}$ of the set of all propositions about a and b, many of which would have nothing at all to do with switching. Let

$$P = (a \text{ is closed}),$$
$$Q = (b \text{ is closed}),$$
$$\bar{P} = (a \text{ is not closed}) = (a \text{ is open}).$$

Then we have in $\mathscr{L}$ the propositions P, $\bar{P}$, Q, $\bar{Q}$, $F \Leftrightarrow P\bar{P} = (a \text{ is closed}$ and a is not closed), $P \vee Q = (a \text{ is closed or } b \text{ is closed})$, $\bar{P}Q = (a \text{ is open and } b \text{ is closed})$, and so on. The complete set may be constructed quickly with the help of Table 3.9.2.

It is interesting to observe that the truth sets of the elements $P(x_1, x_2, \ldots, x_n)$ of a Boolean algebra $\mathscr{L} \subseteq \mathscr{P}$ constitute a *field of subsets* (Section 2.13) of the universal set $\{\xi\}$ of all allowable assignments of values to the variables $x_1, x_2, \ldots, x_n$.

3.11 Boolean Algebras of Truth Functions

Consider again a Boolean algebra $\mathscr{P}$ of propositional functions of a fixed set of variables $x_1, x_2, \ldots, x_n$. Let P and Q belong to $\mathscr{P}$. For the corresponding truth functions p and q we define equality thus: $p = q$ if and only if $p(\xi) = q(\xi)$ for all ξ, that is, if and only if $P \Leftrightarrow Q$. Similarly we define $0 \leqslant 0$, $0 \leqslant 1$, $1 \leqslant 1$, and $p \leqslant q$ if and only if $p(\xi) \leqslant q(\xi)$ for all ξ, that is, if and only if $q(\xi) = 1$ whenever $p(\xi) = 1$, or equivalently, if and only if $P \Rightarrow Q$. We thus have constructed, here and in Sections 3.3 and 3.4, a one-to-one correspondence between propositional functions and their truth functions in such a way as to guarantee the set of correspondences shown in Table 3.11.1. From the given definitions, the listed correspondences, and the last theorem of Section 3.4, it follows that to

Table 3.11.1

Propositional Formula	Corresponding Truth Formula
F	0
T	1
P	p
$\bar{P}$	$\bar{p}$
$P \vee Q$	$p \vee q$
PQ	pq
$P \Rightarrow Q$	$p \leqslant q$
$P \Leftrightarrow Q$	$p = q$

every relation in the Boolean algebra $\mathscr{P}$, there corresponds a structurally analogous relation in the algebra of truth functions. For example, to the equivalence $P \vee PQ \Leftrightarrow P$ corresponds the identical equality $p \vee pq = p$. Hence *the set of all truth functions corresponding to propositional functions of the Boolean algebra $\mathscr{P}$ is also a Boolean algebra.*

To illustrate, let C denote a combinational two-terminal relay switching circuit involving the contact variables, $x_1, x_2, \ldots, x_n$. Then a simple and important example of the correspondence just described is obtained from the set $\mathscr{P}$ of propositional functions, "The circuit C is closed for the combination $(x_1, x_2, \ldots, x_n)$," one such function being defined by each circuit, so that $\mathscr{P}$ is an infinite set. The corresponding truth functions are simply the 2^{2^n} switching functions of $x_1, x_2, \ldots, x_n$. Since in this case the truth functions are so much easier to manipulate formally than are the corresponding propositional functions, the latter are mentioned very little in practical discussions of switching circuits, but of course they are implicitly there. The fact that truth functions are readily manipulated is important because that fact permits an intelligent choice from the infinitely many circuits which all give rise to the same truth function.

3.12   Exercises

In the following exercises, propositional functions $P, Q, R, \ldots$, appearing in the same formula should always be assumed to be arbitrary functions of the same set of variables.

1. Prove the following equivalences algebraically:

(a) $P \oplus P \Leftrightarrow F$, (d) $\overline{P \oplus Q} \Leftrightarrow P \oplus \bar{Q} \Leftrightarrow \bar{P} \oplus Q$,

(b) $P \oplus F \Leftrightarrow P$, (e) $(P \oplus Q) \oplus R \Leftrightarrow P \oplus (Q \oplus R)$,

(c) $P \oplus T \Leftrightarrow \bar{P}$, (f) $P \oplus Q \oplus PQ \Leftrightarrow P \vee Q$.

Then list further properties of the exclusive-or that you would expect to be true, and prove them.

2. Prove that the following are tautologies by algebraically reducing them in each case to T:

(a) $[(P \rightarrow Q)(\bar{P} \rightarrow Q)] \rightarrow Q$, (e) $(P \rightarrow Q) \vee P$,

(b) $[(P \rightarrow Q)(\bar{P} \rightarrow Q)] \leftrightarrow Q$, (f) $PQ \rightarrow P$,

(c) $[(P \rightarrow Q)(P \rightarrow \bar{Q})] \rightarrow \bar{P}$, (g) $(P \rightarrow Q) \vee (Q \rightarrow P)$,

(d) $[(P \rightarrow Q)(P \rightarrow \bar{Q})] \leftrightarrow \bar{P}$, (h) $(P \rightarrow Q) \rightarrow [(Q \rightarrow R) \rightarrow (P \rightarrow R)]$.

Each of these tautologies may be specialized to a simple, familiar, verbal rule concerning implication. What are these verbal rules?

3. Establish that the following relations hold for all P, Q, and R:

(a) $(P \rightarrow Q) \Leftrightarrow [(P \vee Q) \rightarrow Q]$,

(b) $(P \rightarrow Q) \Rightarrow (PR \rightarrow QR)$,

(c) $(P \rightarrow Q) \Rightarrow [(P \vee R) \rightarrow (Q \vee R)]$,

(d) $(P \rightarrow Q) \Leftrightarrow ([PR \rightarrow QR][(P \vee R) \rightarrow (Q \vee R)])$,

(e) $(PQ \rightarrow R)\bar{R} \Rightarrow (\bar{P} \vee \bar{Q})$,

(f) $P \Rightarrow (Q \rightarrow P)$,

(g) $(\bar{P} \rightarrow \bar{Q}) \Leftrightarrow (Q \rightarrow P)$.

What familiar verbal rules concerning implication follow from these?

4. Prove that the following relations hold for all P and Q:

(a) $\overline{P \leftrightarrow Q} \Leftrightarrow P \oplus Q$,

(b) $\overline{P \mid Q} \Leftrightarrow \bar{P} \| \bar{Q}$,

(c) $(P \mid Q) \oplus (P \| Q) \Leftrightarrow P \oplus Q$.

5. Write the following functions in both the disjunctive and conjunctive normal forms (three variables):

(a) $PQ \oplus \bar{P}R$, (d) $(P\bar{Q} \rightarrow R) \leftrightarrow (Q \rightarrow R)$,

(b) $PQ \vee \bar{P}R$, (e) $(\overline{PQ} \vee R) \leftrightarrow (\bar{Q} \vee R)$,

(c) $(P \rightarrow Q)(Q \leftrightarrow R)$, (f) $P \oplus PQ \oplus PQR$.

6. Suppose that $P \oplus Q$ is a tautology, for given P and Q. Does it follow that exactly one of P and Q is a tautology? Explain. What relation *does* exist between P and Q?

7. Use (L–17a, b) to prove (L–12b). (These laws are found in Section 3.10 and Exercise 1, Section 3.8, respectively.)

8. Prove that $(p \mid q) \mid r = p \mid (q \mid r)$ if and only if $p = r$.

9. Prove that $[(p \mid p) \mid q] \mid [p \mid (q \mid q)] = [p \mid (p \mid q)] \mid [(p \mid q) \mid q]$.

10. Show that the binary connective $*$, defined by $P * Q = P\bar{Q}$, and the constant function T, together suffice to generate all sixteen logical functions of P and Q. Then dualize.

11. Give six examples of significant types of "if..., then..." statements. For example: "If the voltage on lead B exceeds 100, transistor number 6 will fail." Make two of the examples technical, two mathematical, and two social in nature.

12. Prove that $(x^2 + y^2 \leqslant 1) \Rightarrow (|y| \leqslant 1)$ and that $(x + y \leqslant 1) \not\Rightarrow (|y| \leqslant 1)$. (The symbol "$\not\Rightarrow$" means "does not imply.")

13. Show that all sixteen logical functions of P and Q can be expressed in terms of the double stroke.

14. Express all sixteen functions of P and Q in terms of *and* and *not* only. Then express them in terms of *or* and *not* only.

15.. Express all sixteen functions of P and Q in terms of "$\rightarrow$" and "$\bar{}$" only. Begin by proving $(P \vee Q) \Leftrightarrow (\bar{P} \rightarrow Q)$ and $PQ \Leftrightarrow \overline{P \rightarrow \bar{Q}}$.

16. Prove that the following relations hold for all P, Q, R:

(a) $[P \rightarrow (Q \rightarrow R)] \Leftrightarrow (PQ \rightarrow R)$,
(b) $[(P \vee Q) \rightarrow PQ] \Leftrightarrow (P \leftrightarrow Q)$,
(c) $PQ \Rightarrow (PR \vee Q\bar{R})$,
(d) $[P \rightarrow (Q \vee R)] \Leftrightarrow [(P \vee R) \leftrightarrow (PQ \vee R)]$.

17. Prove that

$$PQ \oplus QR \oplus RP \Leftrightarrow PQ \vee QR \vee RP \Leftrightarrow (P \vee Q)(Q \vee R)(R \vee P).$$

18. Prove the following distributive laws for the connective "$\rightarrow$" and the relation "$\Rightarrow$":

(a) $[P \rightarrow (Q \vee R)] \Leftrightarrow [(P \rightarrow Q) \vee (P \rightarrow R)]$,
(b) $[(P \Rightarrow R)(Q \Rightarrow R)] \Rightarrow (PQ \Rightarrow R)$

In (a), why can we not replace each of the symbols "$\rightarrow$" by the symbol "$\Rightarrow$"?

19.   Given that $\bar{P} \Rightarrow Q$ and $Q \Rightarrow P$, for some fixed function Q, prove that $P \Leftrightarrow T$.

20.   Let Q be a given propositional function. For what functions P do we have $PQ \Leftrightarrow F$? $P \vee Q \Leftrightarrow T$? Both $PQ \Leftrightarrow F$ and $P \vee Q \Leftrightarrow T$?

21.   Prove that if $\bar{P} \Rightarrow \bar{Q}$, then $Q \Rightarrow P$ and that if $\bar{P} \Rightarrow (Q \Leftrightarrow R)$, then $Q\bar{P} \Leftrightarrow R\bar{P}$. Are the converses also true?

22.   Prove that

$$[P \Rightarrow (Q \vee R)] \Leftrightarrow [(PQ \vee R) \Leftrightarrow (P \vee R)].$$

This is an important simplification formula, for it says that if one *knows* $P \Rightarrow (Q \vee R)$, then one also knows $(PQ \vee R) \Leftrightarrow P \vee R$; that is, that one may replace $PQ \vee R$ by $P \vee R$. (See reference [7].)

23.   Prove that the following rule is correct: To determine whether or not a product $Q = P_1^{e_1} P_2^{e_2}, \ldots, P_n^{e_n}$ implies any formula R, throughout R we replace all the uncomplemented P_j's occurring also in Q by T's and all the complemented P_j's occurring also in Q by F's. The formula obtained from R in this way reduces to a tautology if and only if $Q \Rightarrow R$. (See reference [7].)

24.   Use the disjunctive normal form to show that if c is the number of logical operations required for a representation of a given logical function of $P_1, P_2, \ldots, P_n$, then $c \leqslant n \cdot 2^{n-1}$. (We never need to use more than 2^{n-1} complete products, and each complete product can be reduced to a form having at most one complement.)

25.   Simplify $(P_1 \oplus P_2) \vee (P_2 \oplus P_3) \vee (P_3 \oplus P_1)$ algebraically and with the help of a truth table.

26.   Show that each of the following functions reduces to a single conditional:

(a) $(PQ \rightarrow R) \rightarrow (Q \rightarrow R)$,
(b) $PQ \rightarrow (Q \leftrightarrow PR)$.

Under what conditions on P, Q, R do we have, respectively,

(c) $(PQ \rightarrow R) \Rightarrow (Q \rightarrow R)$

and

(d) $PQ \Rightarrow (Q \leftrightarrow PR)$?

27.   Express in the simplest possible equivalent form:

(a) $(P \rightarrow Q)(Q \rightarrow P)(P \vee Q)$,
(b) $(P \rightarrow Q)(Q \rightarrow R)(R \rightarrow P)(P \vee Q \vee R)$.

Then, in each case, formulate a corresponding verbal statement about implication.

28.   A technician is sorting diodes into two identical trays, each of which contains several hundred diodes. Tray A is to contain only diodes which meet a certain specification; tray B is to contain only diodes which do not. In a moment of confusion, he throws one good diode into the tray of rejects and one faulty diode into the tray of good ones. Then the janitor moves the trays, which the technician forgot to label. The technician decides to test up to three diodes from one tray in order to identify the trays. Consider the following propositional functions:

P:	The technician chooses tray A.
Q:	The first diode selected meets specifications.
R:	The second diode selected meets specifications.
S:	The third diode selected meets specifications.

Prove that the following relations hold in this case:

(a) $QR \Rightarrow P$,   (d) $\bar{P}Q \Rightarrow \bar{R}\bar{S}$,

(b) $\bar{Q}\bar{R} \Rightarrow \bar{P}$,   (e) $QR \vee QS \vee RS \Leftrightarrow P$,

(c) $P\bar{Q} \Rightarrow RS$,   (f) $\bar{Q}\bar{R} \vee \bar{Q}\bar{S} \vee \bar{R}\bar{S} \Leftrightarrow \bar{P}$.

29.   Not infrequently, incorrect reasoning yields a correct result. For example, the formula

$$\overline{PQ \vee QR \vee RP} \Leftrightarrow \bar{P}\bar{Q} \vee \bar{Q}\bar{R} \vee \bar{R}\bar{P}$$

is valid even though one could have gotten it by incorrectly assuming negation to be completely distributive. Explain this situation in terms of the concept of implication.

30.   Prove the following properties of the exclusive-or, where it is assumed that multiplication precedes "addition":

(a) $x \oplus \bar{x}y = x \vee y$,

(b) $xy \oplus \bar{x}z = xy \vee \bar{x}z$,

(c) $x \oplus x\bar{y} = xy$,

(d) $x_1\bar{x}_2 \oplus \bar{x}_1x_2 = x_1 \oplus x_2$,

(e) $(x \oplus y = x \vee y) \Leftrightarrow (xy = 0)$.

31.   Let P, Q, R belong to a Boolean algebra $\mathscr{P}$ of propositional functions. Show by means of counterexamples that, from the fact that $PR \Leftrightarrow QR$ for all ξ belonging to the common domain of these functions, one cannot conclude that $P \Leftrightarrow Q$. What about the case $PR \Leftrightarrow QR$ for all $R \in \mathscr{P}$?

32. Given the ternary operation θ defined by

$$\theta(P, Q, R) = \bar{P} \oplus \bar{Q}R$$

and a nonempty set $\mathscr{P}$ of propositional functions, prove that if $\mathscr{P}$ is closed with respect to θ, then $\mathscr{P}$ is a Boolean algebra.

33. Let $\mathscr{P}$ be the set of all true propositions. What properties of a Boolean algebra does $\mathscr{P}$ possess?

34. Let $\mathscr{P}$ be a Boolean algebra of propositional functions. Let $\mathscr{R}$ be the set of all propositions of the form $P * Q$ where $*$ is either $\Rightarrow$ or $\Leftrightarrow$ and where P and Q are elements of $\mathscr{P}$. What properties of a Boolean algebra does $\mathscr{R}$ possess?

3.13 Electronic Realization of Logical Connectives

In this section, basic electronic circuit elements, called **logic elements,** of a nature to be discussed presently, are represented by small circles. We use arrows leading to such circles to denote **leads** (wires) by which voltages may be applied at appropriate points of the circuit. These are called **input leads.** We let an arrow leading from the circle denote a lead on which a voltage resulting from the applied voltages may be sensed; this is an **output lead** (Figure 3.13.1).

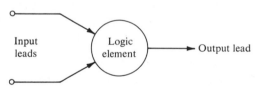

Symbol for a logic element
Figure 3.13.1

The applied voltages and the output voltage, commonly called **signals,** may be of relatively long duration or they may be in the nature of brief voltage changes, positive or negative **voltage pulses** as they are called, applied at specifically determined time intervals.

Now assume that a certain high voltage (or voltage pulse) on a lead constitutes *one* type of signal on that lead and that a certain low voltage (or voltage pulse) constitutes an *opposite* type of signal. Then, for purposes of analysis and synthesis of circuits that realize logical functions of truth values, we can assign to the *high* voltage signal on a lead the symbol "1," and to the *low* voltage signal the symbol "0." At times, it is convenient to use exactly the opposite convention. This is of course a matter of engineering rather than of logic and depends on the types of components and circuitry we use. In the design of logic circuits, we ignore so far as possible the specific voltages involved, which in fact vary considerably, depending on the particular devices (such as transistors, diodes, magnetic cores, and so on) that may be used to realize the circuit. Of course, since no device behaves in quite the ideal fashion that we assume for the purposes of "logical design," the input and output voltages involved must ultimately be taken into account and may well decide how we choose between several circuits that realize the same logical function.

Consider now any circuit with two input leads such that there appears a signal "1" on the output lead if and only if there appears a signal "1" on one input lead, or on the other input lead, or on both at once. Such a device, called an **OR-element** or an **OR-gate,** is symbolized in Figure 3.13.2, where a commonly used alternative representation is also shown.

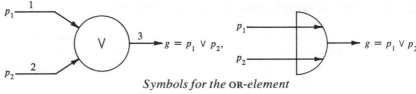

Symbols for the OR-*element*
Figure 3.13.2

If the truth values of the propositions, "There is a signal '1' on lead number 1," "There is a signal '1' on lead number 2," and "There is a signal '1' on lead number 3," are respectively p_1, p_2, and g, then it follows that, consistently with the name "OR-element,"

$$g = p_1 \lor p_2.$$

This equation may be interpreted in another way: If on lead number 1 we input signals representing values of the truth function p_1 of P_1, and on lead number 2 we input signals representing corresponding values of the truth function p_2 of P_2, then the output signal on lead number 3 will represent the truth values of the logical function $G = P_1 \lor P_2$. (Note that we have employed here the verb *to input*, a usage originated by computer people.)

Interpreting the operation of the circuit physically, we observe that, if a high voltage on a lead represents a signal "1," then the voltage on lead number 3 is high if and only if there is a high voltage on lead number 1 or on lead number 2 or on both at once. Similarly, if a low voltage constitutes a signal "1".

There are also circuits such that there appears a signal "1" on the output lead if and only if there appear signals "1" on both input leads at the same time. If the same meanings are attached to g, p_1, and p_2 as above, such a circuit realizes the truth function

$$g = p_1 p_2$$

and hence is called an AND-**element** or an AND-**gate.** It is symbolized in Figure 3.13.3, where two commonly used representations appear.

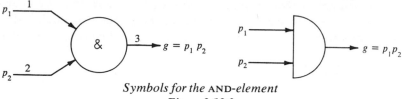

Symbols for the AND-*element*
Figure 3.13.3

Finally, there are circuits which realize the values of the truth function $\bar{p}$ (Figure 3.13.4).

Symbols for the NOT-*element*
Figure 3.13.4

Such devices are called NOT-**elements** or **inverters.** Here if the voltage on lead number 1 is high, the voltage on lead number 2 is low, and vice versa.

There exist also OR-elements and AND-elements with more than two input leads. They may be represented as in Figure 3.13.5.

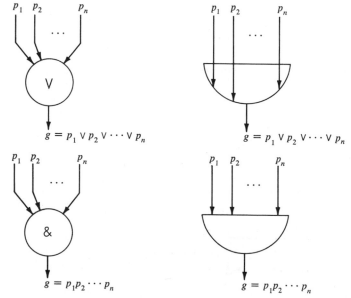

Symbols for multiple-input AND- *and* OR-*elements*
Figure 3.13.5

Discussions of realizations of these truth functions by the use of several types of electronic devices appear in Appendix 2. For the purposes of the remainder of this chapter, we need only to know that such realizations are possible. Physical realizations of the stroke, the double stroke, and the function $p_1\bar{p}_2$ are also simple to attain (Figure 3.13.6). These

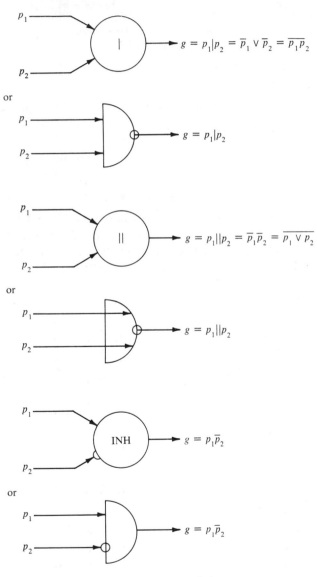

Symbols for other logical elements

Figure 3.13.6

elements are called respectively the NAND-**element** (not and), the NOR-**element** (not or), and the **inhibitor** (an input 1 on the p_2 lead "inhibits" the output signal, that is, holds it at 0). The NAND-element and the NOR-element are also called respectively the stroke element and the double-stroke element in this book. Generalized NAND- and NOR-elements will be introduced later.

3.14   Realization of Truth Values of Logical Functions

Since the truth values of the three logical connectives *and, or,* and *not* can be realized using electronic circuitry, we would expect that the truth value of *any* logical function could be realized using such circuitry, for any logical function can be expressed in terms of *and, or,* and *not*. We illustrate how this is done with some examples.

The truth function $s = p \oplus q = p\bar{q} \vee \bar{p}q$ has, as one realization, the circuit shown in Figure 3.14.1. Here p and $\bar{q}$ are inputs to one AND-

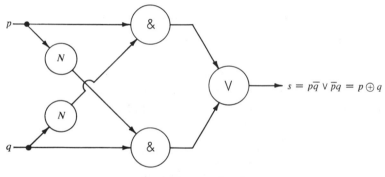

Exclusive–or circuit
Figure 3.14.1

element while $\bar{p}$ and q are inputs to the other. The outputs $p\bar{q}$ and $\bar{p}q$ of these two AND-elements are then used as inputs to an OR-element, the output of which is $p\bar{q} \vee \bar{p}q = s$.

This function may be realized another way. We can write

$$s = (p \vee q)(\bar{p} \vee \bar{q}) = (p \vee q)\overline{pq},$$

which has the more economical realization shown in Figure 3.14.2. Here p and q are used as inputs of an AND-element, the output of which is then inverted to yield $\overline{pq}$. The signals p and q are also used as inputs of an OR-element. The outputs of the OR-element and of the NOT-element are then used as inputs of an AND-element, which yields $(p \vee q) \cdot \overline{pq}$ as its output.

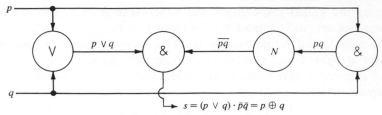

$$s = (p \lor q) \cdot \bar{p}\bar{q} = p \oplus q$$

A simpler exclusive–or circuit
Figure 3.14.2

If inhibitors are available, then $s = p\bar{q} \lor \bar{p}q$ can be realized still more simply, since the algebraic form of the expression calls at once for two of these elements (Figure 3.14.3).

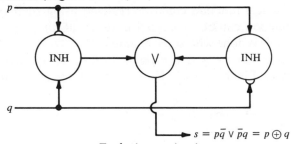

$$s = p\bar{q} \lor \bar{p}q = p \oplus q$$

Exclusive-or circuit
Figure 3.14.3

The same task can be performed exclusively with the use of stroke elements, if one wishes. Since $p \lor q = \bar{p} \mid \bar{q}$ and since $\bar{p}\bar{q} = p \mid q$, we have

$$
\begin{aligned}
s &= p\bar{q} \lor \bar{p}q \\
&= \overline{p\bar{q}} \mid \overline{\bar{p}q} \\
&= (\bar{p} \lor q) \mid (p \lor \bar{q}) \\
&= (\bar{p} \lor pq) \mid (pq \lor \bar{q}) \\
&= (p \mid \overline{pq}) \mid (\overline{pq} \mid q) \\
&= [p \mid (p \mid q)] \mid [(p \mid q) \mid q].
\end{aligned}
$$

The corresponding circuit is shown in Figure 3.14.4. The relative simplicity of this circuit depends on the insertion of redundant symbols

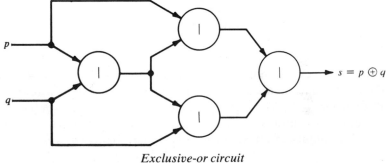

$$s = p \oplus q$$

Exclusive-or circuit
Figure 3.14.4

p and q in the fourth line of the reduction. This permits a sharing of the output $p \mid q$ in a useful way. The reduction of $p \oplus q$ to a form involving the stroke function alone should be studied carefully, for the methods used are important.

For a second example, we note that the function

$$g = (\bar{p}q \lor p\bar{q})r \lor p\bar{r}$$

may be rewritten as

$$g = (p \lor q)\overline{pq} \cdot r \lor p\bar{r}$$

so that we can exploit the result of the previous example to realize it. The result is shown in Figure 3.14.5. Note that this circuit uses a three-input AND-element.

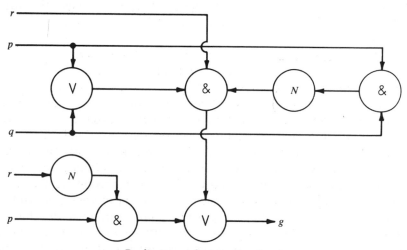

Preliminary design of a circuit
Figure 3.14.5

Once again we can, however, use algebra to obtain a more economical realization of the function. We have, with the help of some identities,

$$g = \bar{p}qr \lor p\bar{q}r \lor p\bar{r}$$
$$= \bar{p} \cdot qr \lor p(\bar{q} \lor \bar{r})$$
$$= p \oplus qr.$$

This leads at once to the circuit of Figure 3.14.6, since we already know how to realize the $\oplus$-operation.

These examples serve to illustrate a basic problem of the design of logic circuits: Is the circuit that is used to realize a given truth function the most economical circuit possible? Unfortunately, it is not known at present how to represent an arbitrary function in a form that demonstrably requires the minimum amount of hardware. In practice, we do the best

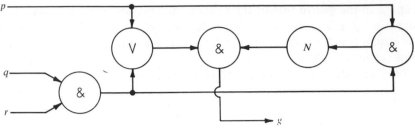

Simplified form of preceding circuit
Figure 3.14.6

we can, with the help of limited algebraic tools, by inspection, comparison, and inspiration. By exploiting the device used in preceding examples, namely, by rearranging the switching function of the circuit to be designed so that component functions appear repeatedly wherever possible, we can frequently obtain much more economical designs than would otherwise be the case.

It should also be pointed out that what constitutes simplicity requires precise definition. In the above two examples, there is no doubt as to which is the simpler AND-OR-NOT circuit. But suppose one has five AND-elements, six OR-elements, and two NOT-elements in one circuit, whereas another equivalent circuit, that is, one which realizes the same truth function, has five AND-elements, five OR-elements, and three NOT-elements. Then which is simpler? If NOT-elements cost one-third as much as OR-elements, then the latter circuit must certainly be regarded as the more economical. If they cost twice as much as OR-elements, then the former circuit is more economical. This point of view is considered in detail in reference [6]. *For our purposes, however, we shall arbitrarily define one circuit built of AND-, OR-, and NOT- elements as being simpler than another, equivalent, AND-OR-NOT circuit if and only if the former has a smaller total number of input arrows entering its various logic elements.* This criterion serves to provide useful practice in algebraic manipulation. When stroke elements alone are being used, the criterion will be that the number of stroke elements must be less in order for a circuit to be simpler. A NOT-element will be regarded as a stroke element with identical inputs.

The preceding example serves to illustrate another point. In the diagram of a relay circuit, the contacts appear in the branches connecting the nodes of the circuit diagram. In a logic circuit, the logical elements are in effect the nodes of the diagram. This helps to explain why relay circuits are often easily simplified by inspection but logic circuits are not, and why algebraic procedures that are useful in one technology may be less useful in the other. For example, the substitution of $\bar{x}\bar{y}$ for $\bar{x} \vee \bar{y}$ is often helpful in the design of logic circuits, but is ordinarily not helpful in the design of relay circuits. This is reflected in the fact that the function xy has an easy geometrical representation in the logic case, but not in the relay case.

3.15 Logic Circuits and Computation

Suppose now that we need to perform operations of addition in the binary system and we wish to have an electronic machine do the work for us. The computation can be described by a set of propositions which say that the values of certain symbols are the digits 1 or 0. If we let one state of a lead denote the digit 1, and let the other state denote the digit 0, then the propositions of our arithmetic can be made to correspond in one-to-one fashion to the states of certain leads of an electronic circuit.

For example, suppose we wish to add two binary digits p and q. Then, in addition to the **augend** p (the digit which is to be augmented) and the **addend** q (the digit which is added to the augend), the digits we must represent are the **sum digit** s and the **carry digit** c, whose values in the four possible cases are given in Table 3.15.1. Whereas in hand computation a carry digit 0 is simply ignored, a computer cannot do this; it always records either a 1 or a 0, whichever is appropriate. That is, we need these values for design purposes, as Table 3.15.1 suggests.

Table 3.15.1

Summary of Binary Addition Facts

p	0	0	1	1
q	0	1	0	1
cs	$\overline{00}$	$\overline{01}$	$\overline{01}$	$\overline{10}$

p	q	c	s
0	0	0	0
0	1	0	1
1	0	0	1
1	1	1	0

We can interpret the *binary digits* in the columns of this table as *truth values* of the following four propositions:

P: The augend p has the value 1.
Q: The addend q has the value 1.
C: The carry digit c has the value 1.
S: The sum digit s has the value 1.

Thus the addition table also plays the role of a truth table. Now we can represent these truth values, that is, the digits themselves, as signals on the leads of a logic circuit. For c and s we can write, from the table, the truth functions

$$c = pq,$$
$$s = p \oplus q = (p \lor q)\overline{pq}.$$

If we now draw the circuit for *s* just as in the previous section, the inclusion of an additional output lead just in front of the element that inverts *pq* will provide us with the output *c*. This is shown in Figure 3.15.1. This circuit is called a **half-adder** because it adds two digits without adding also the carry from a previous stage of addition.

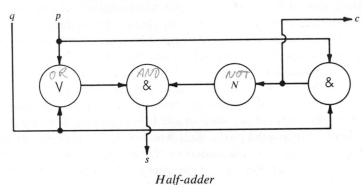

Half-adder

Figure 3.15.1

If stroke elements are to be used, we begin with the exclusive-or circuit of Figure 3.14.4 and note that the output of the first stroke element is $\overline{pq}$. Inverting this (an inverter is simply a stroke element with identical inputs), we generate *pq* and thus have a complete half-adder (Figure 3.15.2).

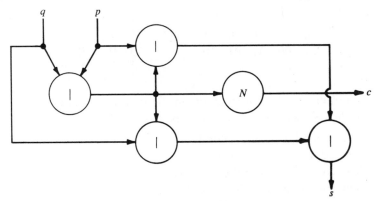

Stroke half-adder

Figure 3.15.2

Suppose next that we wish to add three binary digits: a digit *p*, a digit *q*, and a carry-in digit c_{in}, coming from a previous addition (Table 3.15.2). Note that in any row of the table, the sum of the digits in the first three columns is represented in binary form in the last two columns.

Table 3.15.2
Addition with Carry

p	q	c_{in}	c_{out}	s
0	0	0	0	0
0	0	1	0	1
0	1	0	0	1
0	1	1	1	0
1	0	0	0	1
1	0	1	1	0
1	1	0	1	0
1	1	1	1	1

Now s is the ring sum of p, q, and c_{in}, that is, as the reader may verify,

$$s = (p \oplus q) \oplus c_{in}.$$

From Table 3.15.2, the carry-out digit is defined by

$$c_{out} = \bar{p}qc_{in} \vee p\bar{q}c_{in} \vee pq\bar{c}_{in} \vee pqc_{in}$$
$$= (\bar{p}q \vee p\bar{q})c_{in} \vee pq(\bar{c}_{in} \vee c_{in})$$
$$= (p \oplus q)c_{in} \vee pq.$$

These forms of the functions for s and c suggest that we realize $p \oplus q$ and pq as in the previous example, employing the results so obtained to

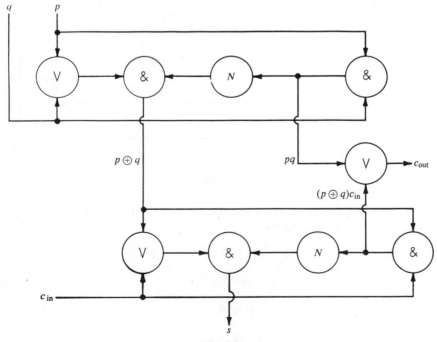

Full adder
Figure 3.15.3

realize both s and c_{out}, with the help of another half-adder, as shown in Figure 3.15.3. This circuit is called a **full adder.** This example illustrates the fact that an important aim in circuit design is to develop simple, basic circuits which can be used repeatedly as building blocks in the construction of more complex circuits. It also illustrates the importance of arranging the algebraic expressions so that outputs at internal points of the circuit can be shared so far as possible in order to save hardware.

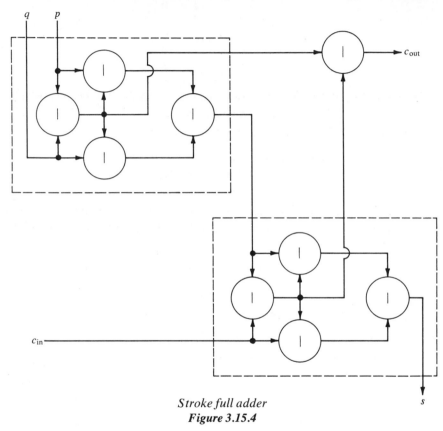

Stroke full adder
Figure 3.15.4

The full adder can also be designed using stroke elements (NAND-elements) exclusively. We have

$$p \oplus q = [p \mid (p \mid q)] \mid [(p \mid q) \mid q]$$

and

$$s = (p \oplus q) \oplus c_{in}.$$

If we put

$$z = p \oplus q$$

then

$$s = z \oplus c_{in}$$

and we use two stroke $\oplus$-elements for the realization of s. Also,

$$c_{\text{out}} = zc_{\text{in}} \vee pq$$
$$= \overline{zc_{\text{in}} \mid \overline{pq}}$$
$$= (z \mid c_{\text{in}}) \mid (p \mid q)$$

and both $z \mid c_{\text{in}}$ and $p \mid q$ are available in the circuits realizing $p \oplus q$ and $z \oplus c_{\text{in}}$. From these expressions we have the circuit shown in Figure 3.15.4. Here, two $\oplus$-elements are employed in the construction of the full adder. Because of the built-in negation of the stroke element, the inverters appearing in stroke half-adders are not required.

3.16 Generalized NAND and NOR Functions

We can also define, and realize electronically, generalized NAND and NOR functions (see Appendix 2). For the **generalized stroke** or NAND, let us make the definition:

$$\sigma(f_1, f_2, \ldots, f_p) = \overline{(f_1 f_2 \cdots f_p)}$$
$$= \bar{f}_1 \vee \bar{f}_2 \vee \cdots \vee \bar{f}_p$$

that is, we allow the arguments of the function to be arbitrary switching functions of the basic variables. For example,

$$\sigma(x_1, x_2) = \overline{x_1 x_2} = \bar{x}_1 \vee \bar{x}_2,$$

$$\sigma(x_1, x_2, x_3) = \overline{x_1 x_2 x_3} = \bar{x}_1 \vee \bar{x}_2 \vee \bar{x}_3,$$

but

$$\sigma(\bar{x}_1, x_2, \bar{x}_3) = \overline{\bar{x}_1 x_2 \bar{x}_3} = x_1 \vee \bar{x}_2 \vee x_3.$$

We can also convert more complex disjunctions into generalized stroke functions. For example,

$$x_1 x_2 \vee x_2 x_3 \vee x_3 x_1 = \sigma(\overline{x_1 x_2}, \overline{x_2 x_3}, \overline{x_3 x_1})$$
$$= \sigma[\sigma(x_1, x_2), \sigma(x_2, x_3), \sigma(x_3, x_1)].$$

For the **generalized NOR-function,** we define

$$\nu(f_1, f_2, \ldots, f_p) = \overline{(f_1 \vee f_2 \vee \cdots \vee f_p)}$$
$$= \bar{f}_1 \bar{f}_2 \cdots \bar{f}_p.$$

For example, one has at once the representations

$$\nu(x_1, x_2, x_3) = \overline{x_1 \lor x_2 \lor x_3} = \bar{x}_1 \bar{x}_2 \bar{x}_3$$

and

$$\nu(\bar{x}_1, \bar{x}_2, x_3, x_4) = \overline{\bar{x}_1 \lor \bar{x}_2 \lor x_3 \lor x_4} = x_1 x_2 \bar{x}_3 \bar{x}_4.$$

We can also convert a more complex product into a NOR-function:

$$(\bar{x}_1 \lor x_2)(\bar{x}_2 \lor x_3)(\bar{x}_3 \lor x_1) = \nu(\overline{\bar{x}_1 \lor x_2}, \overline{\bar{x}_2 \lor x_3}, \overline{\bar{x}_3 \lor x_1})$$
$$= \nu[\nu(\bar{x}_1, x_2), \nu(\bar{x}_2, x_3), \nu(\bar{x}_3, x_1)].$$

Note that these general rules apply: A union (disjunction) may be represented as the NAND of the complements of the terms, and a product (conjunction) may be represented as the NOR of the complements of the factors. Moreover, by definition, any complement of a product is the NAND-function of the factors of the product, and any complement of a union is the NOR-function of the terms of the union.

Symbols for generalized NAND- and NOR-elements appear in Figure 3.16.1.

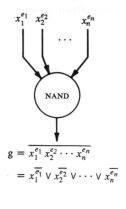
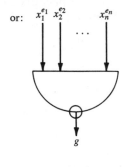
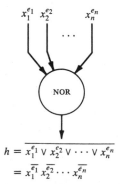
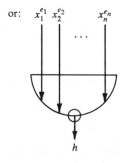

Symbols for generalized NAND- and NOR-elements
Figure 3.16.1

Now when $x_1, x_2, \ldots, x_n$ is the complete set of variables under discussion, $\sigma(x_1^{e_1}, x_2^{e_2}, \ldots, x_n^{e_n})$ is a complete union and hence vanishes at exactly one combination of values of the variables, namely that combination at which each $x_j^{e_j}$ is 1 (because of the complementation). For example, $\sigma(x_1, \bar{x}_2, x_3) = \bar{x}_1 \vee x_2 \vee \bar{x}_3$ vanishes at the combination $(1, 0, 1)$. Thus, we can expand a function into a product of NAND's in a manner similar to that in which we expand it into conjunctive normal form. To illustrate, if we refer to the table for the full adder (Table 3.15.2), we have, *for the function $\bar{s}$:*

$$\bar{s} = \sigma(\bar{p}, \bar{q}, c_{\text{in}}) \cdot \sigma(\bar{p}, q, \bar{c}_{\text{in}}) \cdot \sigma(p, \bar{q}, \bar{c}_{\text{in}}) \cdot \sigma(p, q, c_{\text{in}}).$$

Thus s, being the complement of a product, is also a NAND-function:

$$s = \sigma[\sigma(\bar{p}, \bar{q}, c_{\text{in}}), \quad \sigma(\bar{p}, q, \bar{c}_{\text{in}}), \quad \sigma(p, \bar{q}, \bar{c}_{\text{in}}), \quad \sigma(p, q, c_{\text{in}})].$$

Similarly,

$$\bar{c}_{\text{out}} = \sigma(\bar{p}, q, c_{\text{in}}) \cdot \sigma(p, \bar{q}, c_{\text{in}}) \cdot \sigma(p, q, \bar{c}_{\text{in}}) \cdot \sigma(p, q, c_{\text{in}}),$$

so that

$$c_{\text{out}} = \sigma[\sigma(\bar{p}, q, c_{\text{in}}), \quad \sigma(p, \bar{q}, c_{\text{in}}), \quad \sigma(p, q, \bar{c}_{\text{in}}), \quad \sigma(p, q, c_{\text{in}})].$$

Note that s and c_{out} have one input element in common in these expressions, namely $\sigma(p, q, c_{\text{in}})$. The symmetry of both s and c_{out} in p, q, and c_{in} stands out clearly here.

The above two equations now lead to the following design of a full adder (Figure 3.16.2). In the figure we draw a "bus" for each of p, q, c_{in},

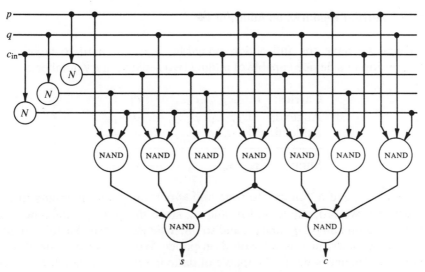

NAND *full adder*

Figure 3.16.2

$\bar{p}, \bar{q}, \bar{c}_{in}$. The rest of the circuit then follows with ease. This algebraic procedure and the corresponding circuit are adapted from material in reference [9].

How does this circuit compare with the circuit of Figure 3.15.4? Assuming that each NOT-element requires one transistor, that each NAND-element requires one transistor, and further that each NAND-element requires one diode for each input lead (see Appendix 2), the earlier circuit requires nine transistors and eighteen diodes whereas the present one requires twelve transistors and twenty-nine diodes. Thus the latter circuit costs more in hardware, but there is an offsetting advantage. In the earlier circuit, some signals must pass through a maximum of six logical elements between input and output (it is thus a "six-stage" circuit), whereas in the present circuit no signal need pass through more than three (it is a "three-stage" circuit). Since every passage through a logical element distorts and delays a signal somewhat, the smaller number of stages could be a decisive advantage in some cases.

Procedures analogous to those used above can be employed to design NOR-logic circuits. NAND-logic and NOR-logic circuits, and the reduction of functions to appropriate algebraic forms, are discussed extensively in reference [10], where further references to the literature are given.

It is interesting to note that in the generalized stroke and double stroke, we have ternary, quaternary,..., connectives. All are, however, expressible in terms of binary connectives.

3.17   Further Remarks on Addition

Once we have the full adder available, it is not hard to develop a description of a device capable of adding two n-digit binary numbers:

Carries:	c_n	c_{n-1}	c_{n-2}	$\cdots$	c_1	0
Augend:	0	p_{n-1}	p_{n-2}	$\cdots$	p_1	p_0
Addend:	0	q_{n-1}	q_{n-2}	$\cdots$	q_1	q_0
Sum:	s_n	s_{n-1}	s_{n-2}	$\cdots$	s_1	s_0

First we need a "clock" to time and synchronize all the inputs to the circuit, for we propose to add p_0 and q_0, store the sum s_0, remember the carry c_1, then add p_1, q_1, and c_1, and so on. That is, we propose to compute the sum *serially*, just as we would on paper. We need also a "delay element" or "memory device" capable of delaying the carry digit for exactly one unit of time, we need a "storage register" capable of remembering the sum digits as they become available, and we need a "steering circuit" to send the sum digits to the right slots for storage. All these things can be done in various ways physically, but the basic tasks are related as is shown in the block diagram in Figure 3.17.1.

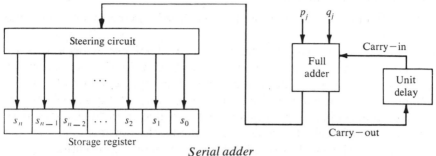

Storage register

Serial adder

Figure 3.17.1

When the addition starts, the delay element contains a "0." At time zero, it delivers the digit 0 to the full adder, and p_0 and q_0 reach it at the same time. The digits s_0 and c_1 are computed and s_0 is steered to the first slot in the storage register. The carry-out digit is delivered to the delay element, which feeds it back into the full adder at the same time that p_1 and q_1 arrive. Now s_1 and c_2 are computed, s_1 is sent to the second slot in the storage register, the carry digit c_2 is again sent to the delay element, p_2, q_2, and c_2 arrive simultaneously at the terminals of the adder, and so on, until the addition is completed. A possible final carry $c_n = s_n = 1$ is allowed for by defining $p_n = q_n = 0$ and performing an $(n+1)$th addition.

An obvious disadvantage of serial addition is that it is slow. A conceivably faster system is that of parallel addition, for which $n-1$ full adders and one half-adder are required (Figure 3.17.2). Here all n addends and all n augends arrive at the same time, and the signals

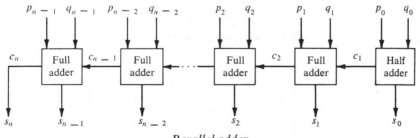

Parallel adder

Figure 3.17.2

remain until the carries have all been forwarded and the circuits have all become stable. A problem here is that one carry digit may result in a series of following carries and thus slow the addition process considerably since each such carry costs the time it takes a half-adder to operate. (Why?). It is possible to design circuits that tend to reduce this sort of delay.

3.18   Codes and Translators

We conclude this chapter with some brief comments on codes and translators.

In order for information to be processed effectively by persons or by machines, it must be represented in a symbolic form that is appropriate for the operations to be performed on it. The representation of integers in decimal form for hand calculation is a case in point. So is the representation of integers in binary form for machine calculation. Such a system of representation is called a **code** — for example, the decimal code and the binary code. The symbol or sequence of symbols representing a given item of information in a given code is called a **code word** or **word** or **code point** of that code.

Many special codes have been devised for various special purposes. With each new code always comes the problem of translating a word in one code into the corresponding word in another code. A circuit that performs this task is called a **translator**. For example, a commonly used code is the **reflected binary** or **Gray code.** Two-digit and three-digit reflected binary codes are shown in Table 3.18.1. In the table, the pairs (α_1, α_0) and the triples $(\alpha_2, \alpha_1, \alpha_0)$ are the Gray code translation of the corresponding binary words to their left. The α_0 column of the left two-digit table may be obtained by "reflecting" the lower *half* of the a_0 column in its center point. The α_1 column of the right, three-digit table may be obtained in the same way from the a_1 column. The α_0 column on the right may be obtained by applying the same principle of reflection to the second and fourth *quarters* of the a_0 column. The important property of the reflected binary codes is that, in proceeding from one code point to the next, one changes only a single digit in each case.

Table 3.18.1
Two-Digit and Three-Digit Gray Codes.

a_1	a_0	α_1	α_0
0	0	0	0
0	1	0	1
1	0	1	1
1	1	1	0

a_2	a_1	a_0	α_2	α_1	α_0
0	0	0	0	0	0
0	0	1	0	0	1
0	1	0	0	1	1
0	1	1	0	1	0
1	0	0	1	1	0
1	0	1	1	1	1
1	1	0	1	0	1
1	1	1	1	0	0

The algebraic definitions of these codes, from which the α-entries of Table 3.18.1 are computed, are respectively

$$\begin{cases} \alpha_1 = a_1 \\ \alpha_0 = a_1 \oplus a_0 \end{cases} \quad \text{and} \quad \begin{cases} \alpha_2 = a_2 \\ \alpha_1 = a_2 \oplus a_1 \\ \alpha_0 = \qquad a_1 \oplus a_0 \end{cases}$$

so that a translator is particularly easy to design in each case (Figure 3.18.1). All we need is a supply of $\oplus$-elements.

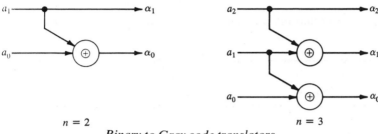

$n = 2$ $n = 3$

Binary to Gray code translators
Figure 3.18.1

The passage of a signal through a logical element ordinarily delays it somewhat. If there is a delay of D units of time in each exclusive-or circuit, and if the output signals must be synchronized, we must insert a delay device or memory element capable of delaying a signal by D units of time in each of the top leads in these two circuits, to the right of the terminal at which the lead to the exclusive-or element is connected (Figure 3.18.2). Such a delay device may be regarded as a logic element realizing the identity function.

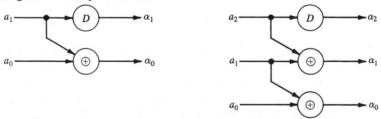

Figure 3.18.2

The n-digit reflected binary code is defined by the set of equations

(3.18.1)

$$\begin{cases} \alpha_{n-1} = a_{n-1} \\ \alpha_{n-2} = a_{n-1} \oplus a_{n-2} \\ \alpha_{n-3} = \qquad a_{n-2} \oplus a_{n-3} \\ \quad \vdots \\ \alpha_1 = \qquad\qquad\qquad a_2 \oplus a_1 \\ \alpha_0 = \qquad\qquad\qquad\qquad a_1 \oplus a_0. \end{cases}$$

Summing the first k equations, for $k = 1, 2, \ldots, n$, we obtain respectively, since $x \oplus x = 0$,

(3.18.2)
$$\begin{cases} a_{n-1} = \alpha_{n-1} \\ a_{n-2} = \alpha_{n-1} \oplus \alpha_{n-2} \\ a_{n-3} = \alpha_{n-1} \oplus \alpha_{n-2} \oplus \alpha_{n-3} \\ \vdots \\ a_1 = \quad \alpha_{n-1} \oplus \alpha_{n-2} \oplus \cdots \oplus \alpha_1 \\ a_0 = \quad \alpha_{n-1} \oplus \alpha_{n-2} \oplus \cdots \oplus \alpha_1 \oplus \alpha_0. \end{cases}$$

From these equations we can easily obtain the circuits shown in Figure 3.18.3.

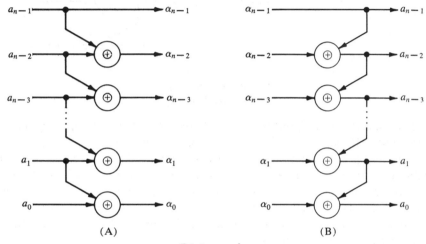

n-Digit translators
Figure 3.18.3

Just as in the case of the two-digit and three-digit Gray codes, the n-digit Gray code (reflected binary code) also has the property that only one digit changes as we proceed from one code point to the next. To see this, let $a = a_{n-1}a_{n-2} \cdots a_1 a_0$ denote any n-digit binary integer and let $\alpha_{n-1}\alpha_{n-2} \cdots \alpha_1 \alpha_0$ be the representation of a in the reflected binary code. Compute $s = a + 1$ and let $\alpha' = \alpha'_{n-1} \; \alpha'_{n-2} \cdots \alpha_1' \; \alpha_0'$ be the reflected binary representation of s. If a contains at least one digit 0, let the rightmost zero-digit in a be a_k. Then, because of the carries, $s_0 = a_0 \oplus 1 = \bar{a}_0$, $s_1 = a_1 \oplus 1 = \bar{a}_1, \ldots, s_k = a_k \oplus 1 = \bar{a}_k$, but $s_{k+1} = a_{k+1}, \ldots, s_{n-1} = a_{n-1}$ because of the absence of further carries:

$$\begin{array}{c} a_{n-1} \cdots a_{k+1} a_k \, a_{k-1} \cdots a_1 a_0 \\ 1 \\ \hline a_{n-1} \cdots a_{k+1} \bar{a}_k \bar{a}_{k-1} \cdots \bar{a}_1 \bar{a}_0 \end{array}$$

Hence, if $k < n-1$,

$$\alpha_j' = s_{j+1} \oplus s_j$$
$$= (a_{j+1} \oplus 1) \oplus (a_j \oplus 1)$$
$$= a_{j+1} \oplus a_j$$
$$= \alpha_j, \qquad j = 0, 1, 2, \ldots, k-1$$

while

$$\alpha_k' = s_{k+1} \oplus s_k$$
$$= a_{k+1} \oplus (a_k \oplus 1)$$
$$= \alpha_k \oplus 1$$
$$= \overline{\alpha_k},$$

and

$$\alpha_j' = s_{j+1} \oplus s_j$$
$$= a_{j+1} \oplus a_j$$
$$= \alpha_j, \qquad j = k+1, k+2, \ldots, n-2$$

and, finally,

$$\alpha'_{n-1} = a_{n-1} = \alpha_{n-1}.$$

Thus only the entry in the kth position is altered. If $k = n-1$, then $\alpha_j' = \alpha_j, j = 0, 1, 2, \ldots, n-2$, but $\alpha'_{n-1} = a_{n-1} \oplus 1 = \bar{a}_{n-1}$, and the property holds. If the binary representation of a contains no zeros at all, then adding 1 and retaining only the first n digits yields a sequence of n zeros. That is, the sequence of digits which *follows* $11 \ldots 1$ is the sequence $00 \ldots 0$. The corresponding *reflected* binary representations are respectively $100 \ldots 0$ and $000 \ldots 0$, which differ only in the first digit, so that the property holds in every case.

That the reflected binary code also contains all 2^n distinct sequences of n 0's and 1's follows from the fact that the linear equations (3.18.1) have the *unique* solution given by equations (3.18.2), and vice versa. There is thus a one-to-one correspondence between binary code points and reflected binary code points, so that the number of distinct code points in the reflected binary code must be 2^n.

The reflected binary code is often called a **unit distance code** because, if the code points $\alpha = (\alpha_{n-1}, \alpha_{n-2}, \ldots, \alpha_1, \alpha_0)$ and $\beta = (\beta_{n-1}, \beta_{n-2}, \ldots, \beta_1, \beta_0)$ are interpreted as coordinates of vertices of a unit cube in n-dimensions, and if the distance formula used is $d = \sum_{j=0}^{n-1} |\alpha_j - \beta_j|$, then the distance between two successive code points is 1. The integer d yielded by this formula is always the minimum number of edges of the n-cube that must be traversed in going from the vertex α to the vertex β along the edges of the n-cube.

A few other codes and translators will be referred to in following pages. More details and an extensive bibliography will be found in reference [11].

3.19 Exercises

1. Compare the outputs of the four circuits shown in Figure 3.19.1 and explain what happens.

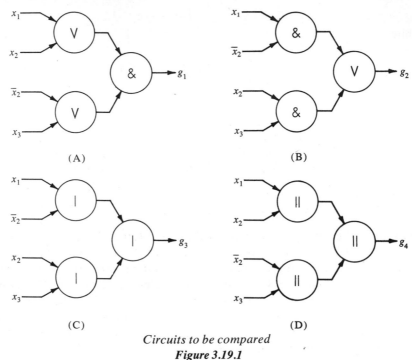

(A)   (B)

(C)   (D)

Circuits to be compared
Figure 3.19.1

2. Synthesize networks, using only AND-, OR-, and NOT-elements as in examples above, which realize the following truth functions in the simplest possible manner, that is, with the smallest number of input arrows:

$$\text{(a)} \quad g = p(q \lor \bar{r}) \lor \bar{q}r,$$
$$\text{(b)} \quad g = \bar{p}\bar{q}\bar{r} \lor \bar{p}\bar{q}r \lor \bar{p}qr \lor pqr,$$
$$\text{(c)} \quad g = (p \lor qr)(\bar{p} \lor \bar{q} \lor \bar{r}),$$
$$\text{(d)} \quad g = \bar{p}q \lor \bar{q}r \lor \bar{r}p,$$
$$\text{(e)} \quad g = \bar{p}\bar{q}\bar{r} \lor \bar{p}qr \lor p\bar{q}r \lor pq\bar{r},$$
$$\text{(f)} \quad g = (ab \lor \bar{c})(\bar{a} \lor \bar{b} \lor c),$$
$$\text{(g)} \quad g = x_1\bar{x}_2 \lor x_2\bar{x}_3 \lor x_3\bar{x}_1,$$
$$\text{(h)} \quad g = \bar{x}_1 \lor \bar{x}_2 \lor \bar{x}_3 \lor x_3(x_1\bar{x}_2 \lor \bar{x}_1x_2),$$
$$\text{(i)} \quad g = x_1\bar{x}_2 \lor x_2\bar{x}_3 \lor \bar{x}_2x_3 \lor x_4,$$
$$\text{(j)} \quad g = ab \oplus (a \lor b),$$
$$\text{(k)} \quad g = ab\bar{c} \lor \bar{a}b\bar{c} \lor \bar{a}bc \lor \bar{a}bc,$$
$$\text{(l)} \quad g = x_1x_2\bar{x}_3 \lor \bar{x}_1x_3x_4 \lor \bar{x}_2x_3x_4.$$

3. Synthesize networks for the functions of Exercise 2, assuming that you have also INH-elements available.

4. In many instances, the complement of every input signal is also available and need not be generated in a logic circuit. For example, the exclusive-or circuit now is as shown in Figure 3.19.2. Redesign the networks of Exercise 2 on the assumption that the complements of all inputs are available. Use AND-, OR-, NOT-elements only.

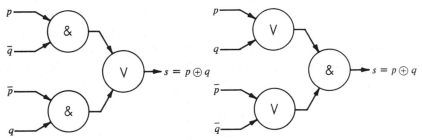

Exclusive–or circuits
Figure 3.19.2

5. Synthesize AND-OR-NOT circuits that will realize the functions g, h, and k defined by Table 3.19.1, (a) assuming complements of all inputs available, and, (b) assuming complements of inputs *not* available.

Table 3.19.1

p	q	r	g	h	k
0	0	0	0	0	d
0	0	1	1	1	0
0	1	0	1	0	0
0	1	1	1	1	1
1	0	0	1	1	0
1	0	1	0	1	1
1	1	0	0	0	d
1	1	1	0	1	d

6. Synthesize a circuit realizing the function
$$g = p\bar{q}r \lor \bar{p}q\bar{r}$$
with AND- and OR-elements and precisely one NOT-element. Do not assume complements of inputs are available.

7. Design the most economical AND-OR-NOT, two-input, three-output circuit corresponding to Table 3.19.2. Complements of inputs are not available.

Table 3.19.2

x	y	a	b	c
0	0	0	1	1
0	1	1	0	1
1	0	1	0	1
1	1	0	1	0

8. A logic circuit is to have two outputs defined as in Table 3.19.3. Design the circuit as economically as possible, using AND-, OR-, NOT-, and $\oplus$-elements, assuming complements of inputs not available (sixteen arrows or less.)

Table 3.19.3

p	q	r	s	t
0	0	0	0	1
0	0	1	1	1
0	1	0	1	0
0	1	1	0	0
1	0	0	0	0
1	0	1	0	1
1	1	0	1	1
1	1	1	1	0

9. Show that if you have a constant input signal 1 available and all the inhibitors you need, you can realize any logical circuit using no other logical elements. Realize $p \oplus q$ using only inhibitors (constant input 1 is permissible).

10. If you were designing an exclusive-or package for shelf stocks, to be drawn on as needed in a variety of circuits, what terminals would you make standard on it?

11. Design a full adder that gives the carry and sum pair in Gray code rather than in binary code. Assume you have exclusive-or packages available.

12. Let ϕ denote the both-or-neither connective (biconditional); that is, define

$$p \phi q = pq \vee \bar{p}\bar{q}.$$

(a)   Prove that, for the operation ϕ just defined,
$$p \phi q = q \phi p,$$
$$p \phi (q \phi r) = (p \phi q) \phi r,$$
$$p \phi 0 = \bar{p},$$
$$p \phi 1 = p,$$
$$p \phi p = 1,$$
$$p \phi \bar{p} = 0,$$

and that $p \phi a = b$ if and only if $p = b \phi a$.

(b)   Design the most economical AND-OR-NOT logic circuit for $p \phi q$ and *use it alone* to realize $p_1 \oplus p_2 \oplus p_3$. Generalize.

(c)   Show that if you have $\oplus$-elements but no other logic elements available you can still realize the function $p_1 \phi p_2$ provided a fixed input 1 is also available. How would you realize $p_1 \phi p_2 \phi \cdots \phi p_{2k}$ using only $\oplus$-elements?

(d)   Show that Exercise 2(e) can be solved using one ϕ-element and one $\oplus$-element, and no other logic elements.

13.   Design a combinational AND-OR-NOT circuit that will compute the four-digit product "$p_3p_2p_1p_0$" of two two-digit binary numbers "a_1a_0" and "b_1b_0". This provides a good illustration of the sharing of blocks of circuitry and the use of redundancies (seventeen arrows suffice).

14.   Assuming you have only two-input NOR-elements (double stroke elements) and NOT-elements available, design the simplest possible circuits for the following functions:

(a) $g = \bar{p}q \vee p\bar{q}$,
(b) $g = pq \vee \bar{p}\bar{q}$,
(c) $g = (x_1 \vee x_2)(x_3 \vee x_4)$.

Here you need to recall that since $r \| s = \bar{r}\bar{s}$, we have $rs = \bar{r} \| \bar{s}$, so that in each case, g should first be expressed as a product of two unions. The fact that $r \| s = \overline{r \vee s}$ is also often useful. Assume complements of inputs *not* available.

15.   Assuming that you have only generalized NOR-elements and AND-elements available, but that complements of all inputs are available, realize the function
$$g = (x_1 \vee x_2)(x_1 \vee \bar{x}_3)(x_2 \vee \bar{x}_3)(x_2 \vee x_4)$$
as economically as possible.

16.   Assuming that you have only two-input NAND-elements (Scheffer stroke elements) available, design the simplest possible circuits for the following functions:

(a) $g = x_1 \vee x_2x_3$,
(b) $g = pq \vee \bar{p}\bar{q}$,
(c) $g = \bar{p}\bar{q} \vee \bar{p}\bar{r} \vee rp$.

Now you need to recall that, since $r \mid s = \bar{r} \vee \bar{s}$, we have $r \vee s = \bar{r} \mid \bar{s}$, so that, in each case, g should first be expressed as a union of two products. The fact that $r \mid s = \bar{r}\bar{s}$ is also often useful. Assume complements of inputs *not* available.

17. Assuming that you have only generalized NAND-elements and OR-elements available, but that complements of all inputs are available, realize the function

$$g = x_1 x_2 \vee \bar{x}_1 x_3 \vee \bar{x}_2 x_3 \vee \bar{x}_2 \bar{x}_4$$

as economically as possible.

18. Write the function realized by the circuit of Figure 3.19.3, (a) if "$*$" represents "NAND" and (b) if "$*$" represents "NOR". Can you observe any general principles here? (See [10] for more such examples.)

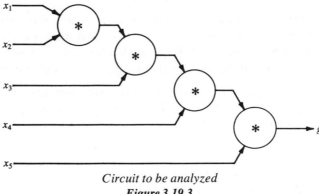

Circuit to be analyzed
Figure 3.19.3

19. Realize the following functions as economically as possible assuming you have only two-input NAND- and NOR-elements and inverters available, complements of inputs again not being available:

(a) $g = x_1 x_2 \bar{x}_3$,
(b) $g = x_1 x_2 (x_3 \vee x_4)$,
(c) $g = x_1 x_2 \vee x_2 x_3 \vee x_3 x_1$,
(d) $g = x\bar{y} \vee \bar{y}z$,
(e) $g = (x \vee y)(\bar{y} \vee z)$.

Assume NAND-, NOR-, and NOT-elements equally expensive so that the number of logic elements is to be a minimum.

20. Write the switching function for the AND-OR-NOT circuit of Figure 3.19.4, then redesign the circuit so as to have a single NOT-element.

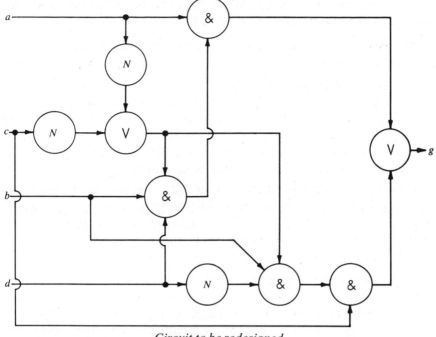

Circuit to be redesigned
Figure 3.19.4

21. Show how to realize the function

$$g = x_1 \oplus x_2 \oplus x_3 \oplus x_1 x_2$$

using only half-adders.

22. A translator is defined by Table 3.19.4. Complements of inputs are available and complements of outputs are needed. Design the circuit using only AND-, OR-, and NOT- elements.

Table 3.19.4

a_2	a_1	a_0	b_2	b_1	b_0
0	0	0	1	1	0
0	0	1	1	0	0
0	1	0	1	0	1
0	1	1	1	1	1
1	0	0	0	1	1
1	0	1	0	0	1
1	1	0	0	0	0
1	1	1	0	1	0

23. Why should we design arithmetic units that can add precisely two binary numbers rather than more, and why are they sufficient?

24. Recall the definition of the connective ϕ (Exercise 12, this section), and prove

(a) $p \oplus q = \bar{p} \phi q = p \phi \bar{q}$,

(b) $(p \oplus q) \phi r = p \oplus (q \phi r) = (p \phi q) \oplus r = p \phi (q \oplus r)$.

(c) Show that if an even number k of the $*$'s in the expression $w = p_1 * p_2 * \cdots * p_n$ are $\oplus$'s and all the rest are ϕ's, then $\oplus$ and ϕ are *totally associative* (that is, the order in which the operations in w are executed does not matter); *totally commutative* (that is, $w = p_{i_1} * p_{i_2} * \cdots * p_{i_n}$ for every permutation $i_1, i_2, \ldots, i_n$ of $1, 2, \ldots, n$; *permutable* (that is, as long as the number of $\oplus$'s and the number of ϕ's remains the same, it does not matter where they appear); and *replaceable in pairs* (that is, for any two $\oplus$'s, two ϕ's may be substituted, and vice versa), in particular, $w = p_1 \phi p_2 \phi \cdots \phi p_n$.

25. Table 3.19.5 defines the translation from the normal binary code to a single-error-detecting, single-error-correcting Hamming code. Complements of inputs are available. Complements of outputs are needed. Design the most economical circuit you can, using AND-, OR-, NOT-, and $\oplus$-elements, as needed.

Table 3.19.5

b_3	b_2	b_1	b_0	h_1	h_2	h_3	h_4	h_5	h_6	h_7
0	0	0	0	0	0	0	0	0	0	0
0	0	0	1	1	1	0	1	0	0	1
0	0	1	0	0	1	0	1	0	1	0
0	0	1	1	1	0	0	0	0	1	1
0	1	0	0	1	0	0	1	1	0	0
0	1	0	1	0	1	0	0	1	0	1
0	1	1	0	1	1	0	0	1	1	0
0	1	1	1	0	0	0	1	1	1	1
1	0	0	0	1	1	1	0	0	0	0
1	0	0	1	0	0	1	1	0	0	1
1	0	1	0	1	0	1	1	0	1	0
1	0	1	1	0	1	1	0	0	1	1
1	1	0	0	0	1	1	1	1	0	0
1	1	0	1	1	0	1	0	1	0	1
1	1	1	0	0	0	1	0	1	1	0
1	1	1	1	1	1	1	1	1	1	1

3.20   References

1. A. Ambrose and M. Lazerowitz, *Fundamentals of Symbolic Logic* (Second Edition). New York: Holt, Rinehart and Winston, 1962.

2. A. Tarski, *Introduction to Logic and to the Methodology of Deductive Sciences*. New York: Oxford University Press, 1939.

3. P. Suppes, *Introduction to Logic*. Princeton: Van Nostrand, 1957.

4. M. Phister, *Logical Design of Digital Computers*. New York: John Wiley, 1958.

5. S. H. Caldwell, *Logical Design and Switching Circuits*. New York: John Wiley, 1958.

6. D. E. Muller, "Complexity in Electronic Switching Circuits," *I.R.E. Trans. on Electronic Computers,* 5, No. 1, March 1956, pp. 15–19.

7. W. V. O. Quine, "The Problem of Simplifying Truth Functions," *Amer. Math. Monthly,* **59,** October 1952, pp. 521–31; "A Way to Simplify Truth Functions," *Ibid,* **62,** November 1955, pp. 627–31.

8. S. H. Washburn, "An Application of Boolean Algebra to the Design of Electronic Switching Circuits," *A. I. E. E. Trans., Part I, Communications and Electronics,* **72,** September 1953, pp. 380–88.

9. N. T. Grisamore, L. S. Ratolo, and G. U. Uyehara, "Logical Design Using the Stroke Function," *Proc. I. R. E., PGEC,* **EC–7,** June 1958, pp. 181–83.

10. G. A. Maley and J. Earle, *The Logic Design of Transistor Digital Computers*. Englewood Cliffs, New Jersey: Prentice-Hall, 1963.

11. W. W. Peterson, *Error Correcting Codes*. New York: John Wiley, 1961.

12. R. E. Miller, *Switching Theory, Volume 1: Combinational Circuits*. New York: John Wiley, 1965.

4

The Minimization Problem

4.1   Origin of the Problem

Ordinarily, the operate-requirements of a circuit to be designed are initially stated in verbal form. These statements are next translated via a table of combinations into algebraic form. The resulting function is then simplified in some manner so that the final circuit will be as economical as possible.

We have already given various examples of the algebraic simplification of functions and of the simplification of circuits by inspection. It is the aim of this chapter to discuss more systematic ways of accomplishing the simplification of functions.

The Map Method

4.2   The Veitch–Karnaugh Map of a Boolean Function

Of primary importance in the study of Boolean functions of n variables are the 2^n combinations of n 0's and 1's. We have already seen that these may be represented as the vertices of an n-cube. Another geometrical representation, due originally to Veitch [10] and revised by Karnaugh [1], is convenient for purposes of simplifying a given function. We consider first functions in two, three, or four variables.

170

In the Veitch-Karnaugh scheme, the four combinations of values of two binary variables x_1 and x_2 are represented as a linear array of four squares (Figure 4.2.1). It is convenient for later purposes to list the combinations in the order 00, 01, 11, 10, which is known as the *Gray*

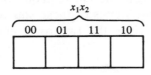

Map for two variables
Figure 4.2.1

code. Since the squares corresponding to the combinations are used for recording information, the combinations are customarily written above the squares.

In the case of three variables the representation is an array of eight squares (Figure 4.2.2).

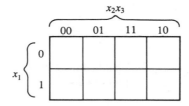

Map for three variables
Figure 4.2.2

For four variables it is a square array of sixteen squares (Figure 4.2.3).

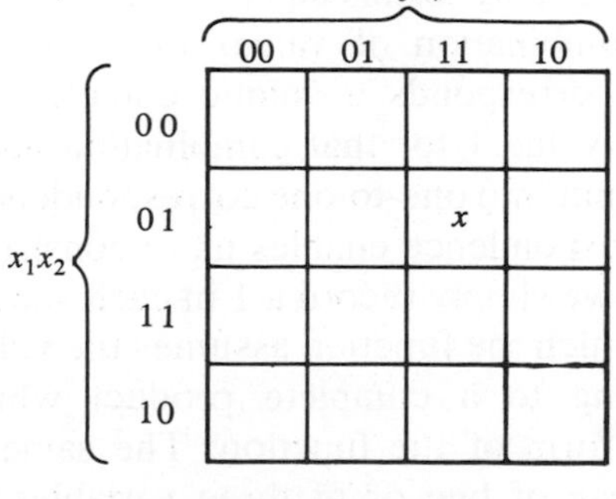

Map for four variables
Figure 4.2.3

The square labeled x in Figure 4.2.3 corresponds to the combination of values 0, 1, 1, 1 of the variables x_1, x_2, x_3, x_4, respectively. Here the

pair of digits to the left of any given square of the array may be interpreted as a "row-coordinate" for the square, whereas those above it may
be used as a "column-coordinate." The row-coordinate then provides the
first two digits and the column-coordinate the last two digits of the
combination corresponding to the square in question.

The labeling of the coordinates of these squares may be simplified as
shown in Figure 4.2.4. Here the two rows embraced by the symbol

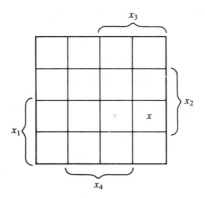

Simplified labeling of map
Figure 4.2.4

"$x_1\{$" are those in which the variable x_1 has the value 1. The rows not
embraced by the symbol "$x_1\{$" are those in which x_1 has the value 0,
and similarly for x_2, x_3, and x_4. Thus, for the square marked x in Figure
4.2.4, the coordinates are $x_1 = 1$, $x_2 = 1$ and $x_3 = 1$, $x_4 = 0$, so that the
combination corresponding to this square is 1110.

Now, to each combination of values e_1, e_2, e_3, e_4 of the variables
x_1, x_2, x_3, x_4 there corresponds a unique complete product $x_1^{e_1}x_2^{e_2}x_3^{e_3}x_4^{e_4}$,
which takes on the value 1 for that combination and no others, so that
the squares may be put into one-to-one correspondence with the complete
products. This correspondence enables us to construct a **map** of a given
switching function: we simply record a 1 in each square corresponding to
a combination for which the function assumes the value 1, that is, in each
square corresponding to a complete product which appears in the
disjunctive normal form of the function. The same procedure applies,
of course, in the case of two or of three variables. Figure 4.2.5 gives
maps of a variety of functions expanded into disjunctive normal form.

The squares in which 1's are recorded are called the **p-squares** of the
function ("p" for "product").

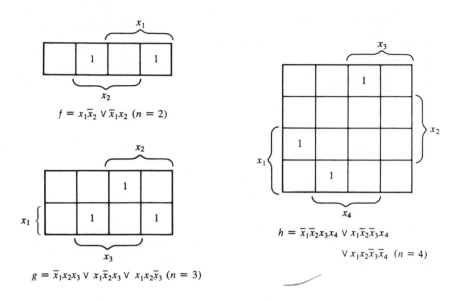

$f = x_1\bar{x}_2 \lor \bar{x}_1 x_2 \ (n = 2)$

$g = \bar{x}_1 x_2 x_3 \lor x_1 \bar{x}_2 x_3 \lor x_1 x_2 \bar{x}_3 \ (n = 3)$

$h = \bar{x}_1 \bar{x}_2 x_3 x_4 \lor x_1 \bar{x}_2 \bar{x}_3 x_4$

$\lor x_1 x_2 \bar{x}_3 \bar{x}_4 \ (n = 4)$

Maps of various functions
Figure 4.2.5.

4.3   Exercises

1.   Draw maps of the following functions:

(a) $f = x_1 x_2 \lor \bar{x}_1 \bar{x}_2$ $(n = 2)$
(b) $f = x_1(x_2 \lor x_3) \lor \bar{x}_1 \bar{x}_2 \bar{x}_3$ $(n = 3)$
(c) $f = x_1 \bar{x}_2 \lor \bar{x}_1 x_2 \lor x_2 x_3$ $(n = 3)$
(d) $f = x_1 \bar{x}_2 \lor \bar{x}_1 x_2 \lor x_1 x_3$ $(n = 3)$
(e) $f = (x_1 x_2 x_3 \lor x_4)(x_1 \lor x_2 \lor x_3)$ $(n = 4)$
(f) $f = x_1 \bar{x}_2 \lor x_2 \bar{x}_3 \lor x_3 \bar{x}_4 \lor x_4 \bar{x}_1$ $(n = 4)$

2.   Show how to cut a cube (Figure 4.3.1(A)) so that when it is flattened the regions about the vertices are arranged as are the corresponding squares in the three-variable Veitch-Karnaugh map.

3.   Show how to divide the surface of a torus (Figure 4.3.1(B)) into sixteen regions, and then cut it and flatten it to get a four-variable Veitch-Karnaugh map.

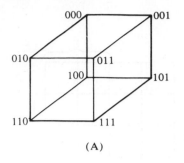

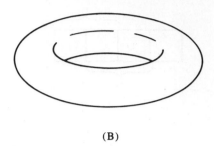

(A)   (B)

Figures on which maps can be drawn
Figure 4.3.1

4. For each of the maps in Figure 4.3.2, write the disjunctive normal form of the function represented by the map. Simplify the function in each case. Is the simplified form in any way suggested by the map?

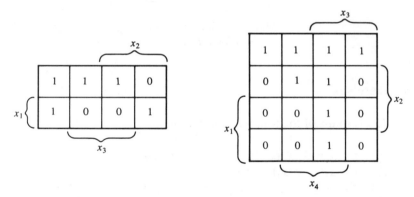

Maps of functions to be determined
Figure 4.3.2

4.4   Simplification of Functions

Once the map of a function is plotted, we can often write a simple algebraic expression for it by noting the arrangement of the 1's on the map. A clue to how this is done is given in the maps shown in Figure 4.4.1, as will be explained subsequently. Note that in each case here the two 1's are in squares whose combinations differ by only one digit. Two such squares are called **adjacent.** If the combinations are interpreted as vertices of a four-dimensional cube, combinations corresponding to adjacent squares determine adjacent vertices of the cube. A two-dimensional projection of a four-dimensional cube (analogous to the two-dimensional

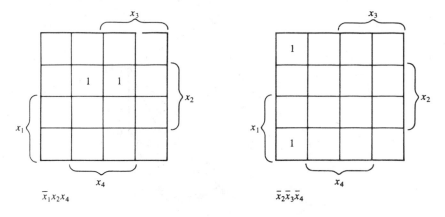

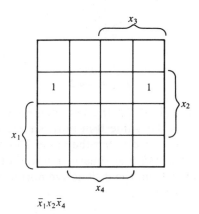

Maps corresponding to three-factor products

Figure 4.4.1

projection of a three-dimensional cube shown in Figure 4.3.1(A)) is shown in Figure 4.4.2. It may be used to check the adjacency of the squares shown in Figure 4.4.1. A study of the cube and of the map shows that for the purpose of determining adjacency, we should consider the left and right edges of the map as identical and also consider the top and bottom edges of the map as identical. That is, we can regard the map as being drawn on a torus as is suggested by Exercise 3, Section 4.3. The preservation of adjacencies throughout the map results from the use of the Gray code in labeling the rows and columns of squares. This improvement of the original Veitch chart is due to Karnaugh [1].

The function corresponding to two adjacent 1's on a map is obtained by writing down the product of all those variables whose values are *fixed* in the two squares in question—uncomplemented if this fixed value

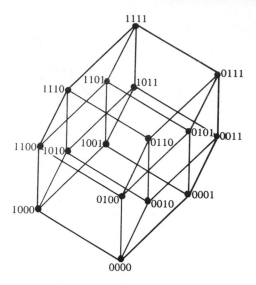

Plane projection of a four-dimensional cube
Figure 4.4.2

is 1, complemented if it is 0. In the first example of Figure 4.4.1, we wrote $\bar{x}_1$ because x_1 has the value 0 in both squares, x_2 because x_2 has the value 1 in both, x_4 because x_4 has the value 1 in both; x_3 was omitted because x_3 has the value 0 in one square, 1 in the other. The legitimacy of this procedure follows from the disjunctive normal form of the function represented by the two squares:

$$f = \bar{x}_1 x_2 \bar{x}_3 x_4 \vee \bar{x}_1 x_2 x_3 x_4 = \bar{x}_1 x_2 x_4 (\bar{x}_3 \vee x_3) = \bar{x}_1 x_2 x_4.$$

The other two examples should be checked in similar fashion.

Two adjacent p-squares are said to constitute a **one-dimensional p-subcube** since they correspond to the endpoints of an edge of the four-cube (Figure 4.4.2).

In Figure 4.4.3, the principles used to write down the functions corresponding to the maps are the same as those used in the preceding examples. Thus, in the first case, we write $\bar{x}_1$ *and* $\bar{x}_2$ because all the 1's are in the $\bar{x}_1$ region, also in the $\bar{x}_2$ region. Both x_3 and x_4 are omitted entirely because they assume the value 0 in some of the squares, 1 in others. Putting it another way, the set of four p-squares intersects both the x_3 and the $\bar{x}_3$ regions, also intersects both the x_4 and the $\bar{x}_4$ regions. Hence x_3 and x_4 are not written. Note also that $\bar{x}_1 \bar{x}_2$, expanded into disjunctive normal form, yields the four complete products corresponding to the 1's on the map. The reader should check carefully the details of the other four examples.

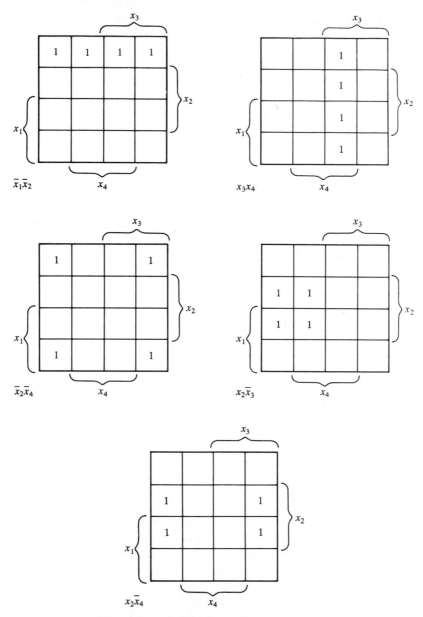

Maps corresponding to two-factor products
Figure 4.4.3

In each of these examples, the four *p*-squares correspond to four vertices of a square face of the four-cube and hence are called **two-dimensional *p*-subcubes** (compare with Figure 4.4.2).

The maps of Figure 4.4.4 illustrate some *three-dimensional p-subcubes*. Again the reader should verify that the indicated functions have indeed the associated maps.

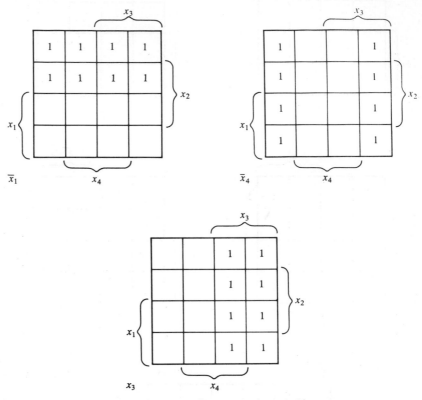

Maps corresponding to single variables
Figure 4.4.4

Notice that to each product of variables and their complements, there corresponds a set of 1, 2, 4, or 8 p-squares on the map. Moreover, because the reduction of a disjunctive normal form to a single product depends on the use of identities like

$$x_1 \lor \bar{x}_1 = 1,$$
$$x_1 x_2 \lor x_1 \bar{x}_2 \lor \bar{x}_1 x_2 \lor \bar{x}_1 \bar{x}_2 = 1,$$

and so on, only blocks of 1, 2, 2^2, 2^3,..., adjacent p-squares can correspond to a single product. If the number of adjacent p-squares is other than a power of two, the union of more than one product will be required. See, for example, the maps of Figure 4.4.5.

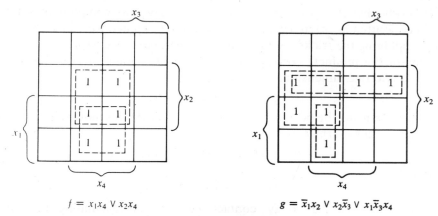

$$f = x_1x_4 \lor x_2x_4 \qquad\qquad g = \bar{x}_1x_2 \lor x_2\bar{x}_3 \lor x_1\bar{x}_3x_4$$

Maps of functions to be determined
Figure 4.4.5.

After these disjunctions of products are written, there remains of course the problem of factoring the resulting expressions effectively for the purpose of designing economical circuits. In this case we obtain, respectively, the easily checked factorizations,

$$f = (x_1 \lor x_2)x_4 \qquad \text{and} \qquad g = (x_2 \lor x_1x_4)(\bar{x}_1 \lor \bar{x}_3),$$

the latter of which becomes, with the aid of DeMorgan's rules,

$$g = (x_2 \lor x_1x_4) \cdot \overline{x_1x_3},$$

a form which is convenient for the realization of the function by an AND-OR-NOT circuit. In the case of the function g, note that each of three p-squares was employed more than once, which is proper since $a \lor a = a$ in this algebra.

Now consider the function f defined by the map of Figure 4.4.6. We could write f as the union of the complete products corresponding to the

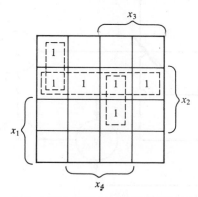

Map of function to be determined
Figure 4.4.6

six p-subcubes. However, by the idempotent law, any complete product can be written as often as desired in this union. Hence we can do better by employing the tricks we have just learned above: we express f as the union of the products corresponding to one two-dimensional p-subcube and to two one-dimensional p-subcubes:

$$f = \bar{x}_1 x_2 \ \lor \ \bar{x}_1 \bar{x}_3 \bar{x}_4 \ \lor \ x_2 x_3 x_4.$$

There remains the possibility of factoring f. To do this most effectively, we join a zero term to f:

$$f = \bar{x}_1 x_2 \ \lor \ \bar{x}_1 \bar{x}_3 \bar{x}_4 \ \lor \ x_2 x_3 x_4 \ \lor \ \bar{x}_3 \bar{x}_4 \cdot x_3 x_4,$$

so that

$$f = (\bar{x}_1 \ \lor \ x_3 x_4) \cdot (x_2 \ \lor \ \bar{x}_3 \bar{x}_4).$$

The series-parallel relay contact network corresponding to this factorization is shown in Figure 4.4.7. It requires 11 springs.

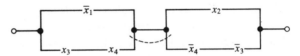

Relay circuit corresponding to preceding map
Figure 4.4.7

If AND, OR, NOT elements are to be used, we can rewrite this factored form as follows:

$$f = (\bar{x}_1 \ \lor \ x_3 x_4) \cdot (x_2 \ \lor \ \overline{x_3 \ \lor \ x_4})$$

The circuit for this factorization is shown in Figure 4.4.8.

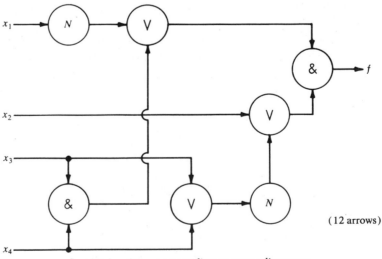

(12 arrows)

Logic circuit corresponding to preceding map
Figure 4.4.8

If we assume complements of all inputs are available, the same factorization that was used for the relay circuit yields the circuit shown in
Figure 4.4.9.

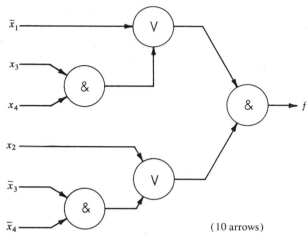

Circuit assuming complements of inputs available
Figure 4.4.9

A disjunction of products of the form $x_{i_1}^{e_1} x_{i_2}^{e_2} \cdots x_{i_k}^{e_k}$ is often called an
OR-polynomial. In the preceding examples, there was in each case a unique,
shortest OR-polynomial which represented the function. Here **shortest**
means "having the smallest possible total number of appearances of the
variables." A unique, shortest OR-polynomial does not always exist, as
some of the exercises in Section 4.3 are intended to suggest. To illustrate
further, consider the function defined by the map in Figure 4.4.10. Here
there are two products that *must* be chosen in the interests of economy.
They are identified by asterisks placed in *p*-squares, each of which is

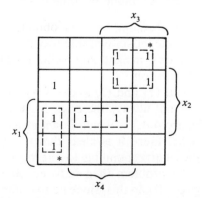

Map of function with two minimal forms
Figure 4.4.10

contained in a *unique largest block* of 2^k adjacent p-squares. Such products, which *must* be chosen to obtain an economical expression for f, are called **essential products.** Next, the two remaining 1's in the third row of the map are most conveniently accounted for by a single product. Finally, the leading 1 in the second row of the map is adjacent to the 1 immediately below it as well as to the 1 at the right end of the second row. Hence there are two ways of accounting for this 1. Thus there are two equally short OR-polynomials representing the function:

$$f = \bar{x}_1 x_3 \ \vee \ x_1 \bar{x}_3 \bar{x}_4 \ \vee \ x_1 x_2 x_4 \ \vee \begin{cases} x_2 \bar{x}_3 \bar{x}_4 \\ \bar{x}_1 x_2 \bar{x}_4 \end{cases}.$$

Which of these two forms is the better? Assuming complements of all input signals available, we have, from the first form of f,

$$f = \bar{x}_1 x_3 \ \vee \ x_1 x_2 x_4 \ \vee \ (x_1 \ \vee \ x_2) \bar{x}_3 \bar{x}_4$$

which, since we assume that multiple-input AND- and OR-elements with arbitrary numbers of input leads are available, requires only thirteen arrows for its realization. The second form of f requires more arrows since it is less extensively factorable.

The preceding examples suggest the following rules for obtaining an economical representation of a function as a union of products, that is, as an OR-polynomial:

1. Determine the essential products that must appear in any representation of f; then
2. select additional products corresponding to p-subcubes which are as large as possible and as few in number as possible but include every p-square at least once. As the last example shows, the results may not be unique in some cases.

After a reasonable expression for f is obtained, there remains the problem of factoring it in the most favorable way possible for the purposes at hand. This still requires insight and skill: no algorithm exists for obtaining the best factorization.

The accomplishment of (1) and (2) above was simple in the example given above, but this is not always the case. M. Karnaugh provided the example shown in Figure 4.4.11, which is about as involved as a four-variable problem can be. Here it is clear that we must use three one-dimensional p-subcubes corresponding to the terms $\bar{x}_1 \bar{x}_3 x_4$, $\bar{x}_1 x_3 \bar{x}_4$, and $x_1 x_3 x_4$, respectively. The problem then is to account for the 1's in the remaining four p-squares. To do this, since no two-dimensional p-subcube contains all four of these p-squares, will require two more terms. To keep these terms as simple as possible we employ two previously used adjacent

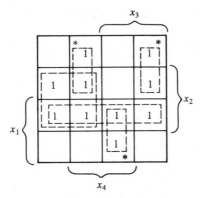

Karnaugh's example
Figure 4.4.11

p-squares which enable us to use two two-dimensional subcubes, as shown in the figure. These steps finally yield

$$f = \bar{x}_1\bar{x}_3x_4 \lor \bar{x}_1x_3\bar{x}_4 \lor x_1x_3x_4 \lor x_1x_2 \lor x_2\bar{x}_3.$$

Factoring, we can obtain the various forms:

$$f = x_2(x_1 \lor \bar{x}_3) \lor \bar{x}_1(\bar{x}_3x_4 \lor x_3\bar{x}_4) \lor x_1x_3x_4$$
$$= x_2(x_1 \lor \bar{x}_3) \lor \bar{x}_1 \cdot (x_3 \lor x_4) \cdot \overline{x_3x_4} \lor x_1 \cdot x_3x_4$$
$$= x_2(x_1 \lor \bar{x}_3) \lor (x_3 \lor x_4)\overline{(x_1 \lor x_3x_4)} \lor x_1 \cdot x_3x_4.$$

The AND-OR-NOT realization, assuming complements not automatically available, requires nineteen arrows, provided the second factored form of the function is used.

A second possible form of f is shown in Figure 4.4.12. We now have

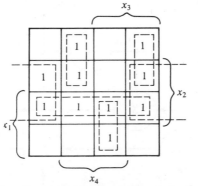

Second treatment of preceding example
Figure 4.4.12

$$f = \bar{x}_1\bar{x}_3x_4 \lor \bar{x}_1x_3\bar{x}_4 \lor x_1x_3x_4 \lor x_1x_2 \lor x_2\bar{x}_4$$
$$= x_2(x_1 \lor \bar{x}_4) \lor \bar{x}_1(x_3 \lor x_4)\overline{x_3x_4} \lor x_1x_3x_4.$$

The AND-OR-NOT realization again requires nineteen arrows.

A third possibility is shown in Figure 4.4.13. In this case

$$f = \bar{x}_1\bar{x}_3x_4 \vee \bar{x}_1x_3\bar{x}_4 \vee x_1x_3x_4 \vee x_2\bar{x}_3 \vee x_2\bar{x}_4$$
$$= x_2 \cdot \overline{x_3x_4} \vee x_1 \cdot x_3x_4 \vee \bar{x}_1(x_3 \vee x_4)\overline{x_3}\overline{x_4}.$$

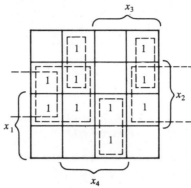

Third treatment of preceding example
Figure 4.4.13

The AND-OR-NOT realization now requires sixteen arrows. The improvement results from the frequent appearance of the product x_3x_4. See Figure 4.4.14.

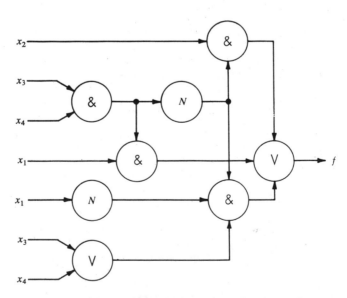

Circuit corresponding to preceding map
Figure 4.4.14

4.5   Use of the Complement in Minimization

Consider again Karnaugh's example, which was used in the preceding section. The function f is, of course, 0 for every combination for which it is not 1. Hence, it can equally well be represented by the map shown in Figure 4.5.1. From such a map we can write a unique, shortest OR-polynomial for $\bar{f}$, whose 1's are the 0's of f:

$$\bar{f} = x_1\bar{x}_2\bar{x}_3 \lor x_1\bar{x}_2\bar{x}_4 \lor \bar{x}_2\bar{x}_3\bar{x}_4 \lor \bar{x}_1x_3x_4$$
$$= x_1\bar{x}_2(\bar{x}_3 \lor \bar{x}_4) \lor \bar{x}_2\bar{x}_3\bar{x}_4 \lor \bar{x}_1x_3x_4,$$

from which

$$f = (\bar{x}_1 \lor x_2 \lor x_3x_4)(x_2 \lor x_3 \lor x_4)(x_1 \lor \overline{x_3x_4}).$$

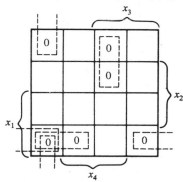

Simplification using the complement

Figure 4.5.1

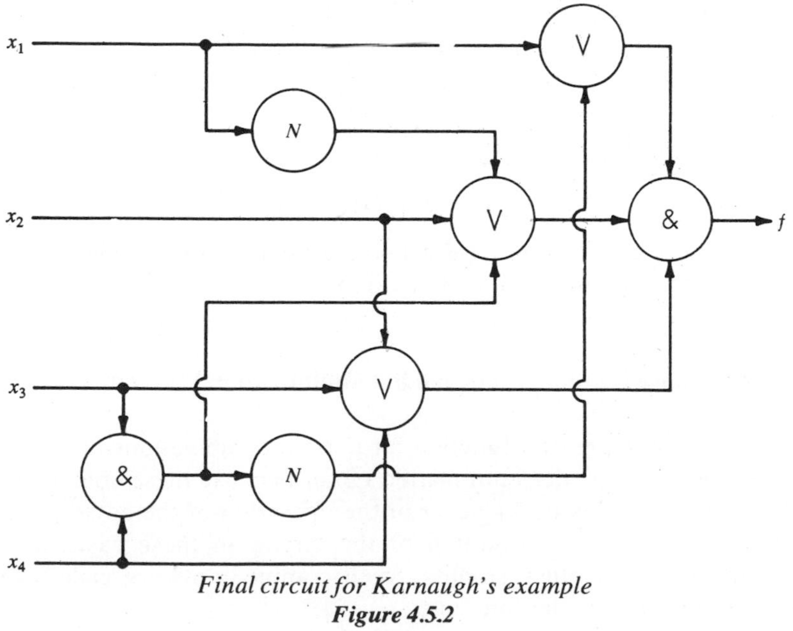

Final circuit for Karnaugh's example

Figure 4.5.2

This form of f employs a product of unions in contrast to the union of products the previous process initially yields. The AND-OR-NOT realization now requires only fifteen arrows because of the possibility of using three three-input elements (Figure 4.5.2). This example emphasizes the importance of computing both f and $(\bar{f})$ and comparing the results.

As another example, consider again the function defined in Figure 4.4.6. The complementary function, $\bar{f}$, is derived from Figure 4.5.3. Here we can write the function in terms of two-factor products exclusively if we exploit adjacencies properly and use some of the squares more than once. We obtain

$$\bar{f} = x_1\bar{x}_3 \vee x_1\bar{x}_4 \vee \bar{x}_2 x_3 \vee \bar{x}_2 x_4$$
$$= x_1(\bar{x}_3 \vee \bar{x}_4) \vee \bar{x}_2(x_3 \vee x_4).$$

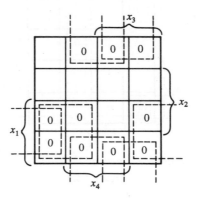

Simplification using the complement

Figure 4.5.3

Hence, taking the complement, we have

$$f = (\bar{x}_1 \vee x_3 x_4)(x_2 \vee \bar{x}_3 \bar{x}_4),$$

which is the same factored form obtained earlier by joining a not-so-obvious zero term to the original function f.

4.6   Don't-Care Combinations and the Minimization Problem

At times the value of a function for certain combinations of the input variables $x_1, x_2, \ldots, x_n$ does not matter, either because these combinations of the input variables never occur in the operation of the corresponding circuit or because the condition of the circuit in these cases has no important effect on other circuits. Such combinations are called **don't-care combinations** for the function.

On the map of the function, we record d's in the squares corresponding to its don't-care combinations. Then we assign the value 1 to selected d's, and 0's to the others, in such a way as to

1. increase the dimensions of the p-subcubes wherever possible, and
2. combine p-subcubes into others of higher dimension wherever possible, but
3. without making it necessary to select more p-subcubes than would be necessary if fewer d's were made 0's.

Consider for example the map of Figure 4.6.1. Here the obvious thing

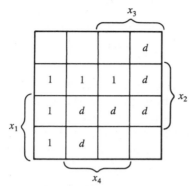

Map showing don't-care combinations

Figure 4.6.1

to do is to assign the value 0 to the d in the first row and the value 1 to all the rest. We then have

$$f_1 = x_2 \vee x_1\bar{x}_3,$$

which requires five arrows. This same map gives

$$\bar{f}_1 = \bar{x}_1\bar{x}_2 \vee \bar{x}_2 x_3 = \bar{x}_2(\bar{x}_1 \vee x_3)$$

which yields the same expression for f_1 when the complement is formed.

At times, in finding the complement, one may decide to make a different assignment of 0's and 1's than when obtaining f directly. In the present example, the most favorable assignment for $\bar{f}$ might appear to be that shown in Figure 4.6.2. This yields

$$\bar{f}_2 = \bar{x}_1\bar{x}_2 \vee x_1 x_3,$$

or

$$f_2 = (x_1 \vee x_2)\overline{x_1 x_3}$$

which requires seven arrows and hence is less desirable than the previous result. That is, the first assignment of 0's and 1's is better, whether one

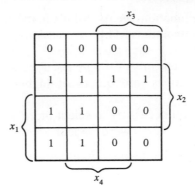

Second assignment for don't-cares in preceding map
Figure 4.6.2

is computing f directly or with the aid of $\bar{f}$. Note that f_2 and f_1 are not identical but that they both take on the value 1 where required, and the value 0 where required, and hence differ only at the don't-care combinations. If we can get $x_1 x_3$ from another circuit, f_2 is better.

As a second example, consider the map shown in Figure 4.6.3. Here,

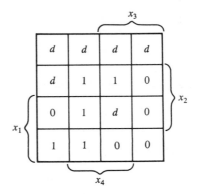

Another don't-care example
Figure 4.6.3

if we make the first three d's in the top row equal to 1 and assign all others the value 0, we have

$$f_1 = \bar{x}_2 \bar{x}_3 \ \vee \ \bar{x}_3 x_4 \ \vee \ \bar{x}_1 x_4,$$

so that

$$f_1 = x_2 \ \vee \ x_3 \ \vee \ x_4 \, \overline{x_1 x_3},$$

which calls for ten arrows, complements being assumed not available.

On the other hand, if we make the first two d's in the top row and the single d in the third row equal to 1, then assign the value 0 to the remaining d's, we have

$$f_2 = \bar{x}_2\bar{x}_3 \lor x_2x_4 = \overline{x_2 \lor x_3} \lor x_2x_4,$$

a form which requires only seven arrows. Further, if we assign the d's in rows 2 and 3 the value 0, all others being given the value 1, we obtain

$$\bar{f}_3 = x_2\bar{x}_4 \lor x_1x_3,$$

so that

$$f_3 = (\bar{x}_2 \lor x_4) \cdot \overline{x_1x_3}.$$

We thus have a form that requires eight arrows. Another possibility is

$$\bar{f}_4 = \bar{x}_2x_3 \lor x_2\bar{x}_4,$$

so that

$$f_4 = (x_2 \lor \bar{x}_3)(\bar{x}_2 \lor x_4),$$

which also requires eight arrows. Under the assumed conditions, f_2 appears to be the best choice.

The reader should be aware that *because the practical object of minimization is to find the most economical circuit, there are times when a less-than-minimal form for a function is to be preferred* because some of the outputs of its component functions are already available as outputs from other circuitry and hence require no additional logic elements.

4.7   Five-Variable and Six-Variable Maps

Consider the map shown in Figure 4.7.1. As the figure suggests, two four-variable charts may be used to map and simplify a five-variable function. The function shown is given by

$$f = x_3x_5 \lor \bar{x}_1x_3x_4 \lor x_1x_3\bar{x}_4 = x_3x_5 \lor x_3 \cdot (x_1 \lor x_4) \cdot \overline{x_1x_4},$$

where the first term is determined by the central *column* of eight 1's, the second by the four upper right 1's and the third by the four lower left 1's.

In the case of six variables, four four-variable maps are required. A $4 \times 4 \times 4$ plastic three-dimensional array is easier to work with than four maps on the same sheet of paper. (Such $4 \times 4 \times 4$ plastic arrays may often

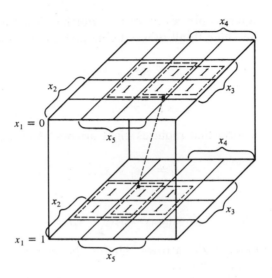

or:

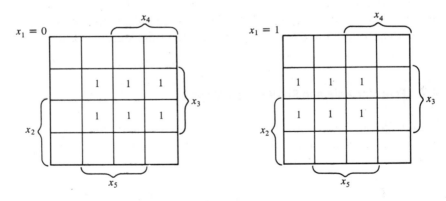

Two forms of five-variable map
Figure 4.7.1

be found in toy stores.) An example appears in Figure 4.7.2. The function shown is

$$f = \bar{x}_1\bar{x}_3\bar{x}_5 \lor x_1x_3x_5 \lor \bar{x}_3x_4\bar{x}_5x_6.$$

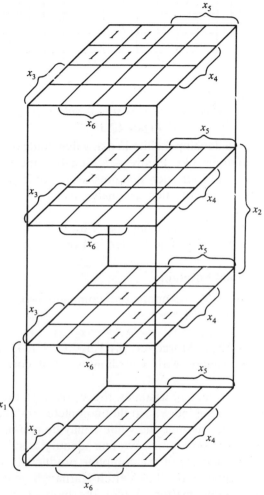

Example of six-variable map
Figure 4.7.2

There are two half-columns of eight adjacent p-squares and a full column of four adjacent p-squares.

The six-variable map may also be represented by four-variable maps arranged in the plane (Figure 4.7.3). The preceding example has been plotted on the array of four maps in Figure 4.7.3 and again is simple to identify from the location of the adjacent p-squares.

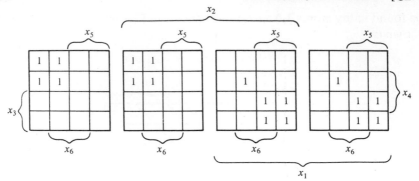

Alternative form of six-variable map

Figure 4.7.3

It is not difficult to develop facility in using five- and six- variable charts. Two $4 \times 4 \times 4$ columns like Figure 4.7.2 enable one to handle seven-variable problems and four such columns serve for eight-variable problems. The effective use of such extensive maps requires considerable practice.

There are other ways of drawing maps for more than four variables, but adjacencies always become harder to keep track of as n increases.

4.8   A More Compact Notation

Earlier (Section 1.17) we numbered complete products in a simple way. For example, if $n = 4$, we have

$$p_{12} = x_1{}^1 x_2{}^1 x_3{}^0 x_4{}^0 = x_1 x_2 \bar{x}_3 \bar{x}_4$$

because $1100_{\text{bin}} = 12_{\text{dec}}$. Moreover, $p_{12}(1,1,0,0) = 1$. Hence, on a four-variable map, the square with coordinates 1100 corresponds to the product $x_1 x_2 \bar{x}_3 \bar{x}_4$.

In general, the product p_j assumes the value 1 at the n-digit binary translation of the decimal index j, so that complete products and the combinations at which they assume the value 1 may be numbered identically.

In view of these observations, we can identify a switching function simply by listing the indices of the complete products it includes, and, if we number the squares of the Veitch-Karnaugh map decimally, it becomes a very simple matter to plot the map of the function. For example, in the case $n = 4$, we write

$$f = \bar{x}_1 \bar{x}_2 \bar{x}_3 \bar{x}_4 \ \lor \ x_1 \bar{x}_2 \bar{x}_3 \bar{x}_4 \ \lor \ x_1 x_2 \bar{x}_3 \bar{x}_4$$
$$\lor \ x_1 x_2 \bar{x}_3 x_4 \ \lor \ x_1 x_2 x_3 \bar{x}_4 \ \lor \ x_1 x_2 x_3 x_4$$

as

$$f = V(0, 8, 12, 13, 14, 15).$$

A decimally numbered four-variable map, with f plotted on it, is shown in Figure 4.8.1. From the map, we have at once

$$f = x_1 x_2 \ \lor \ \bar{x}_2 \bar{x}_3 \bar{x}_4.$$

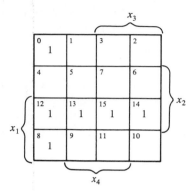

Example of a decimally numbered map
Figure 4.8.1

Similarly, when $n = 5$, the function
$$f = \bar{x}_1\bar{x}_2\bar{x}_3 x_4 x_5 \ \lor\ \bar{x}_1\bar{x}_2 x_3 x_4 x_5 \ \lor\ x_1\bar{x}_2\bar{x}_3 x_4 x_5 \ \lor\ x_1\bar{x}_2 x_3 x_4 x_5$$
$$\lor\ x_1 x_2\bar{x}_3 x_4 x_5 \ \lor\ x_1 x_2 x_3 x_4 x_5$$
is written thus:

$$f = \lor(3,7,19,23,27,31).$$

The map of the function is shown in Figure 4.8.2. From the map, we have

$$f = \bar{x}_2 x_4 x_5 \ \lor\ x_1 x_4 x_5 = (x_1 \ \lor\ \bar{x}_2)x_4 x_5.$$

Notice that the pattern of numbering each row from left to right is *a, b, d, c* and that the same pattern persists in the order in which the rows

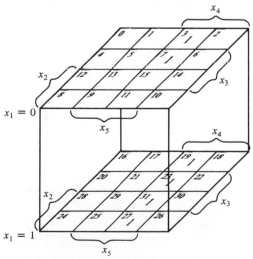

Decimally numbered five-variable map
Figure 4.8.2

are chosen. In the six variable maps it also persists in the order in which the planes are chosen. See Figure 4.16.1.

4.9 Exercises

In these exercises, "an AND-OR-NOT circuit" means one in which complements of inputs are *not* automatically available.

1. Write the shortest possible functions which correspond to the maps of Figure 4.9.1. Then find the best possible AND-OR-NOT circuit in

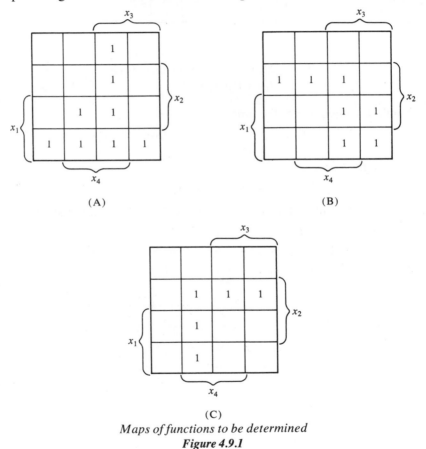

(A)   (B)

(C)
Maps of functions to be determined
Figure 4.9.1

each case. Be sure to consider alternative choices of subcubes as well as the possibility of computing f by first finding $\bar{f}$.

2. Show that the function whose map is shown in Figure 4.9.2 can be determined by the intersection of two regions on the map as

$$f = (x_1\bar{x}_2 \lor \bar{x}_1x_2) \cdot (x_3x_4 \lor \bar{x}_3\bar{x}_4).$$

Draw the best possible AND-OR-NOT circuit for this function.

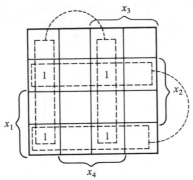

Factorization by intersection
Figure 4.9.2

3. Use the idea of Exercise 2 to find an economical form of the function whose map is shown in Figure 4.9.3.

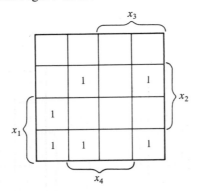

Function to be factored by inspection of map
Figure 4.9.3

4. By tracing the possible series paths, construct by inspection a map for the function realized by the relay circuit of Figure 4.9.4; then use the map to design a simpler circuit.

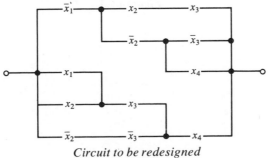

Circuit to be redesigned
Figure 4.9.4

5. Obtain all equally short OR-polynomials representing the functions whose maps are shown in Figure 4.9.5. Then find the form of the function which yields the best AND-OR-NOT circuit.

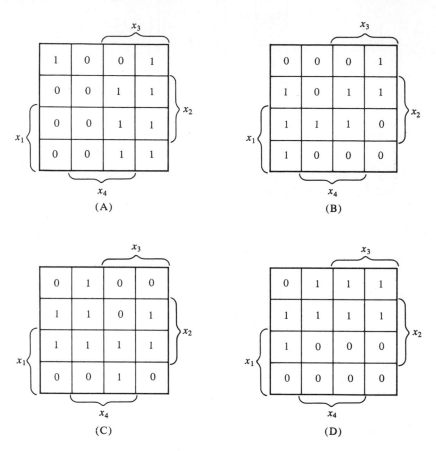

Maps of functions to be determined
Figure 4.9.5.

6. Proceed as in Exercise 5 for Figure 4.9.6.

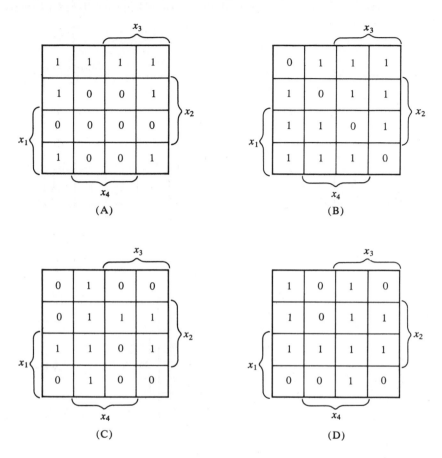

Maps of functions to be determined
Figure 4.9.6

7. Obtain the simplest possible functions, for the purpose of designing
AND-OR-NOT circuits, associated with the maps of Figure 4.9.7 and Figure
4.9.8.

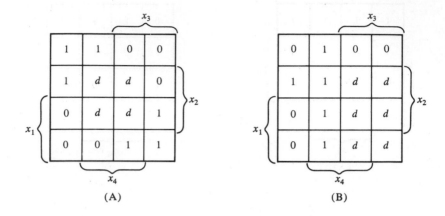

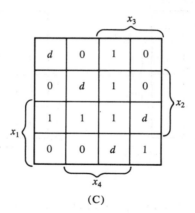

Functions with don't-cares
Figure 4.9.7

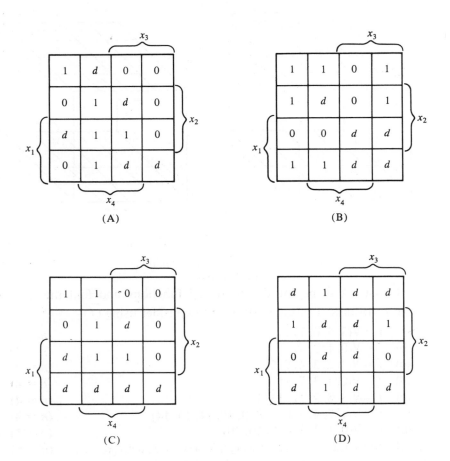

Additional don't-care problems
Figure 4.9.8

8. Obtain the best possible AND-OR-NOT circuits corresponding to the maps shown in Figure 4.9.9, in each case first finding all equally short OR-polynomials that represent the function.

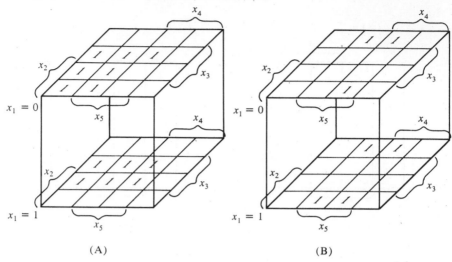

Five-variable functions to be minimized
Figure 4.9.9

9. Construct maps for the following functions and find the best possible AND-OR-NOT circuits. Be sure to consider using $(\bar{f})$.

(a)	$f = V(3, 5, 6, 7)$	$(n = 3)$
(b)	$f = V(0, 1, 2, 4)$	$(n = 3)$
(c)	$f = V(1, 2, 3, 4, 5, 6)$	$(n = 3)$
(d)	$f = V(0, 1, 3, 7, 15)$	$(n = 4)$
(e)	$f = V(3, 8, 9, 12, 13, 15)$	$(n = 4)$
(f)	$f = V(1, 2, 4, 5, 6, 7, 8, 9, 10, 11, 13, 14)$	$(n = 4)$
(g)	$f = V(0, 1, 2, 3, 4, 5, 16, 20)$	$(n = 5)$
(h)	$f = x_1x_2x_3x_5 \lor x_1\bar{x}_3 \lor x_1x_2\bar{x}_4 \lor \bar{x}_1x_3 \lor \bar{x}_1\bar{x}_2\bar{x}_3\bar{x}_4\bar{x}_5$	$(n = 5)$
(i)	$f = x_1x_2 \lor \bar{x}_1x_3 \lor \bar{x}_2x_3 \lor \bar{x}_3x_4 \lor \bar{x}_4x_5 \lor \bar{x}_5x_6$	$(n = 6)$
(j)	$f = V(0, 1, 4, 5, 16, 17, 20, 21, 32, 33, 36, 37, 52, 53)$	$(n = 6)$

10. A function of n variables may at times be written in a form free of x_j (or $\bar{x}_j$) for some $j \leqslant n$. How may this be determined by inspection of the map?

If it is desired to write the function in the form $x_j f_1 \lor \bar{x}_j f_2$, where f_1 and f_2 are free of x_j and $\bar{x}_j$, how may this be done using the map?

If a function f has the form $f = x_j f_1 \lor f_2$, where f_1 and f_2 are free of x_j and $\bar{x}_j$, how may this be detected on the map?

If a function f may be written in a form free of both x_j and $\bar{x}_j$, how is this evidenced by the map?

*11.   Suppose we wish to determine all combinations $\xi = (\xi_1, \xi_2 \ldots, \xi_n)$ that simultaneously satisfy the equations

$$f^{(i)}(x) = g^{(i)}(x), \qquad i = 1, 2, \ldots, k$$

where $x = (x_1, x_2, \ldots, x_n)$. Now $f^{(i)}(\xi) = g^{(i)}(\xi)$ if and only if $f^{(i)}(\xi)g^{(i)}(\xi) \vee \overline{f^{(i)}(\xi)}\,\overline{g^{(i)}(\xi)} = 1$. Hence we have the equivalent problem of solving simultaneously the conditional equations

$$F^{(i)}(x) \equiv f^{(i)}(x)g^{(i)}(x) \vee \overline{f^{(i)}(x)}\,\overline{g^{(i)}(x)} = 1, \qquad i = 1, 2, \ldots, k.$$

The required combinations ξ are those for which every $F^{(i)}$ assumes the value 1. We can map each $F^{(i)}(x)$ (when n is small) and determine all such ξ's from the intersection of the sets of p-squares on the map. Solve simultaneously in this fashion these equations:

(a) $\begin{cases} x_1 x_2 = x_1 \vee x_3 x_4 \\ x_1 \vee x_2 = x_3 \vee x_2 x_4 \end{cases}$ $(n = 4)$

(b) $\begin{cases} (x_1 \vee x_2)\bar{x}_3 = (x_3 \vee x_4)\bar{x}_5 \\ \bar{x}_1 \bar{x}_2 \vee x_3 = \bar{x}_3 x_4 \vee \bar{x}_5 \end{cases}$ $(n = 5)$

12.   If there are n variables, what is the dimension of a p-subcube represented by a product

$$x_{i_1}^{e_1} x_{i_2}^{e_2} \cdots x_{i_k}^{e_k}, \qquad 1 \leqslant k \leqslant n?$$

13.   How many k-dimensional subcubes $(0 \leqslant k \leqslant n)$ exist in an n-cube? (Remember that a vertex is a sequence of 0's and 1's. Now, what is a k-dimensional subcube?)

The Quine-McCluskey Procedure

4.10   Quine's Method of Reduction

We say that a switching function g **implies** a switching function $f(g \leqslant f)$, if and only if f assumes the value 1 at every combination of values of the circuit variables at which g assumes the value 1.

We now adopt some notation, due in part to Quine [3]. A symbol x_i or $\bar{x}_1$ will be called a **literal**. A product of the form $x_{i_1}^{e_1} x_{i_2}^{e_2} \cdots x_{i_k}^{e_k}, k \leqslant n$, in which no two subscripts have the same value, will be called a **fundamental product**. A union of fundamental products (including one product as a special case) will be called an **OR-polynomial**.

A fundamental product π_1 will be said to subsume a fundamental product π_2, if and only if every literal which appears in π_2 also appears in π_1. Thus $x_1\bar{x}_2x_3\bar{x}_4$ subsumes $\bar{x}_2x_3$. If π_1 subsumes π_2, then π_1 implies π_2, since the product π_1 is at least as long as π_2.

A fundamental product π is said to be a **prime implicant** of an OR-polynomial f, if and only if π implies f and also π subsumes no shorter product that implies f. Thus x_1x_2 is a prime implicant of $x_1x_2 \vee \bar{x}_1x_3$ since neither x_1 nor x_2 alone implies $x_1x_2 \vee \bar{x}_1x_3$. We now have the basic

Theorem: *Every shortest* OR-*polynomial g equivalent to a given switching function f is necessarily a union of prime implicants of f.*

Suppose, in fact, that π is one term of a shortest OR-polynomial g which is equivalent to f. Then π implies g and hence implies f. If now π is *not* a prime implicant of f, it subsumes a shorter product π_1 which implies each of g and f. Suppose now $g = \pi \vee h$. Then we have $\pi_1 \vee g = \pi_1 \vee \pi \vee h$, which, because $\pi_1 \leqslant g$ and $\pi \leqslant \pi_1$, reduces to $g = \pi_1 \vee h$, so that g was evidently *not* the shortest OR-polynomial equivalent to f. The contradiction proves the theorem.

The theorem does *not* prove that a shortest OR-polynomial equivalent to f is the union of *all* the prime implicants of f. It still remains to determine which of the prime implicants are to be used. To do this, we first express the given function f in disjunctive normal form and then determine all fundamental products that imply f and are subsumed by the complete products of f. From these, it is not hard to select the prime implicants of f, as examples will show. Thereafter, a mechanical procedure permits selection of a set of prime implicants whose union is a shortest OR-polynomial representing f. At times the process may lead to several equally short polynomials, as examples in the section on the Karnaugh map method illustrate.

To determine prime implicants in the Quine procedure, we first combine pairs of complete products of f so far as possible. For example, when $n = 4$, if the complete products $x_1x_2\bar{x}_3x_4$ and $x_1x_2\bar{x}_3\bar{x}_4$ appear in a function f, they lead to the shorter product $x_1x_2\bar{x}_3$ because $x_1x_2\bar{x}_3x_4 \vee x_1x_2\bar{x}_3\bar{x}_4 = x_1x_2\bar{x}_3$. That is, each of the two complete products subsumes the shorter product $x_1x_2\bar{x}_3$ and, in fact, implies it. Putting it another way, the product $x_1x_2\bar{x}_3$ *includes* each of the complete products from which it was derived. Moreover, for any combination that makes the shorter product assume the value 1, one of the included complete products must also be 1, so that *the shorter product implies f*.

We now illustrate how to find *all* fundamental products that imply a given switching function f. Consider the function

$$f = x_1x_2x_3x_4 \vee x_1\bar{x}_2x_3x_4 \vee x_1x_2x_3\bar{x}_4 \vee x_1x_2\bar{x}_3\bar{x}_4 \vee x_1\bar{x}_2x_3\bar{x}_4$$
$$\vee\ x_1\bar{x}_2\bar{x}_3\bar{x}_4 \vee \bar{x}_1\bar{x}_2\bar{x}_3x_4.$$

The seven complete products of this function are listed in a column at the left in Table 4.10.1. Beginning with the first complete product, we check

Table 4.10.1

Complete Products	Derived Products	
$x_1x_2x_3x_4$ ✓	$x_1x_3x_4$ ✓	x_1x_3
$x_1\bar{x}_2x_3x_4$ ✓	$x_1x_2x_3$ ✓	$x_1\bar{x}_4$
$x_1x_2x_3\bar{x}_4$ ✓	$x_1\bar{x}_2x_3$ ✓	
$x_1x_2\bar{x}_3\bar{x}_4$ ✓	$x_1x_2\bar{x}_4$ ✓	
$x_1\bar{x}_2x_3\bar{x}_4$ ✓	$x_1x_3\bar{x}_4$ ✓	
$x_1\bar{x}_2\bar{x}_3\bar{x}_4$ ✓	$x_1\bar{x}_3\bar{x}_4$ ✓	
$\bar{x}_1\bar{x}_2\bar{x}_3x_4$	$x_1\bar{x}_2\bar{x}_4$ ✓	

successively to see whether or not it can be combined with any of the later products appearing in the first column. We obtain in this way the first two three-factor products in the second column of the table. We place check marks (✓) by the complete products used in this way, to record the fact that they are included in shorter products listed later in the table. Now we determine whether or not the *second* complete product can be combined with any later complete products, then list any new three factor products obtained in this way in the second column, and finally check off all complete products that have been used and have not previously been checked off. Continuing thus, we obtain column two of the table, which we then treat in the same way we treated column one, to generate column three, at which point the process is complete in this example. Note that certain products in these columns remain unchecked because they were not used to obtain any shorter products. Note also that some shorter products were obtained in several ways but were nevertheless listed only once. However, all longer products giving rise to any shorter products were checked.

Now consider the unchecked entries in the three columns of the table. By the manner in which they were obtained, it follows that *the union of these products includes every complete product of f and no others* and hence is equivalent to *f*. Moreover, these unchecked products are the prime implicants of *f* since each of them implies *f* but none subsumes a shorter fundamental product which implies *f*.

It remains to determine which of these prime implicants are required for a minimal OR-polynomial equivalent to *f*. To decide this, we draw up the array shown in Table 4.10.2, in which the prime implicants are used as ordinates and the complete products of *f* are used as abscissas. In each row of the table we put a check mark (an ×) under each complete product included by the prime implicant corresponding to that row.

Table 4.10.2

	$x_1x_2x_3x_4$	$x_1\bar{x}_2x_3x_4$	$x_1x_2x_3\bar{x}_4$	$x_1x_2\bar{x}_3\bar{x}_4$	$x_1\bar{x}_2x_3\bar{x}_4$	$x_1\bar{x}_2\bar{x}_3\bar{x}_4$	$\bar{x}_1\bar{x}_2\bar{x}_3x_4$
$\bar{x}_1\bar{x}_2\bar{x}_3x_4$							×
x_1x_3	×	×	×		×		
$x_1\bar{x}_4$			×	×	×	×	

The problem now is to select from the prime implicants a subset such that

1. each column contains at least one "×" in the rows of the prime implicants selected, and
2. the total number of appearances of variables in the prime implicants selected is as small as possible.

In view of (1), the union of these prime implicants will be identically equal to f, and, in view of (2), no shorter OR-polynomial representing f is possible.

We next observe that if any column contains only one check mark, the prime implicant corresponding to the row in which the check appears *must be* included in the expression for f. Such a prime implicant is called an **essential prime implicant.** We record each of the essential prime implicants, or mark them with an asterisk, and then, to reduce the table, we cross out the columns that forced us to regard these implicants as essential, as well as all other columns headed by products included by these same implicants and therefore requiring no further consideration.

In the case of our example, Table 4.10.2 shows that each prime implicant is essential, so that we have in fact

$$f = \bar{x}_1\bar{x}_2\bar{x}_3x_4 \;\lor\; x_1x_3 \;\lor\; x_1\bar{x}_4$$

as the unique minimal OR-polynomial representing f.

There remains, of course, the problem of factoring f effectively. In this case, it is not hard to obtain the reduced form

$$f = \overline{x_1 \;\lor\; x_2 \;\lor\; (x_3 \lor \bar{x}_4)} \;\lor\; x_1(x_3 \lor \bar{x}_4),$$

the AND-OR-NOT realization of which requires eleven arrows.

As a second example, consider the function whose complete products are listed in the first column of Table 4.10.3, and whose prime implicants are determined in the remainder of the table.

Table 4.10.3

Complete Products	Derived Products
$\bar{x}_1\bar{x}_2\bar{x}_3\bar{x}_4$ ✓	$\bar{x}_1\bar{x}_2\bar{x}_4$ ✓ $\bar{x}_1\bar{x}_4$
$\bar{x}_1\bar{x}_2x_3\bar{x}_4$ ✓	$\bar{x}_1\bar{x}_3\bar{x}_4$ ✓
$\bar{x}_1x_2\bar{x}_3\bar{x}_4$ ✓	$\bar{x}_2\bar{x}_3\bar{x}_4$
$\bar{x}_1x_2x_3\bar{x}_4$ ✓	$\bar{x}_1x_3\bar{x}_4$ ✓
$x_1\bar{x}_2\bar{x}_3\bar{x}_4$ ✓	$\bar{x}_1x_2\bar{x}_4$ ✓
$x_1\bar{x}_2\bar{x}_3x_4$ ✓	$x_1\bar{x}_2\bar{x}_3$
$x_1x_2\bar{x}_3x_4$ ✓	$x_1\bar{x}_3x_4$
$x_1x_2x_3x_4$ ✓	$x_1x_2x_4$

The second table required by the process is Table 4.10.4.

Table 4.10.4

	$\bar{x}_1\bar{x}_2\bar{x}_3\bar{x}_4$	$\bar{x}_1\bar{x}_2x_3\bar{x}_4$	$\bar{x}_1x_2\bar{x}_3\bar{x}_4$	$\bar{x}_1x_2x_3\bar{x}_4$	$x_1\bar{x}_2\bar{x}_3\bar{x}_4$	$x_1\bar{x}_2\bar{x}_3x_4$	$x_1x_2\bar{x}_3x_4$	$x_1x_2x_3x_4$
$\bar{x}_2\bar{x}_3\bar{x}_4$	×				×			
$x_1\bar{x}_2\bar{x}_3$					×	×		
$x_1\bar{x}_3x_4$						×	×	
*$x_1x_2x_4$							×	×
*$\bar{x}_1\bar{x}_4$	×	×	×	×				

In this case, the last two prime implicants are seen to be essential. This leaves the fifth and sixth complete products to be accounted for and we have three prime implicants from which to choose. Clearly, the second is the one to use, for it takes care of both products at once. Hence we have

$$f = \bar{x}_1\bar{x}_4 \lor x_1x_2x_4 \lor x_1\bar{x}_2\bar{x}_3,$$

which factors into

$$f = \overline{x_1 \lor x_4} \lor x_1(x_2x_4 \lor \overline{x_2 \lor x_3}),$$

a form requiring fourteen arrows for an AND-OR-NOT realization.

At times there may be no essential prime implicants, and there may also be more than one shortest form for the function. Both of these cases are illustrated by the next example.

Consider the function

$$f = x_1\bar{x}_2 \lor \bar{x}_1x_2 \lor x_2\bar{x}_3 \lor \bar{x}_2x_3$$
$$= x_1\bar{x}_2x_3 \lor x_1\bar{x}_2\bar{x}_3 \lor \bar{x}_1x_2x_3 \lor \bar{x}_1x_2\bar{x}_3 \lor x_1x_2\bar{x}_3 \lor \bar{x}_1\bar{x}_2x_3.$$

First, we determine the prime implicants (Table 4.10.5).

Table 4.10.5

Complete Products	Derived Products
$x_1\bar{x}_2x_3$ ✓	$x_1\bar{x}_2$
$x_1\bar{x}_2\bar{x}_3$ ✓	$\bar{x}_2x_3$
$\bar{x}_1x_2x_3$ ✓	$x_1\bar{x}_3$
$\bar{x}_1x_2\bar{x}_3$ ✓	$\bar{x}_1x_2$
$x_1x_2\bar{x}_3$ ✓	$\bar{x}_1x_3$
$\bar{x}_1\bar{x}_2x_3$ ✓	$x_2\bar{x}_3$

Then, in Table 4.10.6, we determine the essential prime implicants.

Table 4.10.6

	$x_1\bar{x}_2x_3$	$x_1\bar{x}_2\bar{x}_3$	$\bar{x}_1x_2x_3$	$\bar{x}_1x_2\bar{x}_3$	$x_1x_2\bar{x}_3$	$\bar{x}_1\bar{x}_2x_3$
$x_1\bar{x}_2$	×	×				
$\bar{x}_2x_3$	×					×
$x_1\bar{x}_3$		×			×	
$\bar{x}_1x_2$			×	×		
$\bar{x}_1x_3$			×			×
$x_2\bar{x}_3$				×	×	

Here there are *no essential prime implicants.*

In the final representation of f as a union of prime implicants, every complete product of f must be included by at least one of these prime implicants. (When a complete product is included in this sense by a selected prime implicant, it is also included, as we have seen, in the set-theoretic sense, in the set of complete products that appear in the disjunctive normal form of f. The word "include" may therefore be interpreted either way in what follows.)

Suppose therefore that, to include the complete product entered in the first column, we pick the prime implicant $x_1\bar{x}_2$. Then the complete product entered in the second column is also included. There would be no economy to picking either of the next two prime implicants, for by picking $\bar{x}_1x_3$ and $x_2\bar{x}_3$ we can account for the remaining four columns. That is,

$$f = x_1\bar{x}_2 \lor \bar{x}_1x_3 \lor x_2\bar{x}_3.$$

An equally good choice is

$$f = \bar{x}_1x_2 \lor x_1\bar{x}_3 \lor \bar{x}_2x_3,$$

but any other choice would involve at least four terms.

It is instructive to note how this simplification may be performed algebraically. By applying (S–12b) to f as originally given, we can write

$$f = x_1\bar{x}_2 \lor \bar{x}_1 x_2 \lor x_2\bar{x}_3 \lor \bar{x}_2 x_3 \lor x_1\bar{x}_3.$$

Now the terms $x_1\bar{x}_2$ and $x_2\bar{x}_3$ may be removed by (S–12b) again and we have

$$f = \bar{x}_1 x_2 \lor \bar{x}_2 x_3 \lor x_1\bar{x}_3.$$

The other equally good form may be obtained from the original form of f in a similar fashion.

If we were to express f not in its shortest form but rather as the union of all its prime implicants, the factorizations

$$f = (x_1 \lor x_2 \lor x_3)(\bar{x}_1 \lor \bar{x}_2 \lor \bar{x}_3)$$

and

$$f = (x_1 \lor x_2 \lor x_3)\overline{x_1 x_2 x_3}$$

would be readily discovered. These two forms lead to the relay and AND-OR-NOT circuits shown in Figure 4.10.1. Even when complements

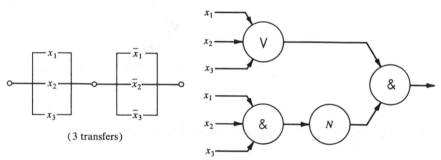

Circuits corresponding to simplified function
Figure 4.10.1

of inputs are available, the factored form is more economical. This example emphasizes the fact that *the minimum OR-polynomial representing a function does not always lead to the simplest circuit realizing the function.*

Some additional observations are in order: After the table has been reduced by removal of the columns and rows corresponding to essential products, we have to determine, by inspecting all the possibilities, which is the best choice for the remaining columns. This may be a difficult task. A further simplification that may be possible is this: If all members of any set of columns in the reduced table have checks in exactly the same rows, that is, are identical with respect to check marks, only one of these columns needs to be retained, for including the complete product of any one of these columns by the selection of a suitable prime implicant automatically includes all the rest. The other columns of the set may therefore be deleted.

The Quine method executes essentially the same process as does the map method presented earlier. When the number of variables is not small but the number of complete products included in f is reasonably small, the Quine process is often less unwieldy than the map method.

A disadvantage of Quine's method is the large amount of writing it requires. This can be reduced by a numerical method, invented by McCluskey, which will be presented in Section 4.12.

4.11   Exercises

1.   Simplify the function

$$f = x_1 x_2 x_3 \lor x_1 \bar{x}_3 \lor x_1 x_2 \bar{x}_4 \lor \bar{x}_1 x_3 \lor \bar{x}_1 \bar{x}_2 \bar{x}_3 \bar{x}_4.$$

There are four equally short forms. Your work may be checked in Quine's article [3].

2.   Use Quine's method to find $\bar{f}$ in each of the examples of Section 4.10 and see whether or not this leads to a more useful expression for f.

3.   Solve some of the problems of Section 4.9, Exercise 9, by Quine's method.

4.12   McCluskey's Mechanization of Quine's Method

In Quine's procedure, we first combine complete products. For example, when $n = 4$, $x_1 x_2 \bar{x}_3 x_4$ and $x_1 x_2 \bar{x}_3 \bar{x}_4$ lead to the derived product $x_1 x_2 \bar{x}_3$ because $x_1 x_2 \bar{x}_3 x_4 \lor x_1 x_2 \bar{x}_3 \bar{x}_4 = x_1 x_2 \bar{x}_3$. This same operation can be accomplished more compactly by combining the corresponding sequences of values of the x's: 1101 and 1100 lead to the sequence 110– in which the dash indicates which variable has been absorbed, for the subscripts are no longer present to show that.

The product $x_1 x_2 \bar{x}_3$ includes the products $x_1 x_2 \bar{x}_3 x_4$ and $x_1 x_2 \bar{x}_3 \bar{x}_4$. Equivalently, the sequence 110– will be said to **include** the sequences 1101 and 1100, because effectively the dash indicates that the corresponding variable may take on either 1 or 0 as its value.

The second stage of combining products in the case $n = 4$ is illustrated in the next example:

$$\left. \begin{array}{l} x_1 x_2 \bar{x}_3 \\ x_1 x_2 x_3 \end{array} \right\} \text{ yield } x_1 x_2 \text{ or, equivalently, } \left. \begin{array}{l} 110- \\ 111- \end{array} \right\} \text{yield } 11--.$$

If two sequences are to be combined, as here, they must agree in all positions but one, and in that position one sequence must have a "0" and the other a "1."

The product $x_1 x_2$ includes the four complete products $x_1 x_2 \bar{x}_3 \bar{x}_4$, $x_1 x_2 \bar{x}_3 x_4$, $x_1 x_2 x_3 \bar{x}_4$, and $x_1 x_2 x_3 x_4$. Equivalently, the sequence 11-- includes the four sequences 1100, 1101, 1110, and 1111, since a dash represents both a 0 and a 1.

The combining of sequences of 0's, 1's, and –'s is executed in similar fashion at each succeeding stage and it yields prime implicants in the same way as Quine's process does. To illustrate, we give in Table 4.12.1 the numerical form of an example given originally by Quine. Beside each sequence, we list the decimal numbers of the complete products that the product corresponding to that sequence includes. (The usefulness of these decimal numbers in the minimization process was pointed out in Section 4.8.) As before, a check mark ($\checkmark$) is placed by each sequence used to obtain a later sequence. The unchecked sequences represent the prime implicants. In the example,

$$f = \bar{x}_1 \bar{x}_2 x_3 x_4 \ \vee \ x_1 \bar{x}_2 \bar{x}_3 \bar{x}_4 \ \vee \ x_1 \bar{x}_2 \bar{x}_3 x_4 \ \vee \ x_1 x_2 \bar{x}_3 \bar{x}_4 \ \vee \ x_1 x_2 \bar{x}_3 x_4 \ \vee \ x_1 x_2 x_3 x_4$$

Table 4.12.1

Complete Sequences of f	Derived Sequences		
3: 0011	8, 9: 100– $\checkmark$	8,9,12,13: 1–0–	
8: 1000 $\checkmark$	8, 12: 1–00 $\checkmark$		
9: 1001 $\checkmark$	9, 13: 1–01 $\checkmark$		
12: 1100 $\checkmark$	12, 13: 110– $\checkmark$		
13: 1101 $\checkmark$	13, 15: 11–1		
15: 1111 $\checkmark$			

Prime implicants:	0011	11–1	1–0–
or:	$x_1 \bar{x}_2 x_3 x_4$	$x_1 x_2 x_4$	$x_1 \bar{x}_3$
Included complete products:	3	13, 15	8, 9, 12, 13

The reader should remember that in constructing such a table of prime implicants, every sequence in a given column should be compared with every sequence that follows it in that column, regardless of whether or not these sequences have previously been checked.

Note, on the other hand, that the last derived sequence in Table 4.12.1 could be obtained in two ways: 8, 9 combined with 12, 13 and 8, 12 combined with 9, 13. The sequence is listed only once but all four of the preceding sequences, that is, 8, 9; 12, 13; 8, 12; 9, 13 must be checked since all are included by the sequence 8, 9, 12, 13.

In the present example, the prime implicants must all appear in any representation of f as a union of prime implicants because each prime implicant includes at least one complete product that no other prime implicant includes. This is easy to see from the decimal numbers of complete products associated with the sequences throughout the table.

These decimal numbers are useful in another way. Two sequences can be combined only if they differ in exactly one place: "0" in the one, "1" in the other. Hence their decimal numbers must differ by a power of 2. If this is not the case, one does not compare them any further. However, not all sequences that differ by a power of two can be combined. For example ($n = 4$), we cannot combine

$$7: \quad 0111$$

with

$$8 = 7 + 1 = 7 + 2^0: \quad 1000,$$

but we can combine

$$\left.\begin{array}{ll} 7: & 0111 \\ 15 = 7 + 2^3: & 1111 \end{array}\right\}: \quad -111.$$

with

The difficulty in the first example lies in the fact that sometimes adding a power of 2 causes carries in the sequence, whereas at other times it does not. The requirement that the difference of the decimal numbers be a power of 2 is thus a necessary condition, but not a sufficient one, for the combining of sequences. Nevertheless, use of the condition reduces the labor of comparison to a significant extent.

The same type of condition exists at all stages. For example, since the digits do not all differ by powers of 2, there is no use in trying to combine

$$\left.\begin{array}{ll} 8, \ 9: & 100- \\ 14, 15: & 111- \end{array}\right\}.$$

However, we can combine in these cases:

$$\left.\begin{array}{ll} 8, \ 9: & 100- \\ 12, 13: & 110- \end{array}\right\}: 1-0-; \qquad \left.\begin{array}{ll} 17, 21: & 10-01 \\ 25, 29: & 11-01 \end{array}\right\}: \quad 1--01.$$

On the other hand, we cannot combine in these cases:

$$\left.\begin{array}{ll} 4, 5: & 010- \\ 8, 9: & 100- \end{array}\right\}; \qquad \left.\begin{array}{ll} 21, 23: & 101-1 \\ 25, 27: & 110-1 \end{array}\right\},$$

even though, in each case, differences of horizontal and vertical pairs of digits are powers of 2 and the dashes correspond.

These observations may be used at each stage to abbreviate the comparison process and thus to speed up the determination of the prime implicants.

Once the prime implicants have been determined, we have again the problem of determining the *essential* prime implicants. This is accomplished just as in Quine's method, but only the decimal numbers need to be used. The table for this work has the decimal numbers of the complete products of f as abscissas and the sets of numbers associated with the prime implicants as ordinates. The prime implicants are listed in descending order with respect to the number of complete products they include.

For each decimal integer in the set of integers identifying a given row, we mark an $\times$ in the column identified by that integer. This is illustrated in Table 4.12.2, from which

$$f = x_2 x_3 \vee \bar{x}_1 \bar{x}_2 \bar{x}_3 \vee \bar{x}_1 \bar{x}_2 x_4 = x_2 x_3 \vee \bar{x}_1 \bar{x}_2 \bar{x}_3 \vee \bar{x}_1 x_3 x_4.$$

Table 4.12.2

$(n = 4)$ $f = \vee (0,1,3,6,7,14,15)$

0:	0000 ✓	0,1:	000–	6,7,14,15: –11–
1:	0001 ✓	1,3:	00–1	
3:	0011 ✓	3,7:	0–11	
6:	0110 ✓	6,7:	011– ✓	
7:	0111 ✓	6,14:	–110 ✓	
14:	1110 ✓	7,15:	–111 ✓	
15:	1111 ✓	14,15:	111– ✓	

	0	1	3	6	7	14	15
*6,7,14,15				⊗	×	⊗	⊗
* 0,1	⊗	×					
1,3		×	×				
3,7			×		×		

In Table 4.12.2, the first two rows are marked with asterisks to denote the fact that the corresponding products are essential. This is determined by the lone $\times$'s in columns 6 and 0. Then we strike out every column containing an $\times$ in at least one of the essential rows. The remaining columns then identify the complete products of f that must still be accounted for. The only such column here is column "3." It may be accounted for in two ways, which gives rise to the two expressions listed above for f.

4.13   McCluskey's Method for Determining All Minimal Forms

Assume that all essential prime implicants have been determined so that there remains only a set of columns, each of which contains two or more ×'s. At this stage, it is desirable to obtain a simple, systematic way of listing all possible choices that will complete an acceptable representation of f.

Suppose we ignore all the canceled columns and the essential rows and then copy down the rest of the table. We obtain in this way a table similar to the arbitrarily selected Table 4.13.1. This table shows the complete products still to be included, and the prime implicants available for the purpose.

Table 4.13.1

	C_1	C_2	C_3	C_4	C_5	C_6
R_1	×	×	×			×
R_2	×		×	×		
R_3		×		×	×	
R_4			×		×	×

What is, in this case, the best choice of a set of prime implicants from R_1, R_2, R_3, R_4 to complete a representation of f?

First of all, we determine *all* choices as follows. To include the complete products corresponding to $C_1, C_2, \ldots, C_6$, we must choose, respectively, R_1 or R_2, *and* R_1 or R_3, *and* R_1 or R_2 or R_4, and so on. These necessities and alternatives may be represented by the product

$$(R_1 \lor R_2)(R_1 \lor R_3)(R_1 \lor R_2 \lor R_4)(R_2 \lor R_3)(R_3 \lor R_4)(R_1 \lor R_4),$$

which expands to

$$R_1 R_3 \lor R_1 R_2 R_4 \lor R_2 R_3 R_4.$$

The *products* here identify the alternative sets of rows that will complete a representation of f. Thus, there are three sets of rows that will do the job. We form the *union* of the prime implicants corresponding to each acceptable set of rows and choose the form that is shortest. This is illustrated in Table 4.13.2. There may be several equally short forms.

Table 4.13.2

$(n=5)$ $f=V(0,1,3,4,7,13,15,19,20,22,23,29,31)$

Prime implicants are

$3,7,19,23$:	$-0-11$	$0,1$: $\;0000-$	$4,20$: $\;-0100$
$7,15,23,31$:	$--111$	$0,4$: $\;00-00$	$20,22$: $\;101-0$
$13,15,29,31$:	$-11-1$	$1,3$: $\;000-1$	$22,23$: $\;1011-$

	0	1	3	4	7	13	15	19	20	22	23	29	31
* 3,7,19,23					×		×	⊗			×		
7,15,23,31					×		×				×		×
*13,15,29,31						⊗	×					⊗	×
A 0,1	×	×											
B 0,4	×			×									
C 1,3		×	×										
D 4,20				×					×				
E 20,22									×	×			
F 22,23										×	×		

The product corresponding to $7,15,23,31$ may be ignored since it is rendered useless by the essential prime implicants.

To account for the five remaining columns 0, 1, 4, 20, 22, we must select one of the terms in the expansion of the product of five factors

$$(A \lor B)(A \lor C)(B \lor D)(D \lor E)(E \lor F),$$

that is, we must select one of the terms of

$$ABE \lor ADE \lor ADF \lor BCE \lor BCDF$$

to determine the remaining prime implicants to be used. This yields the following set of four equivalent expressions for f:

$$f = \bar{x}_2 x_4 x_5 \lor x_2 x_3 x_5 \lor \bar{x}_1 \bar{x}_2 \bar{x}_3 \bar{x}_4 \quad \bar{x}_1 \bar{x}_2 \bar{x}_4 \bar{x}_5 \lor x_1 \bar{x}_2 x_3 \bar{x}_5,$$
$$f = \bar{x}_2 x_4 x_5 \lor x_2 x_3 x_5 \lor \bar{x}_1 \bar{x}_2 \bar{x}_3 \bar{x}_4 \quad \bar{x}_2 x_3 \bar{x}_4 \bar{x}_5 \lor x_1 \bar{x}_2 x_3 \bar{x}_5,$$
$$f = \bar{x}_2 x_4 x_5 \lor x_2 x_3 x_5 \lor \bar{x}_1 \bar{x}_2 \bar{x}_3 \bar{x}_4 \quad \bar{x}_2 x_3 \bar{x}_4 \bar{x}_5 \lor x_1 \bar{x}_2 x_3 x_4,$$
$$f = \bar{x}_2 x_4 x_5 \lor x_2 x_3 x_5 \lor \bar{x}_1 \bar{x}_2 \bar{x}_4 \bar{x}_5 \quad \bar{x}_1 \bar{x}_2 \bar{x}_3 x_5 \lor x_1 \bar{x}_2 x_3 \bar{x}_5.$$

The last set of rows B, C, D, F is *not* used because it involves more than the minimum number of literals.

4.14   Don't-Cares in the Quine–McCluskey Procedure

In many cases of importance, for certain combinations of values of the variables, the value assumed by a function to be determined is irrelevant. Such combinations are the "don't-care" combinations we have dealt with earlier. In the Quine–McCluskey procedure, we list the don't care combinations along with those for which the function is to be 1 in forming the list of prime implicants. This has the effect of increasing the number of possible prime implicants.

When it comes to determining the essential prime implicants, however, the decimal numbers corresponding to *the don't-care combinations are not listed across the top of the table.* If we did list them, this would amount to choosing all the don't-care values of f as 1, which might not be the best choice. By not listing them, we leave the choice open: If we use a prime implicant derived from one of the don't-care combinations, then we are assigning f the value 1 there. If we use no prime implicant derived from a given don't-care combination, then we are assigning f the value 0 there. Since, however, we have more prime implicants to choose from than would be obtained from the 1-combinations only, we may well be able to find a simpler form for f than would otherwise be possible.

Otherwise the process is fundamentally the same as before, as the example to follow shows (Table 4.14.1).

Table 4.14.1

$(n = 5)$ $f = 1$ at combinations $1,3,5,7,13,28,30,31$;
don't-care combinations: $0,4,12,21,23,29$.

Prime implicants are

$0,1,4,5$:	$00\text{–}0\text{–}$	$5,13,21,29$:	$\text{–}\text{–}101$
$1,3,5,7$:	$00\text{–}\text{–}1$	$12,13,28,29$:	$\text{–}110\text{–}$
$4,5,12,13$:	$0\text{–}10\text{–}$	$21,23,29,31$:	$1\text{–}1\text{–}1$
$5,7,21,23$:	$\text{–}01\text{–}1$	$28,29,30,31$:	$111\text{–}\text{–}$

		1	3	5	7	13	28	30	31
†	$0,1,4,5$	✳		✳					
*	$1,3,5,7$	✳	⊗	✳	✳				
	$4,5,12,13$			✳		×			
†	$5,7,21,23$			✳	✳				
	$5,13,21,29$			✳		×			
	$12,13,28,29$					×	✳		
†	$21,23,29,31$								✳
*	$28,29,30,31$						✳	⊗	✳

Here there are two essential prime implicants and three (marked †) that can perform no useful service at all, because they are eliminated in effect by the essential prime implicants. There are, in consequence, three forms for f, all equally good but *not identically equal* since different don't-care combinations are chosen as 1-combinations:

$$f_1 = \bar{x}_1\bar{x}_2 x_5 \ \lor \ x_1 x_2 x_3 \ \lor \ \bar{x}_1 x_3 \bar{x}_4,$$
$$f_2 = \bar{x}_1\bar{x}_2 x_5 \ \lor \ x_1 x_2 x_3 \ \lor \ x_3 \bar{x}_4 x_5,$$
$$f_3 = \bar{x}_1\bar{x}_2 x_5 \ \lor \ x_1 x_2 x_3 \ \lor \ x_2 x_3 \bar{x}_4.$$

The third form permits the best factorization under any conditions.

An additional remark is in order. In constructing the table of prime implicants, *we do not bother to combine purely don't-care products with other purely don't-care products to get shorter products.* These would have the value 1 only at don't-care combinations and hence would provide no ×'s at all in the table used to determine the minimal forms.

4.15   Exercises

Minimize by the Quine–McCluskey procedure. In each case it is helpful to check the results by the map method. Find all equally short OR-polynomials representing the given functions. Factorizations and circuit diagrams are not required.

(1) $f = V(4, 5, 6, 8, 9, 12, 14)$ $(n = 4)$
(2) $f = V(2, 3, 5, 6, 7, 8, 9, 12, 13, 14, 15)$ $(n = 4)$
(3) $f = V(1, 3, 4, 6, 7, 8, 9, 12, 13, 15)$ $(n = 4)$
(4) $f = V(0, 1, 3, 4, 5, 6, 7, 12, 13, 16, 17, 18, 19, 22, 23)$ $(n = 5)$
(5) $f = V(4, 5, 6, 7, 13, 15, 22, 31, 32)$ $(n = 6)$
(6) $f = V(8, 9, 10, 11, 12, 13, 15, 28, 29, 58, 75, 79, 92)$ $(n = 7)$
(7) $f = V(4, 5, 12, 13, 16, 17, 18, 19, 20, 21, 28, 29, 33, 35, 36, 37,$
          $38, 39, 44, 45, 46, 47, 54, 55, 62, 63)$ $(n = 6)$

(Exercise 7 is designed to show that the map method should not be discarded lightly.)

Minimize by the Quine-McCluskey procedure, taking account of the indicated don't-care conditions. In problem 10, $n = 6$.

(8) $f = V(2, 6, 8, 9, 13)$;   don't-cares: $(0, 4, 15)$ $(n = 4)$
(9) $f = V(4, 5, 8, 9, 12, 14)$;   don't-cares: $(1, 6, 7, 11)$ $(n = 4)$
(10) $f = V(4, 5, 6, 7, 13, 15, 22, 31, 52)$;   don't-cares: $(20, 23, 30, 36)$.

4.16   Use of Coverings to Reduce the Problem

Whereas we have outlined basic procedure fully, cases arise in which the selection of nonessential prime implicants to complete a minimum representation of f may be considerably shortened. Consider first the following case: After all columns accounted for by essential prime implicants have been struck out, there may remain a row that has un-canceled ×'s only in columns in which another row has uncanceled ×'s. If these two rows correspond to *products of the same or decreasing length* and if the second contains *at least as many* uncanceled ×'s as the first, the second is said to **cover** the first.

Now let one of two rows cover the other. If the covering row contains *more* uncanceled ×'s, it is chosen in preference to the covered row, on the grounds of efficiency. We now strike out (one at a time) each row covered by one of the still remaining rows corresponding to products of *equal or shorter length*. Of products of equal length, with identical un-canceled ×'s, only one need be retained. The columns containing the ×'s canceled out by this process are *not* struck out, however, because the *rows* being struck out will *not* be involved in any representation of f and hence will not account for any complete products.

Note that this type of cancellation never causes us to choose a longer product than would otherwise be needed, nor can it force us to choose more terms than would otherwise be needed.

The cancellation of covered rows may result in columns containing only one uncanceled ×. That is, we now have a new type of "essential" product, namely, one that has been rendered essential by the cancellation of covered rows. To indicate this fact, we mark rows corresponding to such essential products with double asterisks, then cross out the columns in which they have ×'s, just as before. Thereafter we look again for cover-ings, cancel out covered rows as before, and mark any new essential products with three asterisks, and so on. The process is continued as long as it results in changes in the table.

When the preceding process is complete, it is possible that all columns have been crossed out. In that event, the union of the products found at the various stages to be essential is a minimal representation of f, for at each stage we have made certain that only the most inclusive products will be chosen.

On the Karnaugh map, this process is interpreted as follows: Assume the essential prime implicants have been determined, so that they account for a certain set of p-squares. Let a given k-dimensional p-subcube K include certain p-squares not previously accounted for. Then a k'-dimen-sional p-subcube K' which includes all the p-squares in K is to be pre-ferred over K if it also includes at least one *additional* p-square not previously covered. If $k' = k$, there may, as above, be no preference.

It is also possible that after the preceding process is complete, there remain columns containing more than one entry. In this case the problem of making a suitable choice from the class of all possible choices must again be faced. These observations are illustrated in the following examples (Tables 4.16.1 and 4.16.2).

Table 4.16.1

$(n = 6) f = V(3, 7, 11, 13, 19, 20, 21, 22, 23, 29, 31, 39, 51, 52, 54, 63)$

3:	000011 ✓	3,7:	000–11 ✓	3,7,19,23:	0–0–11
7:	000111 ✓	3,11:	00–011	20,21,22,23:	0101––
11:	001011 ✓	3,19:	0–0011 ✓	20,22,52,54:	–101–0
13	001101 ✓	7,23:	0–0111 ✓	21,23,29,31:	01–1–1
19:	010011 ✓	7,39:	–00111		
20:	010100 ✓	13,29:	0–1101		
21:	010101 ✓	19,23:	010–11 ✓		
22:	010110 ✓	19,51:	–10011		
23:	010111 ✓	20,21:	01010– ✓		
29:	011101 ✓	20,22:	0101–0 ✓		
31:	011111 ✓	20,52:	–10100 ✓		
39:	100111 ✓	21,23:	0101–1 ✓		
51:	110011 ✓	21,29:	01–101 ✓		
52:	110100 ✓	22,23:	01011– ✓		
54:	110110 ✓	22,54:	–10110 ✓		
63:	111111 ✓	23,31:	01–111 ✓		
		29,31:	0111–1 ✓		
		31,63:	–11111		
		52,54:	1101–0 ✓		

Table 4.16.2

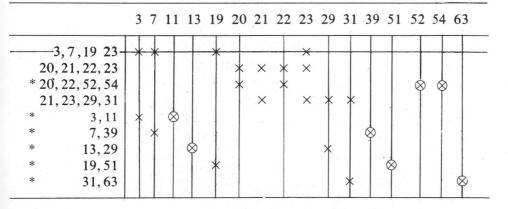

After the essential prime implicants have been determined and the corresponding columns have been crossed out, rows 1, 2, and 4 appear as nonessential. The first of these nonessential rows is covered by each of the other two. Hence we cross out this row (but none of the columns still unaccounted for). We could now cancel another of the non-essential rows. If we do not, we have a choice of expressions for f:

$$f = x_2\bar{x}_3x_4\bar{x}_6 \lor \bar{x}_1\bar{x}_2\bar{x}_4x_5x_6 \lor \bar{x}_2\bar{x}_3x_4x_5x_6 \lor \bar{x}_1x_3x_4\bar{x}_5x_6 \lor x_2\bar{x}_3\bar{x}_4x_5x_6$$
$$\lor\; x_2x_3x_4x_5x_6 \lor \begin{cases} \bar{x}_1x_2\bar{x}_3x_4 \\ \bar{x}_1x_2x_4x_6. \end{cases}$$

The factoring problem that now presents itself is not trivial in a case like this. This problem would be less tedious on a Karnaugh map. (Figure 4.16.1).

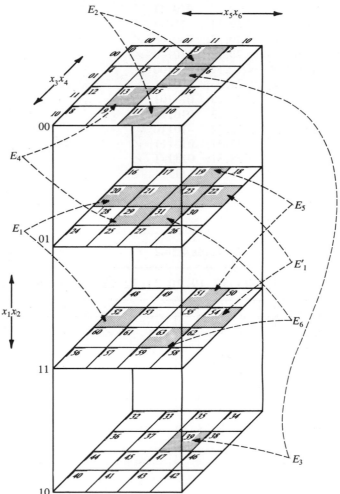

Map for preceding six variable example. (The E's denote essential products. E_1 and E'_1 refer to the same product.)

Figure 4.16.1

If the figure is drawn large enough, or if a three-dimensional plastic array is used, one can lay pennies on all the p-squares, then lay dimes on the pennies in those squares belonging to essential products. (The essential products should be recorded as they are noted.) Thereafter, the choices for covering the remaining p-squares are not hard to see.

The use of the covering process often leads more rapidly to the determination of a minimal OR-polynomial representing a given function, but it may drastically reduce the number of possible choices and thereby yield a form less favorable for factorization or less economical for interconnection with other circuits. For example, consider Exercise 8, Section 4.15. Here we have

$$f = V(2,6,8,9,13); \text{ don't-cares: } (0,4,15); (n = 4).$$

The prime implicants are readily computed to be

$$
\begin{array}{ll}
0, 8: & -000 \\
8, 9: & 100- \qquad 0,2,4,6: \quad 0--0. \\
9, 13: & 1-01 \\
13, 15: & 11-1
\end{array}
$$

This yields Table 4.16.3.

Table 4.16.3

	2	6	8	9	13
* 0, 2, 4, 6	⊗	⊗			
0, 8			×		
8, 9			×	×	
9, 13				×	×
13, 15					×

Here 0, 2, 4, 6 is essential. By the covering rule, we should discard the products $0, 8$ and $13, 15$ since they are covered by $8, 9$ and $9, 13$, respectively. Hence, there remains but one choice for f:

$$f_1 = \bar{x}_1\bar{x}_4 \ \vee \ x_1\bar{x}_2\bar{x}_3 \ \vee \ x_1\bar{x}_3x_4.$$

However, equally short representations are

$$f_2 = \bar{x}_1\bar{x}_4 \ \vee \ \bar{x}_2\bar{x}_3\bar{x}_4 \ \vee \ x_1\bar{x}_3x_4$$

and

$$f_3 = \bar{x}_1\bar{x}_4 \ \vee \ x_1\bar{x}_2\bar{x}_3 \ \vee \ x_1x_2x_4.$$

Moreover, these last two forms permit more favorable factorizations if AND-OR-NOT circuits are to be designed.

Thus, reduction by deletion of covered rows is not unconditionally helpful. On the other hand, in some problems the total number of alternative, equally short forms is extremely large, so that, unless we use the covering process, finding even one minimal OR-polynomial may be quite discouraging.

It should be noted that the selection of the covered rows which are to be deleted is not always unique. For example, we may be in a position to delete one row, or another, but not both. Hence deletion of covered rows may well yield different sets of answers to the same problem, depending on how the reduction process is applied.

4.17   Exercises

1. Rework the exercises of Section 4.15, deleting covered rows wherever possible. Compare with results previously obtained.

2. Apply the covering process in this instance ($n = 5$):

$$f = V(0, 1, 2, 5, 6, 7, 8, 16, 18, 20, 21, 22, 23, 24, 25, 26, 27, 29, 31).$$

Also, by McCluskey's procedure, determine the total number of minimal forms.

4.18   Summary and Conclusions

In designing digital circuits, it is important to have methods of reducing bulky switching functions to manageable forms, from which acceptable factored forms may be determined. The two most widely used methods, the Karnaugh map method and the Quine–McCluskey procedure, both adapted to paper and pencil work, have been presented in detail.

Since many problems involve so many variables or such bulky functions that paper and pencil procedures become too unwieldy to be useful, much attention has been directed to the development of improved procedures, particularly to the development of methods appropriate for programming for computer solution. Even computer methods have their limitations, for it is possible for relatively simple functions, even for rather small values of n, to have an extremely large number of prime implicants. (To indicate the possibilities, note that when $n = 10$, there are $3^n = 59{,}049$ fundamental products.)

The frustration suggested by this last observation is of small concern in practice, however, for we do not ordinarily want to minimize a single circuit involving a large number of variables since the construction and, even more, the maintenance of such circuits would, in all probability, be prohibitively expensive. The real problem is to decompose large circuits into well-designed systems of small circuits which can be readily and economically replaced or serviced in the event of failure. In short, the minimization problem for large numbers of variables or complicated functions is more of academic rather than of practical interest. The important problem is therefore the one known as "functional decomposition," the nature and scope of which has only been suggested here.

4.19   References

The following include discussions of the material covered in this chapter as well as of further methods of obtaining economical representations of Boolean functions.

1.   M. Karnaugh, "The Map Method for Synthesis of Combinational Logic Circuits," *Trans. Amer. Inst. Elec. Engr.*, **72,** Part 1, 1953, pp. 593–99.

2.   Staff of Harvard University Computation Laboratory, *Synthesis of Electronic Computing and Control Circuits*. Cambridge, Massachusetts: Harvard University Press, 1951, chapter V.

3.   W. V. O. Quine, "The Problem of Simplifying Truth Functions," *Amer. Math. Monthly,* **59,** 1952, pp. 521–31.

4.   W. V. O. Quine, "A Way to Simplify Truth Functions," *Amer. Math. Monthly,* **62,** 1955, pp. 627–31.

5.   W. V. O. Quine, "On Cores and Prime Implicants of Truth Functions," *Amer. Math. Monthly,* **66,** 1959, pp. 755–60.

6.   E. J. McCluskey, Jr., "Minimization of Boolean Functions," *Bell Syst. Tech. J.,* **XXXV,** 1956, pp. 1417–44.

7.   R. H. Urbano and R. K. Mueller, "A Topological Method for the Determination of the Minimal Forms of a Boolean Function," *Inst. Radio Engr., Trans. on Elec. Computers,* **EC–5,** 1956, pp. 126–132.

8.   M. Phister, Jr., *Logical Design of Digital Computers*. New York: John Wiley, 1958, chapter 4.

9.   R. E. Miller, *Switching Theory, Volume I: Combinational Circuits.* New York: John Wiley, 1965.

10.   E. W. Veitch, "A Chart Method for Simplifying Truth Functions," *Proc., Conf. Assn. Computing Machinery,* May 2–3, 1952, pp. 127–133.

11.   E. J. McCluskey, *Introduction to the Theory of Switching Circuits.* New York: McGraw-Hill, 1966.

5

An Abstract Summary of Boolean Algebra

5.1 The Basic Operations of a Boolean Algebra

We present now a brief, abstract treatment of Boolean algebra in order to emphasize that such an algebra is in fact a mathematical structure completely independent of its applications. This chapter should also make it simple to refer to the basic laws.

The postulates are given in an order that is convenient. As before, they are not independent; but they are, of course, consistent. Various independent sets of postulates may be found in the literature. (See, for example, the references cited in [2], Chapter 1, page 3.)

Let B be a set of elements for which, first of all, **equality** $(=)$ means identity; that is, if a and b are elements of B, then $a = b$ if and only if a and b are in fact the same element of B. This does not, of course, exclude the familiar possibility that an element of B may have more than one *representation*, one of which may be more useful for a given purpose than another. For all a,b,c belonging to B, equality is **reflexive**; that is, $a = a$; equality is **symmetric,** that is, if $a = b$ then $b = a$; and equality is **transitive,** that is, if $a = b$ and $b = c$, then $a = c$.

We assume next that there are two binary operations, denoted by "$\vee$" and "$\wedge$" and called **join** and **meet,** respectively, each of which may be applied to any ordered pair of elements of B to produce, in every case, again an element of B. The fact that the join and the meet of two elements of B are always again elements of B is described by saying that B is **closed** with respect to these two operations. We read "$a \vee b$"

223

as "*a* join *b*" or as "the join of *a* and *b*" and "*a* ∧ *b*" as "*a* meet *b*" or as "the meet of *a* and *b*." These operations are required to satisfy, for all elements *a*, *b*, *c* of *B*,

the commutative laws:

(1a)
$$a \lor b = b \lor a,$$
(1b)
$$a \land b = b \land a;$$

the associative laws:

(2a)
$$a \lor (b \lor c) = (a \lor b) \lor c,$$
(2b)
$$a \land (b \land c) = (a \land b) \land c;$$
and

the distributive laws:

(3a)
$$a \land (b \lor c) = (a \land b) \lor (a \land c),$$
(3b)
$$a \lor (b \land c) = (a \lor b) \land (a \lor c).$$

The first of the distributive laws says that *meet distributes across join*, and the second says that *join distributes across meet*. These operations also satisfy

the idempotent laws:

(4a)
$$a \lor a = a,$$
(4b)
$$a \land a = a.$$

The idempotent laws contrast sharply with the laws of the algebra of complex numbers and, in fact, account for many of the special properties of Boolean algebra.

We assume that *B* contains two *distinct* special elements, "0" (zero) and "1" (one) which, for every element *a* of *B*, satisfy

the laws of operation with 0 and 1:

(5a)
$$a \lor 0 = a,$$
(5b)
$$a \land 1 = a,$$
(6a)
$$a \land 0 = 0,$$
(6b)
$$a \lor 1 = 1.$$

Note that in the first pair of these laws, the element *a* always survives so that 0 and 1 are **identity elements** with respect to *join* and *meet*, respectively. The second pair of laws will be described here by saying that 0 and 1 are **dominant elements** with respect to *meet* and *join*, respectively.

We also assume that there is defined in *B* a *unary* operation called **complementation,** denoted by "¯", which assigns to each element *a* of *B* a **complement,** $\bar{a}$, also a member of *B*, which satisfies

the laws of complementarity:

(7a) $a \wedge \bar{a} = 0,$
(7b) $a \vee \bar{a} = 1,$

DeMorgan's laws:

(8a) $\overline{a \vee b} = \bar{a} \wedge \bar{b},$
(8b) $\overline{a \wedge b} = \bar{a} \vee \bar{b},$

and finally

the law of involution:

(9) $(\bar{\bar{a}}) = a.$

The laws (1a) through (9) are the basic laws of Boolean algebra. All else follows from them via definitions and theorems. Before proceeding to prove several basic theorems, we remark that, since equality means identity, it follows that *for all a, b, c belonging to B, if a = b, then $\bar{a} = \bar{b}$, $a \vee c = b \vee c$, and $a \wedge c = b \wedge c$.* We often use these facts in manipulations.

First we note that the definitions imply

(10) $\bar{0} = 1$ and $\bar{1} = 0.$

Indeed, by (7b), (1a), and (5a); then by (7a), (1b), and (5b), we have

$$1 = 0 \vee \bar{0} = \bar{0} \vee 0 = \bar{0}; \qquad 0 = 1 \wedge \bar{1} = \bar{1} \wedge 1 = \bar{1}.$$

Another fact to note is that the postulates (1a) through (8b) are listed in pairs. Each member of a pair may be obtained from the other by interchange of the operations "$\vee$" and "$\wedge$" and the symbols "0" and "1," throughout. The complement symbol, however, remains unchanged. Thus, throughout the list of postulates, the operations "$\vee$" and "$\wedge$," and the symbols "0" and "1" as well, enjoy a certain equality of treatment. This symmetry leads to the **principle of duality,** and the postulates are said to appear in *dual pairs*. Postulate 9 is said to be *self-dual* since it is unaffected by the named interchanges. The importance of the principle of duality is that it enables us to conclude at once, from the proof of a given identity, the truth of the dual identity, *without separate proof.* Indeed, since a step-wise dual proof for the latter identity *could* be written, there is no point to writing it. This principle doubles the usefulness of each of our proofs.

Next we show that *each element a of B has a unique complement.* Indeed, a has at least one complement, $\bar{a}$, by hypothesis. Then $a \wedge \bar{a} = 0$, $a \vee \bar{a} = 1$. Suppose that x is a complement of a so that we also have

$a \wedge x = 0, a \vee x = 1$. Then $x = x \vee 0 = x \vee (a \wedge \bar{a}) = (x \vee a) \wedge (x \vee \bar{a})$
$= (a \vee x) \wedge (x \vee \bar{a}) = 1 \wedge (x \vee \bar{a}) = (a \vee \bar{a}) \wedge (x \vee \bar{a}) = (\bar{a} \vee a) \wedge (\bar{a} \vee x)$
$= \bar{a} \vee (a \wedge x) = \bar{a} \vee 0 = \bar{a}$. Thus $x = \bar{a}$ so that $\bar{a}$ is the *only* complement of a and the theorem is proved. The proof has been given in full detail. The reader may provide the reasons for the steps.

We now *apply* the fact that if $a \wedge x = 0$ and $a \vee x = 1$, x is necessarily $\bar{a}$. We have

$$(a \wedge b) \wedge (\bar{a} \vee \bar{b}) = [(a \wedge b) \wedge \bar{a}] \vee [(a \wedge b) \wedge \bar{b}]$$
$$= [(a \wedge \bar{a}) \wedge b] \vee [a \wedge (b \wedge \bar{b})] = 0$$

and

$$(a \wedge b) \vee (\bar{a} \vee \bar{b}) = [(a \wedge b) \vee \bar{a}] \vee \bar{b} = [\bar{a} \vee (a \wedge b)] \vee \bar{b}$$
$$= [(\bar{a} \vee a) \wedge (\bar{a} \vee b)] \vee \bar{b}$$
$$= [1 \wedge (\bar{a} \vee b)] \vee \bar{b} = (\bar{a} \vee b) \vee \bar{b}$$
$$= \bar{a} \vee (b \vee \bar{b}) = \bar{a} \vee 1 = 1.$$

These show that the unique complement of $a \wedge b$ is $\bar{a} \vee \bar{b}$:

$$\overline{a \wedge b} = \bar{a} \vee \bar{b}.$$

In short, *(8a) follows from earlier postulates* and hence is not independent. Similarly, *we can obtain (8b) from earlier postulates*. The proof is, in fact, dual to the one just given.

There are further postulates that are not independent of the others, and there are further theorems to be proved. Some of these results are given in following exercises.

5.2 Exercises

*1.   Prove that (1)–(9) imply that B *contains a unique zero element and a unique unit element*; that is, if the element z of B is such that $a \vee z = a$ for all a in B, then $z = 0$, and if the element u of B is such that $a \wedge u = a$ for all a in B, then $u = 1$.

*2.   Using the postulates above, prove that $0 \vee 0 = 0$, $0 \vee 1 = 1 \vee 0 = 1 \vee 1 = 1$, $0 \wedge 0 = 0 \wedge 1 = 1 \wedge 0 = 0$, $1 \wedge 1 = 1$.

*3.   Define and discuss the symbols $\bigwedge_{i=1}^{n} b_i$ and $\bigvee_{i=1}^{n} b_i$ where the b_i are elements of B.

*4.   Prove that $\left(\overline{\bigwedge_{i=1}^{n} b_i}\right) = \bigvee_{i=1}^{n} \bar{b}_i$ and $\left(\overline{\bigvee_{i=1}^{n} b_i}\right) = \bigwedge_{i=1}^{n} \bar{b}_i$ where the b_i are elements of B.

*5.   Prove that these identities hold in every set B in which (1)–(9) hold:

(10a)	$a \vee (a \wedge b) = a,$
(10b)	$a \wedge (a \vee b) = a,$
(11a)	$a \vee (\bar{a} \wedge b) = a \vee b,$
(11b)	$a \wedge (\bar{a} \vee b) = a \wedge b,$
(12a)	$(a \vee b) \wedge (\bar{a} \vee c) \wedge (b \vee c) = (a \vee b) \wedge (\bar{a} \vee c),$
(12b)	$(a \wedge b) \vee (\bar{a} \wedge c) \vee (b \wedge c) = (a \wedge b) \vee (\bar{a} \wedge c).$

5.3 The Inclusion Relation

The next step is to define, for elements of B, the binary relation "$\subseteq$," which is called **inclusion.** The expression "$a \subseteq b$" is read, "a is included in b," and may be defined thus:

$$(13) \qquad\qquad a \subseteq b \Leftrightarrow a \wedge \bar{b} = 0.$$

We have at once the following theorems, which hold for all elements a, b, c belonging to B:

the universal bounds property:

$$(14) \qquad\qquad 0 \subseteq a \subseteq 1,$$

the reflexive law:

$$(15) \qquad\qquad a \subseteq a,$$

the antisymmetric law:

$$(16) \qquad\qquad \text{if } a \subseteq b \text{ and } b \subseteq a, \quad \text{then } a = b,$$

the transitive law:

$$(17) \qquad\qquad \text{if } a \subseteq b \text{ and } b \subseteq c, \quad \text{then } a \subseteq c,$$

and last,

the consistency principle:

(18a)	$a \subseteq b$	if and only if $a \wedge b = a,$
(18b)	$a \subseteq b$	if and only if $a \vee b = b.$

The result (14) is obtained thus: by (1a) and (6a), $0 \wedge \bar{a} = \bar{a} \wedge 0 = 0$, so that by (13), $0 \subseteq a$. Since $\bar{1} = 0$, we have by (6a), $a \wedge \bar{1} = a \wedge 0 = 0$, so $a \subseteq 1$. The other results are obtained similarly and are left to the reader as exercises.

5.4   Definition of a Boolean Algebra

Any collection B of elements for which equality means identity and for which a binary relation "$\subseteq$" is defined, which is closed under binary operations "$\vee$" and "$\wedge$" and under a unary operation "$^{-}$," and which contains two distinct special elements "0" and "1," the entire system satisfying (1a) through (18b), is called a **Boolean algebra.** The postulates (1a) through (9), though not independent, are consistent because there exist systems, some of which we have studied in previous chapters, meeting all these requirements.

The postulates, definitions, and theorems (1) through (18b) have many further consequences, a large number of which have appeared in earlier chapters of this book, though at times in less general contexts.

5.5   Normal Forms of Boolean Functions

Next, let $x_1, x_2, \ldots, x_n$ be variables whose common domain is a Boolean algebra B. Then a function $f(x_1, x_2, \ldots, x_n)$, built up from these variables and from elements of B by a finite number of applications of the operations $\vee$, $\wedge$, and $^{-}$, is called a **Boolean function** of the variables $x_1, x_2, \ldots, x_n$. Just as in the case of real or complex functions, the variables may, in particular, *all* be absent from f so that f is a *constant* function equal to some element of B. Also, just as in other connections, we define $f = g$ if and only if $f(\xi_1, \xi_2, \ldots, \xi_n) = g(\xi_1, \xi_2, \ldots, \xi_n)$ for every combination of values $\xi_1, \xi_2, \ldots, \xi_n$ of the x's.

In the case of switching functions, the algebra B is simply the pair of elements $\{0, 1\}$ so that a Boolean function of $x_1, x_2, \ldots, x_n$ contains only $0, 1$, and x's in addition to symbols for grouping and for operations. When B contains elements other than 0 and 1, expressions representing Boolean functions need not be so simple. Nevertheless, disjunctive and conjunctive normal forms are always possible. We begin with

Lemma 1: *Every Boolean function of one variable, $f(x)$, may be written in the form*

$$(5.5.1) \qquad f(x) = (f(1) \wedge x) \vee (f(0) \wedge \bar{x}).$$

The proof is by mathematical induction. First we have, by inspection,

$$a = (a \wedge x) \vee (a \wedge \bar{x}), \qquad (a \text{ any element of } B)$$
$$x = (1 \wedge x) \vee (0 \wedge \bar{x}),$$

and

$$\bar{x} = (0 \wedge x) \vee (1 \wedge \bar{x}).$$

Thus, if $f(x) = a$, $f(x) = x$, or $f(x) = \bar{x}$, we have

$$f(x) = (f(1) \wedge x) \vee (f(0) \wedge \bar{x}).$$

Now let f and g be any two functions having the property announced in the lemma. Then

$$f(x) \vee g(x) = [(f(1) \wedge x) \vee (f(0) \wedge \bar{x})] \vee [(g(1) \wedge x) \vee (g(0) \wedge \bar{x})]$$
$$= [(f(1) \vee g(1)) \wedge x] \vee [(f(0) \vee g(0)) \wedge \bar{x}],$$

so that $f \vee g$ also has the property announced in the lemma. Similarly, since $x \wedge \bar{x} = 0$,

$$f(x) \wedge g(x) = [(f(1) \wedge x) \vee (f(0) \wedge \bar{x})] \wedge [(g(1) \wedge x) \vee (g(0) \wedge \bar{x})]$$
$$= [(f(1) \wedge g(1)) \wedge x] \vee [(f(0) \wedge g(0)) \wedge \bar{x}],$$

so that $f \wedge g$ also has the same property. Since, by DeMorgan, every $f(x)$ can be built up by finitely many joins and meets from $x, \bar{x}$, and elements of B, it now follows by induction that every such function has the property stated in the lemma.

The lemma shows that *there is, in essence, just one type of Boolean function of one variable,* namely,

$$f(x) = (a \wedge x) \vee (b \wedge \bar{x}),$$

where $f(1) = a$ and $f(0) = b$.

By extending the initial identities of the proof of Lemma 1 to the n variables $x_1, x_2, \ldots, x_n$ we prove in the same way

Lemma 2:   *Every Boolean function $f(x_1, x_2, \ldots, x_n)$ may be written in the form:*

(5.5.2) $f(x_1, x_2, \ldots, x_n) = (f(1, x_2, \ldots, x_n) \wedge x_1) \vee (f(0, x_2, \ldots, x_n) \wedge \bar{x}_1).$

Next we apply Lemma 2 to the variable x_2 in each of the functions $f(1, x_2, \ldots, x_n)$ and $f(0, x_2, \ldots, x_n)$ of (5.5.2), thus obtaining the expansion

$$f(x_1, x_2, \ldots, x_n) = [f(1, 1, x_3, \ldots, x_n) \wedge x_1 \wedge x_2]$$
$$\vee [f(1, 0, x_3, \ldots, x_n) \wedge x_1 \wedge \bar{x}_2] \vee [f(0, 1, x_3, \ldots, x_n) \wedge \bar{x}_1 \wedge x_2]$$
$$\vee [f(0, 0, x_3, \ldots, x_n) \wedge \bar{x}_1 \wedge \bar{x}_2].$$

This process may be continued until all the variables have been isolated, in whatever functions they may appear, by the aid of Lemma 2. We obtain finally the join of 2^n terms:

$$f(x_1, x_2, \ldots, x_n) = [f(1, 1, \ldots, 1) \wedge x_1 \wedge x_2 \wedge \cdots \wedge x_n]$$
$$\vee [f(1, 1, \ldots, 1, 0) \wedge x_1 \wedge x_2 \wedge \cdots \wedge x_{n-1} \wedge \bar{x}_n] \vee \cdots$$
$$\vee [f(0, 0, \ldots, 0) \wedge \bar{x}_1 \wedge \bar{x}_2 \wedge \cdots \wedge \bar{x}_n].$$

The pattern here is that if x_j (or $\bar{x}_j$) appears in a meet of the n x's, then the value 1 (or 0) appears in the corresponding position in the symbol for the value of f.

Let us again define the use of exponents as follows:

$$x_j^{\,0} = \bar{x}_j, \qquad x_j^{\,1} = x_j, \qquad e_j = 0 \text{ or } 1.$$

Then each of the bracketed expressions in the above expansion may be written in the form

$$f(e_1, e_2, \ldots, e_n) \wedge x_1^{e_1} \wedge x_2^{e_2} \wedge \cdots \wedge x_n^{e_n}.$$

Thus in every Boolean algebra B we have the

Theorem: *Every Boolean function $f(x_1, x_2, \ldots, x_n)$ may be written in the* **join normal form,**

(19a) $$f(x_1, x_2, \ldots, x_n) = \bigvee_{(e)} [f(e_1, e_2, \ldots, e_n) \wedge x_1^{e_1} \wedge x_2^{e_2} \wedge \cdots \wedge x_n^{e_n}],$$

where the join extends over all combinations (e) of n zeros and ones.

By a dual sort of argument we obtain the companion

Theorem: *Every Boolean function $f(x_1, x_2, \ldots, x_n)$ may be written in the* **meet normal form,**

(19b) $$f(x_1, x_2, \ldots, x_n) = \bigwedge_{(e)} [f(\bar{e}_1, \bar{e}_2, \ldots, \bar{e}_n) \vee x_1^{e_1} \vee x_2^{e_2} \vee \cdots \vee x_n^{e_n}],$$

where the meet extends over all combinations (e) of n zeros and ones.

Applying these theorems by way of illustration to the function $f(x) = (\bar{a} \wedge x_1 \wedge x_2) \vee (b \wedge \bar{x}_3)$, we obtain, by checking all combinations of values of 0's and 1's:

$$f(x) = [\bar{a} \wedge x_1 \wedge x_2 \wedge x_3] \vee [(\bar{a} \vee b) \wedge x_1 \wedge x_2 \wedge \bar{x}_3]$$
$$\vee [b \wedge x_1 \wedge \bar{x}_2 \wedge \bar{x}_3] \vee [b \wedge \bar{x}_1 \wedge x_2 \wedge \bar{x}_3] \vee [b \wedge \bar{x}_1 \wedge \bar{x}_2 \wedge \bar{x}_3],$$

and

$$f(x) = [b \vee x_1 \vee x_2 \vee x_3] \wedge [x_1 \vee x_2 \vee \bar{x}_3] \wedge [b \vee x_1 \vee \bar{x}_2 \vee x_3]$$
$$\wedge [x_1 \vee \bar{x}_2 \vee \bar{x}_3] \wedge [b \vee \bar{x}_1 \vee x_2 \vee x_3] \wedge [\bar{x}_1 \vee x_2 \vee \bar{x}_3]$$
$$\wedge [(\bar{a} \vee b) \vee \bar{x}_1 \vee \bar{x}_2 \vee x_3] \wedge [\bar{a} \vee x_1 \vee x_2 \vee x_3].$$

Note that all eight joins $x_1^{e_1} \vee x_2^{e_2} \vee x_3^{e_3}$ appear in this latter form because the function f does not assume the value 1 for any combination of 0's and 1's.

The identities (19a) and (19b) demonstrate the useful and interesting fact that *for every Boolean algebra B, a Boolean function f of n variables*

$x_1, x_2, \ldots, x_n$ *is completely determined by the values it assumes at the* 2^n *combinations of 0's and 1's.*

For mature and extensive treatments of Boolean algebra as a branch of mathematics, the reader should consult references [1], [2].

5.6   Exercises

1.   Define $a + b = (a \wedge \bar{b}) \vee (\bar{a} \wedge b)$. Prove that the following hold for all a, b, c of B:

$$a + b = b + a,$$
$$a + (b + c) = (a + b) + c,$$
$$a \wedge (b + c) = (a \wedge b) + (a \wedge c),$$
$$(a + b) \wedge c = (a \wedge c) + (b \wedge c),$$
$$a + a = 0, \quad a + 0 = a$$
$$a + \bar{a} = 1, \quad a + 1 = \bar{a}$$
$$x + a = b \Leftrightarrow x = a + b.$$

2.   Prove that in every Boolean algebra B,

$$\overline{(a \wedge x_1) + (\bar{a} \wedge x_2)} = (a \wedge \bar{x}_1) + (\bar{a} \wedge \bar{x}_2).$$

3.   Look up the definition of a ring in a textbook of modern algebra and then show that every Boolean algebra is an idempotent ring (one in which "$a^2 = a$" for all a) with a unit. (Use the results of Exercise 1.)

4.   Expand $(a \wedge x_1) + (b \wedge x_2 \wedge x_3)$ into both the join and the meet normal forms ($n = 3$).

5.   Solve Exercises 1–4 on page 9 of reference [1]. (These exercises give brief systems of postulates for a Boolean algebra.)

6.   Go through previous chapters and determine which further theorems and identities hold in an arbitrary Boolean algebra. Can any of them be generalized in the new context?

7.   Let a, b be distinct real numbers. Define $\bar{a} = b$, $\bar{b} = a$, $a \vee b = \max(a, b)$ and $a \wedge b = \min(a, b)$. Show that with respect to these operations, the set $\{a, b\}$ is a Boolean algebra.

8.   Let D be the set of positive integral divisors of 30. Define $a \vee b = lcm(a, b)$, $a \wedge b = gcd(a, b)$ and $a = 30/a$. Show that with respect to these operations, D is a Boolean algebra. What are the meanings of $a + b$ and $a \subseteq b$ here? Can you generalize this problem?

5.7　References

1. P. R. Halmos, *Lectures on Boolean Algebra*. Princeton: Van Nostrand, 1963.

2. R. Sikorski, *Boolean Algebras* (Second Edition). Berlin: Springer-Verlag, 1964.

The Binary System of Numeration

Since the preceding chapters make a number of references to binary arithmetic, we give in this appendix a brief summary of its more important aspects for the benefit of those not familiar with it.

A1.1 The Decimal System of Numeration

The digits of a decimal integer have **place value.** Thus the decimal integer 426 stands for four *hundreds*, plus two *tens*, plus six *ones*. Since $10^2 = 100$, $10^1 = 10$, and $10^0 = 1$, we can express this compactly thus:

$$426 = 4 \times 10^2 + 2 \times 10^1 + 6 \times 10^0.$$

More generally, the positive decimal integer N, where

$$N = a_k a_{k-1} \ldots a_1 a_0, \qquad 0 \leqslant a_j \leqslant 9$$

can be written

$$N = a_k \cdot 10^k + a_{k-1} \cdot 10^{k-1} + \cdots + a_1 \cdot 10^1 + a_0 \cdot 10^0.$$

The same principle holds for decimal fractions, but negative powers of 10 are involved. Thus the decimal fraction 0.256 stands for two tenths, plus five hundredths, plus six thousandths. Since $\frac{1}{10} = 10^{-1}, \frac{1}{100} = 10^{-2}, \frac{1}{1000} = 10^{-3}$, we may write

$$0.256 = 2 \times 10^{-1} + 5 \times 10^{-2} + 6 \times 10^{-3}.$$

More generally, the decimal fraction F, where

$$F = 0 . a_{-1} a_{-2} \ldots a_{-p}, \qquad 0 \leqslant a_j \leqslant 9$$

can be written

$$F = a_{-1} \cdot 10^{-1} + a_{-2} \cdot 10^{-2} + \cdots + a_{-p} \cdot 10^{-p}$$

and hence the decimal number

$$N + F = a_k a_{k-1} \ldots a_1 a_0 \cdot a_{-1} a_{-2} \ldots a_{-p+1} a_{-p}$$

can be written

$$N + F = a_k \cdot 10^k + a_{k-1} \cdot 10^{k-1} + \cdots + a_1 \cdot 10^1 + a_0 \cdot 10^0 + a_{-1} \cdot 10^{-1}$$
$$+ \cdots + a_{-p} \cdot 10^{-p}$$

or

$$N + F = \sum_{j=-p}^{k} a_j 10^j, \qquad 0 \leqslant a_j \leqslant 9.$$

The numbers N, F, and $N + F$ are said to be expressed in terms of the *base 10* or in the **decimal system.**

A1.2   The Binary System of Numeration

Other positive integral bases than 10 are often used for the representation of numbers. The principle is the same as that illustrated in Section A1.1. The most common among these other bases is the base 2. Numbers expressed in terms of this base are said to be written in the **binary system.** In this system, 0 and 1 have the same meaning as in the decimal system. Since we are counting by 2's, the decimal number 2 will be represented by 10, which means $1 \times 2^1 + 0 \times 2^0$, that is, *one* "2" and *no* "1's." The decimal number 3 will be represented by 11, which means $1 \times 2^1 + 1 \times 2^0$, that is, *one* "2" and *one* "1." The decimal number 4 is represented by 100 in the binary system, that is, as *one* "2^2," *no* "2's," *no* "1's." For the decimal numbers 0 to 10 we have the binary representations shown in Table A1.2.1.

Table A1.2.1
Binary Equivalents of Decimal Integers

Decimal Form	Expansion in Powers of 2	Binary Form
0	0×2^0	0
1	1×2^0	1
2	$1 \times 2^1 + 0 \times 2^0$	1 0
3	$1 \times 2^1 + 1 \times 2^0$	1 1
4	$1 \times 2^2 + 0 \times 2^1 + 0 \times 2^0$	1 0 0
5	$1 \times 2^2 + 0 \times 2^1 + 1 \times 2^0$	1 0 1
6	$1 \times 2^2 + 1 \times 2^1 + 0 \times 2^0$	1 1 0
7	$1 \times 2^2 + 1 \times 2^1 + 1 \times 2^0$	1 1 1
8	$1 \times 2^3 + 0 \times 2^2 + 0 \times 2^1 + 0 \times 2^0$	1 0 0 0
9	$1 \times 2^3 + 0 \times 2^2 + 0 \times 2^1 + 1 \times 2^0$	1 0 0 1
10	$1 \times 2^3 + 0 \times 2^2 + 1 \times 2^1 + 0 \times 2^0$	1 0 1 0

The reader would do well to continue the table up to the decimal integer 20, say.

For fractions a similar principle holds. The decimal fraction $\frac{1}{2}$ is written .1 in binary form, which means 1×2^{-1}. The decimal fraction $\frac{1}{4}$ is .01 in binary form, which means 1×2^{-2}. The fraction $\frac{3}{4} = \frac{1}{2} + \frac{1}{4}$ is written .11, which means $1 \times 2^{-1} + 1 \times 2^{-2}$. The binary equivalents for eighths are shown in Table A1.2.2. The reader should construct a table for sixteenths and possibly also thirtyseconds.

Table A1.2.2

Decimal Form	*Expansion in Powers of 2*	*Binary Form*
$\frac{1}{8}$	$0 \times 2^{-1} + 0 \times 2^{-2} + 1 \times 2^{-3}$	.001
$\frac{1}{4}$	$0 \times 2^{-1} + 1 \times 2^{-2} + 0 \times 2^{-3}$	.010
$\frac{3}{8}$	$0 \times 2^{-1} + 1 \times 2^{-2} + 1 \times 2^{-3}$	.011
$\frac{1}{2}$	$1 \times 2^{-1} + 0 \times 2^{-2} + 0 \times 2^{-3}$	.100
$\frac{5}{8}$	$1 \times 2^{-1} + 0 \times 2^{-2} + 1 \times 2^{-3}$	.101
$\frac{3}{4}$	$1 \times 2^{-1} + 1 \times 2^{-2} + 0 \times 2^{-3}$	.110
$\frac{7}{8}$	$1 \times 2^{-1} + 1 \times 2^{-2} + 1 \times 2^{-3}$	.111

A1.3   Binary Arithmetic

Binary arithmetic is particularly simple because the addition, subtraction, and multiplication facts are so few:

$$0 + 0 = 0, \quad 0 + 1 = 1 + 0 = 1, \quad 1 + 1 = 10$$
$$0 - 0 = 1 - 1 = 0, \quad 1 - 0 = 1, \quad 10 - 1 = 1$$
$$0 \cdot 0 = 0 \cdot 1 = 1 \cdot 0 = 0, \quad 1 \cdot 1 = 1$$

We illustrate addition with an example. The mechanism is entirely analogous to that of the decimal system:

$$
\begin{array}{ccccccc}
 & & & & & & \text{carries} \\
1\,0_1 & 1_1 & 1_0 & 1_1 & 1\overset{\longleftarrow}{}1 & & 55 \\
1 & 0 & 0 & 0 & 1 & & 17 \\
(+)\quad 1 & 1 & 0 & 1 & 0 & & 26 \\
\hline
1\ 1 & 0 & 0 & 0\ 1 & 0 & & 98 \\
\end{array}
$$

Check: $64 + 32 + 2 = 98$

Note that carries are made exactly as in ordinary arithmetic. In the fifth column from the right, the sum of the four 1's is 100 so that the carry is 10 and the 1 of this carry falls in a new column.

Binary subtraction may be performed as in ordinary arithmetic, the borrowing process being fundamentally the same:

$$\begin{array}{l} \quad\quad\quad\quad\quad\quad \longleftarrow \text{borrows} \\ \quad 1\ {}^{0}\not{1}\ {}^{1}0\ 1\ 1\ 1 \quad \text{minuend M} \\ (-)\quad 1\ \ 1\ 0\ 1\ 1 \quad \text{subtrahend S} \\ \hline \\ \quad\quad 1\ \ 1\ 1\ 0\ 0 \quad \text{difference D} \end{array}$$

Here we borrow 1 from the fifth column from the right to make subtraction possible in the fourth column. This leaves 10 in columns six and five. Since $10 - 1 = 1$, the difference has 1's in columns five and four.

The borrowing process may be avoided completely by using the fact that

$$D = M - S = M + (P - S) - P$$

and letting $P = 2^n_{\text{dec}}$, where n is the number of digits in the minuend M, that is, $P = 100\ldots 0_{\text{bin}}$, namely a 1 followed by n zeros. First we form $P - S$ in a mechanical way and *add* it to M. Finally we subtract P by dropping the leftmost 1 of the sum.

The number $P - S$ is called the **two's complement** of S. We illustrate its computation by several examples. In these examples we first separate P into two parts so that the subtraction can be accomplished without borrowing.

$$\begin{array}{ll} n = 6: & P = 1\ 0\ 0\ 0\ 0\ 0 = 1\ 1\ 1\ 1\ 1\ 1 + 1 \\ & S = \quad\quad\quad\quad\quad\quad\quad 0\ 1\ 1\ 0\ 1\ 1 \\ & \overline{} \\ & P - S = \quad\quad\quad\quad\quad 1\ 0\ 0\ 1\ 0\ 0 + 1 = 1\ 0\ 0\ 1\ 0\ 1 \\ n = 4: & P = 1\ 0\ 0\ 0\ 0 = 1\ 1\ 1\ 1 + 1 \\ & S = \quad\quad\quad\quad\quad 1\ 1\ 0\ 0 \\ & \overline{} \\ & P - S = \quad\quad\quad\quad 0\ 0\ 1\ 1 + 1 = 0\ 1\ 0\ 0 \end{array}$$

These examples suggest the following rule for forming $P - S$:

1. Make sure S contains n digits by supplying as many zeros on the left as may be necessary.
2. Subtract each digit of S from 1.
3. Add 1 to the difference.

For example, if $n = 8$, the two's complement of 0 1 1 0 1 1 1 0 is 1 0 0 1 0 0 0 1 + 1 = 1 0 0 1 0 0 1 0.

Now we compare examples of a subtraction, using both schemes.

$$1\ 0\ 1\ 1\ 1\ 1\ 0\ 1 - 0\ 1\ 1\ 0\ 1\ 1\ 1\ 0$$

Regular Subtraction:

```
  1 0 1 ⁰1̸ ¹⁰1̸ ¹⁰1̸ ¹0̸ 1
(−)  1 1 0  1   1   1 0
  ─────────────────────
    1 0 0  1   1 1 1
```

Subtraction Using Two's Complement:

```
    1 0 1 1 1 1 0 1
(+) 1 0 0 1 0 0 1 0
    ─────────────────
  1̸ 0 1 0 0 1 1 1 1
```

The results are of course equal but the two's complement procedure is much simpler, especially for a computer.

Binary multiplication offers no difficulties at all since the procedure is formally the same as in decimal multiplication. We illustrate with two examples. The second shows how to handle terminal zeros in the multiplier.

```
        1 1 1 0 1                    1 1 1 0 1
          1 0 0 1                      1 0 1 0 0
      ─────────────                ─────────────
        1 1 1 0 1                  1 1 1 0 1 0 0
    1 1 1 0 1                      1 1 1 0 1
  ─────────────────            ─────────────────
  1 0 0 0 0 0 1 0 1            1 0 0 1 0 0 0 1 0 0
```

The following example illustrates how a computer multiplies by repeated shifting and adding:

```
      1 1 0 1 1 0 1 ← multiplicand "m"
        1 1 1 0 1 ← multiplier
    ─────────────────
      1 1 0 1 1 0 1 ← m
  1 1 0 1 1 0 1       ← shift m left two places
  ───────────────────
  1 0 0 0 1 0 0 0 0 1 ← sum = first partial product
  1 1 0 1 1 0 1       ← shift m left one place
  ─────────────────────
1 0 1 1 0 0 0 1 0 0 1 ← sum = second partial product
1 1 0 1 1 0 1         ← shift m left one place
─────────────────────
1 1 0 0 0 1 0 1 1 0 0 1 ← sum = completed product
```

Finally, we illustrate binary division with a single example. The principles here, too, are exactly the same as in decimal division.

```
                          1 1 0 1.1
              ┌─────────────────────────
  1 1 0 1 0 │ 1 0 1 0 1 1 1 1 1.0
              1 1 0 1 0
            ───────────
              1 0 0 0 1 1
                1 1 0 1 0
              ───────────
                1 0 0 1 1 1
                  1 1 0 1 0
                ───────────
                  1 1 0 1 0
                  1 1 0 1 0
```

It does not take much practice to develop facility in the binary operations.

A1.4   Conversion from Binary to Decimal Form

To convert a binary integer into decimal form is not difficult. For example,

$$1\ 1\ 0\ 1\ 0\ 1\ 1_{\text{bin}} = 1 \times 2^6 + 1 \times 2^5 + 0 \times 2^4 + 1 \times 2^3 + 0 \times 2^2 + 1 \times 2^1$$
$$+ 1 \times 2^0$$
$$= 64 + 32 + 8 + 2 + 1 = 107_{\text{dec}}.$$

We simply write the expansion of the binary integer in powers of 2, then expand and collect in the decimal system.

To convert a binary fraction into decimal form, we can proceed in the same way, doing all the arithmetic in the decimal system. For example,

$$0.1\ 1\ 0\ 1_{\text{bin}} = \tfrac{1}{2} + \tfrac{1}{4} + \tfrac{1}{16} = 0.5 + 0.25 + 0.0625 = 0.8125_{\text{dec}}.$$

We can also effect this transformation by doing the arithmetic in the binary system. To see how, let an arbitrary positive number $N < 1$ be represented thus:

$$N = (0.d_{-1}d_{-2}\ldots d_{-q}\ldots)_{\text{dec}} = (0.a_{-1}a_{-2}\ldots a_{-p}\ldots)_{\text{bin}}$$

that is,

$$(d_{-1}10^{-1} + d_{-2}10^{-2} + \cdots + d_{-q}10^{-q} + \cdots)_{\text{dec}} = (0.a_{-1}a_{-2}\ldots a_{-p}\ldots)_{\text{bin}}.$$

Since

$$10_{\text{dec}} = 1010_{\text{bin}}$$

we have

$$10_{\text{dec}} \cdot (d_{-1}\ 10^{-1} + d_{-2}\ 10^{-2} + \cdots + d_{-q}\ 10^{-q} + \cdots)_{\text{dec}}$$
$$= (d_{-1} + d_{-2}10^{-1} + \cdots + d_{-q}10^{-q+1} + \cdots)_{\text{dec}}$$
$$= 1\ 0\ 1\ 0_{\text{bin}} \cdot (0.a_{-1}a_{-2}\ldots a_{-p}) + \cdots)_{\text{bin}}$$

Now the whole number parts of these last two expressions must be equal and their fractional parts must also be equal. Hence $(d_{-1})_{\text{dec}} =$ (integer part of right member)$_{\text{bin}}$ and when we transform this integer part of the right member from base 2 to base 10, we obtain $(d_{-1})_{\text{dec}}$. Suppose there remains on the right the binary fraction $0.b_{-1}b_{-2}\ldots b_{-r}\ldots$. Then we must have, as remarked above,

$$(d_{-2}10^{-1} + \cdots + d_{-q}10^{-q+1} + \cdots)_{\text{dec}} = (0.b_{-1}b_{-2}\ldots b_{-r}\ldots)_{\text{bin}}.$$

Now we find $(d_{-2})_{\text{dec}}$ by repeating the above process, and so on. For example, to transform $0.\ 1\ 1\ 0\ 1_{\text{bin}}$ into decimal form, we arrange the work as shown in Table A1.4.1. The tabular form shows that $0.\ 1101_{\text{bin}} = 0.8125_{\text{dec}}$.

Table A1.4.1
Example of Decimal to Binary Conversion

```
                        0. 1 1 0 1
                           1 0 1 0
                        ─────────────
                           1 1 0 1 0
                        1 1 0 1
                        ─────────────
d₋₁ = 8                 1 0 0 0. 0 0 1 0
                             1 0 1 0
                        ─────────────
                           0 0 1 0 0
                         0 0 1 0
                        ─────────────
d₋₂ = 1                 0 0 1. 0 1 0 0
                             1 0 1 0
                        ─────────────
                           0 1 0 0 0
                         0 1 0 0
                        ─────────────
d₋₃ = 2                 0 1 0. 1 0 0 0
                             1 0 1 0
                        ─────────────
                           1 0 0 0 0
                         1 0 0 0
                        ─────────────
d₋₄ = 5                 1 0 1. 0 0 0 0
```

A1.5   Conversion from Decimal to Binary Form

Suppose it is required to convert a decimal integer N into binary form. If we divide N by 2 in the decimal system, and obtain a quotient N_1 and a remainder r_1, we may write

$$N = 2 \cdot N_1 + r_1, \qquad r_1 = 0 \text{ or } 1.$$

Next we divide the quotient N_1 by 2. Assume the new quotient is N_2 and the new remainder r_2. Then

$$N_1 = 2 \cdot N_2 + r_2, \qquad r_2 = 0 \text{ or } 1,$$

so that

$$N = 2(2N_2 + r_2) + r_1 = 2^2 N_2 + r_2 \cdot 2^1 + r_1 \cdot 2^0.$$

If next

$$N_2 = 2N_3 + r_3,$$

we have

$$N = 2^3 N_3 + r_3 \cdot 2^2 + r_2 \cdot 2^1 + r_1 \cdot 2^0.$$

Continuing thus, since $N > N_1 > N_2 > N_3,\ldots$, we must eventually obtain a quotient $N_k = 1$ and a remainder r_k, which is 0 or 1. Then

$$N = 1 \cdot 2^k + r_k \cdot 2^{k-1} + \cdots + r_3 \cdot 2^2 + r_2 \cdot 2^1 + r_1 \cdot 2^0$$

That is, we convert from base 10 to base 2 by repeated divisions by 2. The remainders and the final quotient 1 give us, in order of increasing significance, the binary digits of N. As an example, let us convert 565_{dec} to binary form.

$$
\begin{array}{rll}
2 & \underline{|5\ 6\ 5} & \text{rem.} \\
2 & \underline{|2\ 8\ 2} & -\ 1 \\
2 & \underline{|1\ 4\ 1} & -\ 0 \\
2 & \underline{|7\ 0} & -\ 1 \\
2 & \underline{|3\ 5} & -\ 0 \\
2 & \underline{|1\ 7} & -\ 1 \\
2 & \underline{|8} & -\ 1 \\
2 & \underline{|4} & -\ 0 \\
2 & \underline{|2} & -\ 0 \\
2 & \underline{|1} & -\ 0 \\
& 0 & -\ 1
\end{array}
$$

Hence $565_{dec} = 1000110101_{bin}$.

Every positive decimal fraction $F < 1$ may be transformed into binary notation by repeated multiplication by 2. To see this, we write

$$F_{dec} = a_{-1} \cdot \frac{1}{2} + a_{-2} \cdot \frac{1}{2^2} + a_{-3} \cdot \frac{1}{2^3} + \cdots_{dec},$$

where each a_{-j} is 0 or 1. If we multiply this by 2, we obtain

$$2F_{dec} = a_{-1} + a_{-2} \cdot \frac{1}{2} + a_{-3} \cdot \frac{1}{2^2} + \cdots_{dec}.$$

The integer parts of these two expressions must be equal. Hence the integer part of $2F$, which must be either 0 or 1 since $0 < F < 1$, is simply a_{-1}. Thus $2F = a_{-1} + F_1$ where $0 \leqslant F_1 < 1$ and where

$$F_1 = a_{-2} \cdot \frac{1}{2} + a_{-3} \cdot \frac{1}{2^2} + \cdots.$$

To find a_{-2} we now repeat the process, and so on. This is illustrated in the following example in which we transform 0.8965_{dec} into binary form.

Table A1.5.1

Example of Decimal to Binary Conversion

$$0.\ 8\ 9\ 6\ 5$$
$$2$$

$a_{-1} = 1$ $\quad 1 | .\ 7\ 9\ 3\ 0$
$$2$$

$a_{-2} = 1$ $\quad 1 | .\ 5\ 8\ 6\ 0$
$$2$$

$a_{-3} = 1$ $\quad 1 | .\ 1\ 7\ 2\ 0$
$$2$$

$a_{-4} = 0$ $\quad 0 | .\ 3\ 4\ 4\ 0$
$$2$$

$a_{-5} = 0$ $\quad 0 | .\ 6\ 8\ 8\ 0$
$$2$$

$a_{-6} = 1$ $\quad 1 | .\ 3\ 7\ 6\ 0$
$$2$$

$a_{-7} = 0$ $\quad 0 | .\ 7\ 5\ 2\ 0$
$$2$$

$a_{-8} = 1$ $\quad 1 | .\ 5\ 0\ 4\ 0$
$$2$$

$a_{-9} = 1$ $\quad 1 | .\ 0\ 0\ 8\ 0$

Etc.

There now follows a long sequence of zeros. Correct to nine binary places, we then have

$$0.8965_{\text{dec}} = 0.111001011_{\text{bin}}.$$

Combining results of the last two examples, we have, to nine binary places,

$$565.8965_{\text{dec}} = 1000110101.111001011_{\text{bin}}.$$

The reader should prepare, solve, and check a variety of further examples. Work done in one system can be checked in the other. It is also a simple matter to extend these techniques to other bases.

Semiconductor Logic Elements

A2.1 Basic Assumptions

The following list of informally stated working assumptions concerning electrical circuits is for the person who is not an engineer but who may wish to develop some feeling for how logic elements function physically.

1. Voltage measures the ability of a source of electrical energy to drive an electrical current.
2. In any electric circuit, current always flows from a point at a higher voltage to one at a lower voltage when there exists a conducting path from the first point to the second.
3. Other conditions remaining fixed, the current flowing through a given path increases with the voltage difference between the ends of the path.
4. A resistor is a device that impedes the flow of electrical current. In so doing, it converts some of the electrical energy passing through it into heat energy. A simple example is the heating element of an electric stove.
5. The voltage V (measured in volts) between the two terminals of a resistor (represented by the symbol —/\/\/\/\— in circuit diagrams) is given by the equation $V = IR$ where I is the current (measured in amperes) through the resistor and R is the resistance (measured in ohms) of the resistive device. The current enters the resistor at the terminal which is at the higher voltage.

Often voltages and currents are very small compared with the standard units (volt and ampere). Hence the symbols *mv* and *ma*, for millivolts and milliamperes, are useful: 1,000 mv = 1 volt; 1,000 ma = 1 ampere. Resistances, on the other hand, are commonly very large. The following notations are therefore useful: 1 ohm = 1Ω, 1,000Ω = 1K, 1,000,000Ω = 1 Megohm = 1 Meg. Thus 5.2K stands for a resistance of 5,200Ω, for example.

6. All connecting wires (called *leads* since they lead the current from one terminal to another) are assumed to have zero resistance. Thus the voltage difference between any two points on the same lead is assumed to be zero since nothing to impede the flow of current lies between them. This is, of course, not strictly true under most circumstances, but it is not an impractical assumption. The voltage difference between any two points of a conducting path in a circuit will also be zero if no current is flowing from one to the other: $V = I \cdot R = 0 \cdot R = 0$ in this case.

A2.2   The Semiconductor Diode

One of the simplest devices employed in the design of logic circuits is the **semiconductor diode.** One form of diode consists of a crystal of one of the semiconducting elements germanium or silicon in contact with a gold "cat's whisker" (Figure A2.2.1).

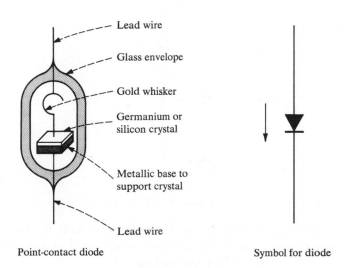

Lead wire

Glass envelope

Gold whisker

Germanium or
silicon crystal

Metallic base to
support crystal

Lead wire

Point-contact diode   Symbol for diode

Diode and symbol for diode
Figure A2.2.1

The characteristic property of the semiconductor diode is that it conducts current relatively freely in the direction indicated by the arrow (resistance as low as 1 to 500 ohms) and almost not at all in the other direction (resistance as high as 100,000 to 1,000,000 ohms). The whole device is only about $\frac{1}{4}$ inch long and $\frac{1}{10}$ inch in diameter.

An *ideal* semiconductor diode offers no resistance to the flow of current in the *forward* direction (indicated by the arrow in Figure A2.2.1), but it offers infinite resistance to the flow of current in the *back* direction. That is, the forward resistance, denoted by R_f, is 0 and the back resistance, denoted by R_b, is ∞. The assumption that $R_b = \infty$ is equivalent to the assumption that current in the back direction is always zero.

This idealization of the physical properties of a diode is very convenient for the purpose of designing logic circuits, just as the idealized concept of a relay was useful in Chapter 1. In any given case, the fact that a diode is *not* an ideal device must ultimately be recognized and dealt with, if necessary, in appropriate ways. These engineering details need not concern us here.

A2.3   A Diode AND- Element

Now assume that the truth value 1 of a proposition is represented by a suitably high voltage on a lead and that the truth value 0 is represented by a relatively low voltage. Then Figure A2.3.1 shows what is called a **diode AND-element.**

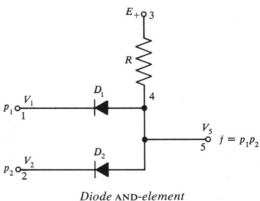

Diode AND-*element*
Figure A2.3.1

In this circuit, assume that point 3 is constantly held at a high voltage E_+, and that points 1 and 2 are normally maintained at a suitable fixed voltage $V_0 < E_+$. Then when the voltage at either of these points is increased to a sufficient extent above V_0, we say there is a *signal present* on the corresponding lead or that the lead is *activated*.

The resistance R in the circuit is made large enough so that any current flowing from point 3 to point 4 is appropriately small (measured in *ma*).

Now consider the following cases:

Case 1:   Neither Input Lead Activated.   Assume points 1 and 2 are maintained at voltage V_0, that is, $V_1 = V_2 = V_0$, so that a small current flows from point 3 via 4 to 1 and 2.

The diodes offer no resistance to current flow from 4 to 1 and 2 so that there is no voltage difference between 4 (*i.e.*, 5) and 1 or 2. Thus $V_5 = V_0$ also.

Case 2:   One Input Lead Activated at Voltage $P \leqslant E_+$. Assume point 1 is maintained at a voltage P, $E_+ \geqslant P = V_1 > V_0$, while at point 2, $V_2 = V_0$.

The diode D_2 provides a resistance-free path from 4 to 2, so there is no voltage difference across it and V_5 is therefore also equal to V_0.

No current flows from 1 to 4, even though P is greater than the voltage V_0 at 4 because the diode D_1 blocks the path.

Similar conclusions apply if the roles of points 1 and 2 are interchanged.

Case 3:   Both Input Leads Activated at Same Voltage $P \leqslant E_+$. Assume points 1 and 2 maintained at the voltage P: $V_1 = V_2 = P$, $E_+ \geqslant P > V_0$. The diodes offer no resistance to the flow of current from 4 to 1 and 2. Hence there is no voltage difference across either diode, so that $V_5 = P$ also.

Case 4:   Both Input Leads Activated But at Unequal Voltages $\leqslant E_+$. Assume $V_1 = P_1$, $V_2 = P_2$, $E_+ \geqslant P_1 > P_2 > V_0$. This is the same as Case 2 with the voltage V_0 replaced by P_2. Now $V_5 = P_2$ and there is no current from 1 to 4 because of the blocking effect of D_1. Current does flow from 3 to 4 to 2 since $P_2 < E_+$.

The input leads are never activated at voltages higher than E_+.

It may now be observed that, in every case, $V_5 = \min [V_1, V_2]$. Hence the voltage V_5 is high relative to V_0 if and only if V_1 and V_2 are both high relative to V_0. If f denotes the truth value of the proposition "the voltage on the output lead is high" and if p_1 and p_2 denote truth values of similar propositions relating to the two input leads, then $f = p_1 p_2$. This explains why the circuit may be used to realize the AND-operation and is called an AND-element.

The high voltage signals on the p_1 and p_2 leads often appear in the form of pulses, that is, temporary rises of voltage to a fixed signal level P, which is the same for both leads and which is less than E_+. Then there is an output pulse on the f-lead if and only if there is an input pulse on each of the p_1 and p_2 leads.

Suppose now that the inputs and outputs of an AND-element are read (observed) only at times 0, 1, 2,..., which are determined by some sort

of clocking device. Then an example of sequences of input signals and
the corresponding output signals may be represented by the graph in
Fig. A2.3.2. Here the input voltages V_1 and V_2 are assumed given and
the output voltage V_5 is found from the rule, $V_5 = \min [V_1, V_2]$. The vertical lines represent the reading times and the logical (Boolean) equivalents
of the inputs are written below the voltage axes.

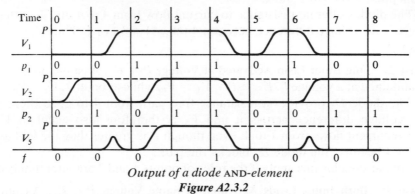

Output of a diode AND-*element*

Figure A2.3.2

The curves are intended to show that the voltages rise and fall sharply
but not instantaneously. This causes no difficulty if the reading times are
properly spaced.

The small rises in the output voltage V_5 occur between reading times
and hence are not interpreted as the signal " 1."

A2.4   A Diode OR -Element

Assume again that a high voltage represents truth value 1 and that a low
voltage represents truth value 0. Then Figure A2.4.1 represents a **diode
OR-element.**

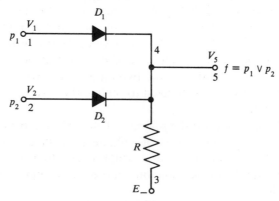

Diode OR-*element*

Figure A2.4.1

Here we assume point 3 is maintained constantly at a (relatively) low voltage E_- and that points 1 and 2 are normally at a voltage $V_0 \geqslant E_-$. Again, if either lead is at a voltage high relative to V_0, or if a pulse of high voltage is present on a lead, we say that a signal is present on the lead or that the lead is activated. There are the following cases to consider:

Case 1:   Neither Input Lead Activated. In this case point 5 is also at voltage V_0 and there is a small current flowing from points 1 and 2 to point 3 , the only voltage difference being across R.

Case 2:   One Input Lead Activated at Voltage $P > V_0$. Assume $V_1 = P > V_0$. Then point 4, and hence point 5 also, is at the voltage P since D_1 has 0 forward resistance.

No current flows from point 1 to point 2 because of the back resistance of the diode D_2.

Case 3:   Both Input Leads Activated at Same Voltage $P > V_0$. Assume now that points 1 and 2 are maintained at a common voltage P: $V_1 = V_2 = P > V_0$.

There is no voltage difference across either diode, so $V_5 = P$.

The voltage difference across R results in a current from 1 and 2 to 3.

Case 4:   Both Input Leads Activated But at Unequal Voltages. Assume $V_1 = P_1$, $V_2 = P_2$, $P_1 > P_2 > V_0$. This is the same as Case 2 with V_0 replaced by P_2. Current flows from 1 to 3 but not from 1 to 2 because of the back resistance of D_2. Since there is no voltage difference across D_1, the voltage at 4 and 5 is P_1.

In every case, $V_5 = \max [V_1, V_2]$. Thus the voltage V_5 is high relative to V_0 if either V_1 or V_2 is high or if both are high. Letting f, p_1, p_2 denote the truth values of the propositions that the corresponding leads carry high voltages, we then have $f = p_1 \vee p_2$. This explains why the circuit is called an OR-element.

As in the case of the AND-element, assume that the input and output signals of an OR-element are read only at times 0, 1, 2,.... If sequences of input voltages V_1 and V_2 are given, then an output voltage graph may be constructed by the rule $V_5 = \max [V_1, V_2]$. An example, showing the logical values as well as the actual voltages, is given in Figure A2.4.2. The reader should check the details with care.

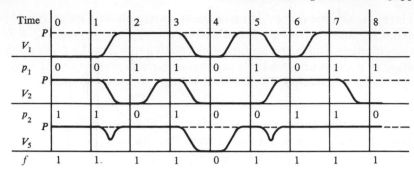

Output of a diode OR-*element*
Figure A2.4.2

A2.5 An Alternative Procedure: Negative Logic

It is often convenient to use what is called **negative logic:** a low voltage represents truth value 1, the truth value 0 being represented by a normally high voltage. It is not hard to show that in the case of negative logic, the above AND-element becomes an OR-element, and vice versa. The details are left to the reader.

It is also possible to use a **mixed logic,** letting a high voltage denote 1 at certain terminals, 0 at others.

A2.6 Multiple Input Elements

A diode element may have more than two input leads, as is shown in Figure A2.6.1.

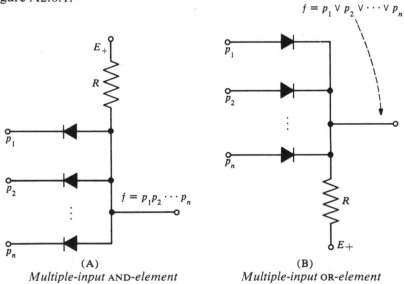

(A)   (B)
Multiple-input AND-*element*   *Multiple-input* OR-*element*
Multiple-input diode logic elements
Figure A2.6.1

The analysis of the behavior in these two cases is essentially the same as that given for the two-input case.

A2.7   Some Simple Diode Circuits

We shall assume for the purpose of these examples that the device which generates a given input signal p also generates its complement $\bar{p}$. Some simple examples of diode circuits are shown in Figure A2.7.1. Notice that factoring saves diodes here just as it saves contacts when one is using relays.

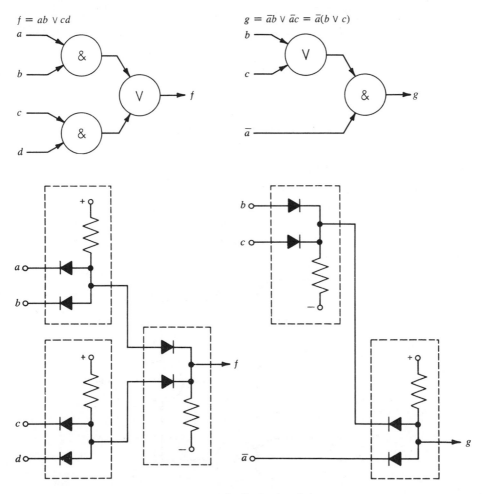

Some simple diode circuits
Figure A2.7.1

The given two circuits are called **two-stage circuits** because some signals must travel through two diodes but none must travel through more. Every logical function *f* which is written as a union of products can be realized as a two-stage diode circuit: one multiple-input AND-element for each product in *f*, the outputs of these AND-elements then being used as inputs of a single, multiple-input OR-element. If *f* is factored into a product of unions, it may be realized by a set of multiple-input OR-elements whose outputs form the inputs of a single, multiple-input AND-element, which again yields a two-stage circuit.

An example of a three-stage realization of a function is shown in Figure A2.7.2. This circuit requires only eight diodes. The two-stage realization requires nine (Figure A2.7.3).

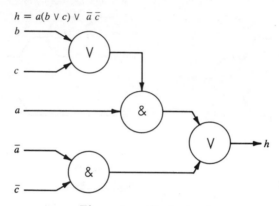

$$h = a(b \lor c) \lor \bar{a}\,\bar{c}$$

Three-stage diode circuit
Figure A2.7.2

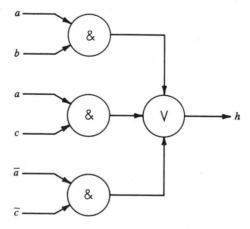

Equivalent two-stage diode circuit
Figure A2.7.3

Since the difficulties arising from the fact that diodes do not in fact
have the ideal character ascribed to them increase with the number of
stages, it may at times be desirable to employ a less economical circuit
(in terms of the number of diodes) in order to reduce the number of stages.

A2.8   The Transistor

It is possible to grow crystals of almost perfectly pure germanium
metal but such "intrinsic" germanium, as it is called, is less useful than
crystals into which small, precisely controlled amounts of impurities have
been introduced. Two types of crystal are commonly made, the "*p*-type"
and the "*n*-type." The *p*-type contains a larger number of positive charge
carriers (called "holes"), and the *n*-type contains a larger number of
negative charge carriers (electrons) than does intrinsic germanium.

When a slice of *p*-type crystal and a slice of *n*-type crystal are perfectly
joined together (which is not a trivial matter) and leads are attached
(Figure A2.8.1) a ***p-n* junction diode** results. A peculiarity of the *p-n*

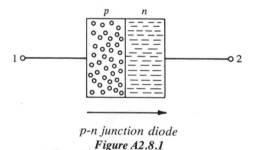

p-n junction diode
Figure A2.8.1

junction diode is that, because of the chemical properties of the types of
germanium, there is a built-in electrostatic potential difference between
terminals 1 and 2 (see figure). This electrostatic potential difference,
although it is not responsible for external current flow, tends to force
the holes to stay in the *p*-type crystal. However, when an external voltage
is applied so as to make terminal 1 sufficiently more positive than terminal
2, this built-in barrier is reduced and positive charge-carrying holes move
into the *n*-type crystal, causing current to flow. On the other hand, applying a voltage so as to make terminal 2 more positive than terminal 1
simply adds to the built-in electrostatic potential barrier, thereby re-
inforcing the isolation of holes from electrons and preventing current from
flowing. Thus we see that the *p-n* junction behaves exactly like the diode
described above. This junction diode may therefore be represented by
the usual symbol for a diode (Figure A2.8.2). We shall assume that the
junction diode is an ideal diode.

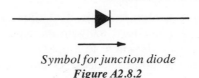

Symbol for junction diode
Figure A2.8.2

When a *p-n-p* junction is formed and leads are attached as shown in Figure A2.8.3, the result is called a ***p-n-p* junction transistor.** The three

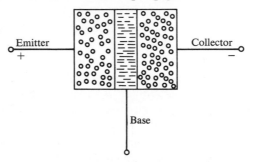

Base

p-n-p junction transistor
Figure A2.8.3

leads are labeled **emitter, collector,** and **base,** which are the names of the parts of the transistor to which these leads are connected. Note that the emitter is shown as being normally held at a high voltage and that the collector is shown as being normally held at a low voltage.

A standard symbol for the *p-n-p* junction transistor is shown in Figure A2.8.4. The arrowhead on the emitter is intended to suggest the fact that the emitter and base together constitute a junction diode as well as to indicate direction of current flow.

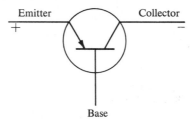

Base

Symbol for p-n-p junction transistor
Figure A2.8.4

From the switching point of view, the important property of a transistor is the fact that when a voltage difference is applied to emitter and collector as shown, then if the base is held at a *high* voltage, the emitter-base diode is blocked to the flow of current. That is, the ability of the emitter to inject positive charges into the base is inhibited so that very little current can flow through the transistor to either base or collector. However, when the base is held at a *low* voltage, the emitter-base diode conducts, the emitter injects positive charges freely into the base, and most of these positive charges diffuse over to, and are carried away by, the collector. Only *a very small* current flows in the emitter-base circuit, but a relatively large current flows from emitter to collector. Such a control of a large current by a small current is called **current amplification.**

In summary, from the switching point of view, when the base voltage is *high* the transistor is OFF and when it is *low*, the transistor is ON. We shall assume that the transistor too is an ideal element, for the purposes of this discussion.

The detailed physical explanation of why the transistor works this way is more involved than is appropriate for these pages, nor is it necessary for the understanding of the switching applications of the device.

A2.9 The Transistor NOT-Element

Consider the circuit shown in Figure A2.9.1. Here if the lead labeled x is at a *high* voltage, namely E_+ or higher, the transistor does not conduct, and the *low* voltage at C is felt at B, for since no current flows through the resistance R, there is no voltage drop across it from B to C. However, if x is *low* relative to E_+, current flows in the path A-B-C through R and hence there is a voltage drop across R. Thus B is at a high voltage relative to the *fixed* negative voltage E_- at C.

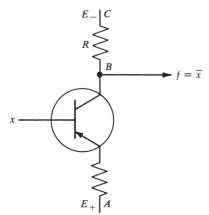

Transistor NOT-*element*
Figure A2.9.1

Thus the transistor performs as an inverter or NOT-element: when x is high, f is low, and when x is low, f is high. If we denote a low voltage by 0 and a high voltage by 1, then when $x = 0$, $f = 1$ and when $x = 1$, $f = 0$. Thus $f = \bar{x}$.

A2.10 Transistor AND- and Stroke-Elements

For the purposes of this section, we assume a "positive" logic: "high" corresponds to 1 and "low" corresponds to 0. The reader would do well to analyze each circuit shown, in terms of negative logic.

Consider first the circuit shown in Figure A2.10.1. Here if either the x or the y voltage is *low* relative to E_+, the corresponding transistor

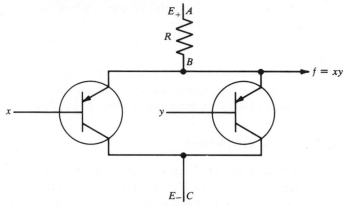

Transistor AND-*element*
Figure A2.10.1

conducts and there is a voltage drop across R, so that point B is at a *low* voltage with respect to the fixed positive voltage at A. Only when the x and y leads are both at *high* voltages, namely voltages $\geq E_+$, will the current be cut off so that there is no voltage drop across R and hence B is at the same *high* voltage E_+ as A. That is, $f = 1$ if and only if $x = y = 1$, so $f = xy$.

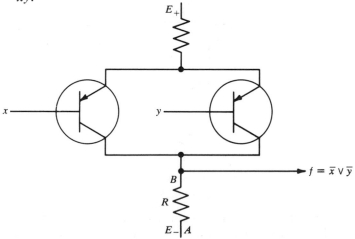

Transistor stroke-element
Figure A2.10.2

A related circuit is shown in Figure A2.102.

Here if the x lead or the y lead is at a *low* voltage relative to E_+, the corresponding transistor conducts, there is a voltage drop across R, and hence point B is at a *high* voltage relative to the fixed negative voltage at A. On the other hand, if both x and y are at *high* voltages, that is, voltages $\geq E_+$, no current flows, there is no voltage drop across R, and hence the *low* voltage E_- at A is felt at B. The truth table is therefore the following:

x	y	f
0	0	1
0	1	1
1	0	1
1	1	0

Thus

$$f = \bar{x} \lor \bar{y}.$$

That is, we have here a transistor element that realizes the Scheffer stroke function. Since every logical function can be realized by means of the Scheffer stroke function alone, this element would theoretically suffice for all logical circuitry.

By connecting more transistors in the same way into the circuits of Figures A2.10.1 and A2.10.2, we could obtain a multiple-input AND-element and a generalized Scheffer stroke element. Transistors connected in this way are said to be connected in *parallel*. The generalized stroke element is shown in Figure A2. 10.3.

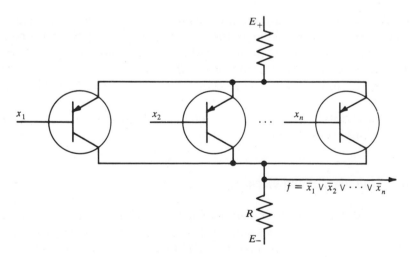

Generalized stroke-element
Figure A2.10.3

A2.11   Transistor OR-Element

There are other ways of operating a transistor than by regulating the base voltage. One can hold the base voltage fixed, for example, and regulate the emitter voltage instead, thus obtaining the same relative effect. In Figure A2.11.1, there appears an OR-element designed in this way.

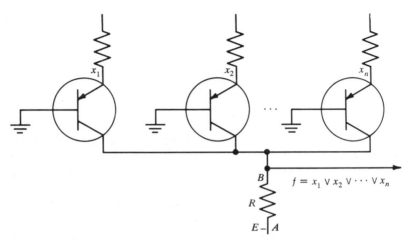

Multiple-input transistor OR-element
Figure A2.11.1

In this case the bases are all connected to ground. If any x is "high" relative to ground, current flows through R so that point B is at a high voltage relative to the fixed negative voltage at A. If *no* x is high relative to ground, no current flows, and hence B is at the same voltage as A; that is, B is "low." Thus $f = x_1 \lor x_2 \lor \cdots \lor x_n$ is the function here realized.

Other methods of connecting and operating transistors are explained in the standard books on transistor circuits.

A2.12   Transistor-Diode Circuits

At times, different types of switching devices are employed in the same circuit. This is of course possible only when the operating voltages and speeds of operation are compatible. An example is the use of diodes and transistors to realize NAND- and NOR-elements as is shown in Figure A2.12.1.

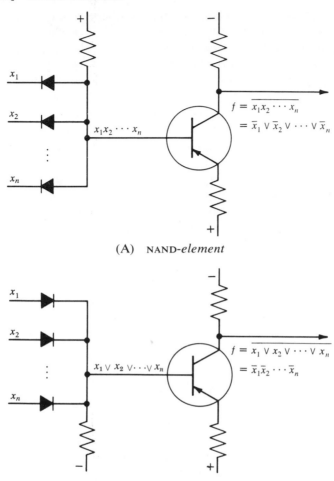

(A)   NAND-*element*

(B)   NOR-*element*

Construction of transistor NAND- *and* NOR-*elements*
Figure A2.12.1

Since the connective $x_1 \| x_2 = \bar{x}_1 \bar{x}_2$ (the double stroke) is sufficient to generate all other connectives, the NOR-element would also suffice for the construction of all logical circuits.

A2.13   General Comments

There are many other types of transistor circuits which are useful for switching purposes. Some of these are described in the book by S. H. Caldwell, *Switching Circuits and Logical Design*. New York: John Wiley, 1958.

In all these circuits the facts that the transistor is never really totally *off* and that it is never really totally *on* can cause difficulty. That is, the "backward resistance" of the transistor is not really ∞, and the "forward resistance" is not really 0. One of the major problems in the engineering of these circuits lies in recognizing and overcoming these difficulties. These are, however, problems of *engineering* rather than of *logical design* although at times the logical design must be altered to make possible the resolution of the engineering problems.

A good basic book on transistor circuit design is D. DeWitt and A. L. Rossoff, *Transistor Electronics*. New York: McGraw-Hill, 1957. Many specific designs for various types of logic elements and circuits will be found in the latest edition of the *G. E. Transistor Manual*. An extensive, introductory treatment of all these matters is found in the series of paperbacks: *SEEC*, volumes 1–7, New York: John Wiley, 1964–1966.

The Cardinality of a Finite Set

A3.1   The Number of Elements in a Union of Disjoint Sets

Consider a universal set $\hat{U}$ and any subset A of U. Let U be *finite* and denote by "$\#(A)$" the number of distinct elements belonging to A. $\#(A)$ is commonly called the **order,** the **power,** or the **cardinality** of A. In particular, if U has p elements, $\#(U) = p$.

Now suppose $A_1, A_2, \ldots, A_n$ are subsets of U, no two of which have any elements in common, that is, which are **mutually disjoint.** Then we have

(A3.1.1) $\#(A_1 \cup A_2 \cup \cdots \cup A_n) = \#(A_1) + \#(A_2) + \cdots + \#(A_n)$,

$$(A_i \cap A_j = \varnothing,\ i \neq j),$$

since each element of the union is accounted for once and only once on the right. Figure A3.1.1(A) illustrates the case $n = 4$.

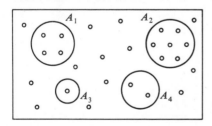

$$\#(A_1 \cup A_2 \cup A_3 \cup A_4) = 14$$

(A)

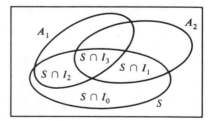

$$\#(S) = \sum_{j=0}^{3} \#(S \cap I_j)$$

(B)

Cardinalities of subsets
Figure A3.1.1

Let $A_1, A_2, \ldots, A_n$ be arbitrary subsets of U and define, as usual,

$$I_j = A_1^{e_1} \cap A_2^{e_2} \cap \cdots \cap A_n^{e_n}$$

where

$$j_{\text{dec}} = e_1 e_2 \cdots e_{n_{\text{bin}}}.$$

Then,

$$U = \bigcup_{j=0}^{2^n-1} I_j \quad \text{and} \quad I_j \cap I_k = \varnothing, \quad j \neq k,$$

and hence, by (A3.1.1), we have

(A3.1.2) $$\#(U) = \sum_{j=0}^{2^n-1} \#(I_j)$$

Similarly, since $A_1, A_1 \cap A_2, \bar{A}_1 \cap \bar{A}_2 \cap A_3, \ldots, \bar{A}_1 \cap \bar{A}_2 \cap \cdots \cap \bar{A}_{n-1}$ $\cap A_n$ are disjoint sets whose union is $A_1 \cup A_2 \cup \cdots \cup A_n$, we have in every case

(A3.1.3) $$\#(A_1 \cup A_2 \cup \cdots \cup A_n) = \#(A_1) + \#(\bar{A}_1 \cap A_2)$$
$$+ \#(\bar{A}_1 \cap \bar{A}_2 \cap A_3) + \cdots + \#(\bar{A}_1 \cap \bar{A}_2 \cap \cdots \cap \bar{A}_{n-1} \cap A_n).$$

Again, let S be any subset of U, and form the sets $S \cap I_j$, $j = 0$, $1, \ldots, 2^n - 1$. These sets are disjoint since the I_j's are disjoint. Moreover $\bigcup_{j=0}^{2^n-1} (S \cap I_j) = S$, so that we have

(A3.1.4) $$\#(S) = \sum_{j=0}^{2^n-1} \#(S \cap I_j).$$

This formula is illustrated for $n = 2$ in Figure A3.1.1(B).

Consider a numerical example. Suppose we inspect a sample of 100 transistors for three possible defects, d_1, d_2, d_3, obtaining the results shown in Figure A3.1.1. In the table, 0 denotes absence of the defect, whereas 1 denotes its presence.

Table A3.1.1

j	d_1	d_2	d_3	$\#$
0	0	0	0	49
1	0	0	1	13
2	0	1	0	12
3	0	1	1	8
4	1	0	0	10
5	1	0	1	6
6	1	1	0	1
7	1	1	1	1
				100

Let A_1, A_2, A_3 denote the subsets of transistors possessing defects d_1, d_2, d_3, respectively. Then (A3.1.2) becomes, in this case,

$$\#(U) = \sum_{j=0}^{7} \#(I_j) = 100.$$

Letting $S = A_1$ in (A3.1.4), we have, since $A_1 \cap I_j = \emptyset$ for $j = 0, 1, 2, 3$,

$$\#(A_1) = \sum_{j=4}^{7} \#(A_1 \cap I_j) = 10 + 6 + 1 + 1 = 18.$$

That is, $\#(A_1)$ is just the sum of the integers (in the #-column of the table) which are in the four rows that contain 1's in the d_1 column. Since

$$\bar{A}_1 \cap A_2 = (\bar{A}_1 \cap A_2 \cap \bar{A}_3) \cup (\bar{A}_1 \cap A_2 \cap A_3)$$

and the sets on the right are disjoint, we have

$$\#(\bar{A}_1 \cap A_2) = \#(I_2) + \#(I_3) = 12 + 8 = 20.$$

Hence an illustration of (A3.1.3) is, in this case,

$$\#(A_1 \cup A_2 \cup A_3) = \#(A_1) + \#(\bar{A}_1 \cap A_2) + \#(\bar{A}_1 \cap \bar{A}_2 \cap A_3)$$
$$= 18 + 20 + 13 = 51;$$

that is, fifty-one transistors possess at least one defect.

A3.2   Counting Formulas Involving the Positive Intersections

Let us call the sets

(A3.2.1)
$$\begin{cases} U \\ A_i, & 1 \leqslant i \leqslant n, \\ A_{i_1} \cap A_{i_2}, & 1 \leqslant i_1 < i_2 \leqslant n \\ \vdots \\ A_1 \cap A_2 \cap \cdots \cap A_n \end{cases}$$

the **positive intersections** of the subsets $A_1, A_2, \ldots, A_n$ of U. Except for the set U, we simply reject or accept each A_i, so there are $1 + (2^n - 1) = 2^n$ such intersections altogether. They are useful in counting the numbers of elements in certain unions. For example,

$$A_1 \cup A_2 = (A_1 \cap \bar{A}_2) \cup (A_1 \cap A_2) \cup (\bar{A}_1 \cap A_2)$$

and since the sets on the right are disjoint, we have, after adding and subtracting $\#(A_1 \cap A_2)$,

$$\#(A_1 \cup A_2) = [\#(A_1 \cap \bar{A}_2) + \#(A_1 \cap A_2)] + [\#(\bar{A}_1 \cap A_2)$$
$$+ \#(A_1 \cap A_2)] - \#(A_1 \cap A_2).$$

Now $(A_1 \cap \bar{A}_2) \cup (A_1 \cap A_2) = A_1$ and $(\bar{A}_1 \cap A_2) \cup (A_1 \cap A_2) = A_2$ and these are unions of disjoint sets. Hence, by (A3.1.1), we have

(A3.2.2) $\#(A_1 \cup A_2) = \#(A_1) + \#(A_2) - \#(A_1 \cap A_2).$

Since $A_1 \cup A_2 \cup A_3 = A_1 \cup (A_2 \cup A_3)$, we have, by (A3.2.2),

$$\#(A_1 \cup A_2 \cup A_3) = \#(A_1) + \#(A_2 \cup A_3) - \#[A_1 \cap (A_2 \cup A_3)].$$

Since $A_1 \cap (A_2 \cup A_3) = (A_1 \cap A_2) \cup (A_1 \cap A_3)$, we obtain, by using (A3.2.2) twice and rearranging terms,

(A3.2.3)
$$\#(A_1 \cup A_2 \cup A_3) = \#(A_1) + \#(A_2) + \#(A_3) - \#(A_1 \cap A_2)$$
$$- \#(A_1 \cap A_3) - \#(A_2 \cap A_3) + \#(A_1 \cap A_2 \cap A_3).$$

By induction, we obtain without difficulty the important formula

(A3.2.4) $\#\left(\bigcup_{i=1}^{n} A_i \right) = \sum_{i=1}^{n} \#(A_i) - \sum_{1 \le i_1 < i_2 \le n} \#(A_{i_1} \cap A_{i_2}) + \sum_{1 \le i_1 < i_2 < i_3 \le n} \#(A_{i_1} \cap A_{i_2} \cap A_{i_3})$
$$- \cdots + (-1)^{n-1} \#(A_1 \cap A_2 \cap \cdots \cap A_n).$$

For example, suppose the internal states of a finite automaton are classified by an experiment into three sets A_1, A_2, A_3 containing 5, 7, and 9 states, respectively. A_1 and A_2 have one state in common, A_1 and A_3 have two states in common, A_2 and A_3 have three states in common. One state belongs to all three sets. How many internal states has the automaton? By (A3.2.3) we have, since $A_1, A_2,$ and A_3 include all states of the automaton, that the number of distinct states in their union is:

$$\#(A_1 \cup A_2 \cup A_3) = 5 + 7 + 9 - 1 - 2 - 3 + 1 = 16.$$

It is well to note the intuitive nature of formulas (A3.2.2) and (A3.2.3): In the sum of $\#(A_1)$ and $\#(A_2)$, any elements *common* to A_1 and A_2 are counted twice, so that we must subtract $\#(A_1 \cap A_2)$, the number of these elements, to make the total correct. In the sum of $\#(A_1)$, $\#(A_2)$, and $\#(A_3)$, the elements common to A_1 and A_2, A_1 and A_3, A_2 and A_3 will each be counted twice (Figure A3.2.1) except for the elements of $A_1 \cap A_2 \cap A_3$ which are counted three times. Since these last-named elements appear in each of $A_1 \cap A_2$, $A_1 \cap A_3$, and $A_2 \cap A_3$, when we subtract $\#(A_1 \cap A_2)$, $\#(A_1 \cap A_3)$, and $\#(A_2 \cap A_3)$ from $\#(A_1) + \#(A_2) + \#(A_3)$ in order to

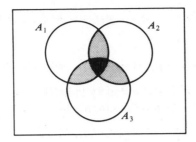

Effect of intersections on counting
Figure A3.2.1

eliminate duplicate counting, we have eliminated the elements of $A_1 \cap A_2 \cap A_3$ from the count altogether. Hence we add the term $\#(A_1 \cap A_2 \cap A_3)$ to correct the result. This sort of reasoning extends also to (A3.2.4).

A3.3   Other Counting Formulas

Again, let $A_1, A_2, \ldots, A_n$ denote arbitrary subsets of a finite set U. Using intersections and complements, we can generate the following 3^n subsets, which we call the **fundamental intersections** determined by the given sets:

$$(A3.3.1) \quad \left\{ \begin{array}{l} U \\ A_i^e, \quad 1 \le i \le n \\ A_{i_1}^{e_1} \cap A_{i_2}^{e_2}, \quad 1 \le i_1 < i_2 \le n \\ \vdots \\ A_1^{e_1} \cap A_2^{e_2} \cap \cdots \cap A_n^{e_n} \end{array} \right.$$

Here each e_i is 0 or 1 so that in forming an intersection of this type, we consider each A_i and reject it completely, accept it, or accept its complement, again omitting $\varnothing$ but including U in the list.

Each of the fundamental intersections can be expanded into a union of complete intersections and hence its cardinality can be determined by summing the entries in the corresponding rows of a table listing the values of $\#(I_j)$.

There are other useful formulas which at times give required cardinalities more simply than by expansion into disjunctive normal form. For example, since $A_i \cup \bar{A}_i = U$ and $A_i \cap \bar{A}_i = \varnothing$, we have, from (A3.1.1),

$$(A3.3.2) \qquad \#(\bar{A}_i) = \#(U) - \#(A_i).$$

Next, since

$$\bar{A}_i \cap \bar{A}_j = \overline{A_i \cup A_j}$$

we have the formula

$$\#(\bar{A}_i \cap \bar{A}_j) = \#(U) - \#(A_i \cup A_j),$$

so that, by (A3.2.2),

(A3.3.3) $\#(\bar{A}_i \cap \bar{A}_j) = \#(U) - \#(A_i) - \#(A_j) + \#(A_i \cap A_j),$

a formula which is readily extended by induction.

Next, because of the disjoint decomposition

$$(A_{i_1} \cap A_{i_2} \cap \cdots \cap A_{i_{k-1}} \cap \bar{A}_{i_k}) \cup (A_{i_1} \cap A_{i_2} \cap \cdots \cap A_{i_{k-1}} \cap A_{i_k})$$

$$= A_{i_1} \cap A_{i_2} \cap \cdots \cap A_{i_{k-1}},$$

we have

(A3.3.4) $\#(A_{i_1} \cap A_{i_2} \cap \cdots \cap A_{i_{k-1}} \cap \bar{A}_{i_k})$

$$= \#(A_{i_1} \cap A_{i_2} \cap \cdots \cap A_{j_{k-1}}) - \#(A_{i_1} \cap A_{i_2} \cap \cdots \cap A_{i_{k-1}} \cap A_{i_k}).$$

Thus, the cardinalities of all intersections involving a single complement are obtainable from those of the positive intersections. Then, by the same type of argument,

(A3.3.5) $\#(A_{i_1} \cap \cdots \cap A_{i_{k-1}} \cap \bar{A}_{i_k} \cap \bar{A}_{i_{k+1}})$

$$= \#(A_{i_1} \cap \cdots \cap A_{i_{k-1}} \cap \bar{A}_{i_k}) - \#(A_{i_1} \cap \cdots \cap A_{i_{k-1}} \cap \bar{A}_{i_k} \cap A_{i_{k+1}}),$$

but the numbers on the right are known by (A3.3.4), so that now the cardinalities of all fundamental intersections involving two complements can be found.

Continuing thus, we can ultimately find the cardinalities of all fundamental intersections. Formulas for the cardinalities of more complicated Boolean functions of $A_1, A_2, \ldots, A_n$ are not hard to find using the principles developed in this and in the preceding section.

To illustrate these remarks, let us return to the example of Section A3.1. By the rules of Sections A3.1 and A3.2, we have

$$\begin{aligned}
\#(U) &= 100, & \#(A_1 \cap A_2) &= 2, \\
\#(A_1) &= 18, & \#(A_1 \cap A_3) &= 7, \\
\#(A_2) &= 22, & \#(A_2 \cap A_3) &= 9, \\
\#(A_3) &= 28, & \#(A_1 \cap A_2 \cap A_3) &= 1.
\end{aligned}$$

Hence, by (A3.3.2),

$$\begin{aligned}
\#(\bar{A}_1) &= 100 - 18 = 82, \\
\#(\bar{A}_2) &= 78, \\
\#(\bar{A}_3) &= 72.
\end{aligned}$$

Then, by (A3.3.4), we have the further cardinalities

$$\#(A_1 \cap \bar{A}_2) = \#(A_1) - \#(A_1 \cap A_2) = 18 - 2 = 16,$$
$$\#(\bar{A}_1 \cap A_2) = 20,$$
$$\#(A_1 \cap \bar{A}_3) = 11,$$
$$\#(\bar{A}_1 \cap A_3) = 21,$$
$$\#(A_2 \cap \bar{A}_3) = 13,$$
$$\#(\bar{A}_2 \cap A_3) = 19.$$

Next, by (A3.3.3), we have

$$\#(\bar{A}_1 \cap \bar{A}_2) = 100 - 18 - 22 + 2 = 62,$$
$$\#(\bar{A}_1 \cap \bar{A}_3) = 61,$$
$$\#(\bar{A}_2 \cap \bar{A}_3) = 59.$$

Again, by (A3.3.4), we have

$$\#(A_1 \cap A_2 \cap \bar{A}_3) = \#(A_1 \cap A_2) - \#(A_1 \cap A_2 \cap A_3) = 2 - 1 = 1,$$
$$\#(A_1 \cap \bar{A}_2 \cap A_3) = 6,$$
$$\#(\bar{A}_1 \cap A_2 \cap A_3) = 8.$$

Now, by (A3.3.5), we have

$$\#(A_1 \cap \bar{A}_2 \cap \bar{A}_3) = \#(A_1 \cap \bar{A}_2) - \#(A_1 \cap \bar{A}_2 \cap A_3) = 16 - 6 = 10,$$
$$\#(\bar{A}_1 \cap A_2 \cap \bar{A}_3) = 12,$$
$$\#(\bar{A}_1 \cap \bar{A}_2 \cap A_3) = 13.$$

We also have

$$\#(\bar{A}_1 \cap \bar{A}_2 \cap \bar{A}_3) = \#(U) - \sum \#(A_i) + \sum \#(A_i \cap A_j)$$
$$- \#(A_1 \cap A_2 \cap A_3) = 100 - (18 + 22 + 28) + (2 + 7 + 9) - 1 = 49,$$

which checks with the entry in the table. Thus we have found the cardinalities of all the fundamental intersections.

To illustrate the handling of other Boolean functions, note that, for the present example,

$$\#[(A_1 \cap \bar{A}_2) \cup (A_2 \cap \bar{A}_3) \cup (A_3 \cap \bar{A}_1)]$$
$$= \#[(A_1 \cup A_2 \cup A_3) \cap (\bar{A}_1 \cup \bar{A}_2 \cup \bar{A}_3)]$$
$$= \#[(A_1 \cup A_2 \cup A_3) \cap \overline{A_1 \cap A_2 \cap A_3}]$$
$$= \#(A_1 \cup A_2 \cup A_3) - \#(A_1 \cap A_2 \cap A_3)$$
$$= 51 - 1 = 50.$$

A3.4 Comments on Counting Problems

In preceding sections we have seen how to compute the cardinality of any Boolean function of sets $A_1, A_2, \ldots, A_n$ provided the cardinalities of the complete intersections are known. There are of course other families of 2^n subsets such that knowing their cardinalities permits calculation of the cardinalities of all other subsets determined by A_1, A_2, ..., A_n. The cardinalities of the positive intersections are an example.

Counting problems involving finite sets are important in switching theory, in automata theory, in probability theory and its applications, and in many other connections. In many cases, the methods we have outlined in this appendix are helpful in the solution of these problems. These methods are part of the larger subject of combinatorial analysis, which treats all types of counting problems relating to the distribution of elements into sets [1], [2].

A3.5   Exercises

1.   A group of 150 graduate students are classified according to marital status a_1, legal age a_2, and sex a_3. The results are listed in Table A3.5.1. In the table, 0's mean unmarried, under-age, and female, respectively, in columns 1, 2, and 3. Compute the cardinalities of the positive intersections.

Table A3.5.1

a_1	a_2	a_3	#
0	0	0	12
0	0	1	5
0	1	0	51
0	1	1	32
1	0	0	6
1	0	1	2
1	1	0	22
1	1	1	20

2.   Show that if A is a subset of a finite subset B of U, then

$$\#(\bar{A} \cap B) = \#(B) - \#(A).$$

3.   If A and B are subsets of U, under what conditions will the following be true?

(a) $\#(A \cup \bar{B}) = \#(A) + \#(\bar{B})$,
(b) $\#(\bar{A} \cup B) = \#(U)$.

4.   Prove that

$$\#(A_1 \cap \bar{A}_2 \cap \bar{A}_3) = \#(A_1) - \#(A_1 \cap A_2) - \#(A_1 \cap A_3)$$
$$+ \#(A_1 \cap A_2 \cap A_3).$$

Obtain a similar formula for

$$\#(A_1 \cap A_2 \cap \bar{A}_3 \cap \bar{A}_4).$$

5.   Prove that

$$\#(U) = \sum_{i=1}^{n} \#(A_i) - \sum_{1 \leq i_1 < i_2 \leq n} \#(A_{i_1} \cap A_{i_2}) + \cdots + (-1)^{n-1} \#(A_1 \cap A_2 \cap \cdots \cap A_n)$$
$$+ \#(\bar{A}_1 \cap \bar{A}_2 \cap \cdots \cap \bar{A}_n).$$

6.   The cardinalities of the positive intersections of three subsets of U are asserted to be as follows:

$$\#(U) = 39, \qquad \#(A_1 \cap A_2) = 10,$$
$$\#(A_1) = 20, \qquad \#(A_1 \cap A_3) = 4,$$
$$\#(A_2) = 30, \qquad \#(A_2 \cap A_3) = 8,$$
$$\#(A_3) = 10, \qquad \#(A_1 \cap A_2 \cap A_3) = 2.$$

Are these figures correct? Why?

7.   The following is a portion of a report submitted by an investigator for a well-known market analysis agency with standards so high that it boasts that an employee's first mistake is his last:

Number of consumers interviewed:	100
Number of consumers using brand X:	78
Number of consumers using brand Y:	71
Number of consumers using both brands:	48

Why was the interviewer discharged?

8.   A famous problem of Lewis Carroll reads thus: "In a very hotly fought battle, 70 percent, at least, of the combatants lost an eye, 75 percent, at least, lost an ear, 80 percent, at least, lost an arm, and 85 percent, at least, lost a leg. How many, at least, lost all four?" (*A Tangled Tale*).

9.   If A_1 and A_2 are subsets of U such that

$$\frac{\#(A_1 \cap A_2)}{\#(A_2)} > \frac{\#(A_1 \cap \bar{A}_2)}{\#(\bar{A}_2)},$$

prove that also

$$\frac{\#(A_1 \cap A_2)}{\#(A_1)} > \frac{\#(\bar{A}_1 \cap A_2)}{\#(\bar{A}_1)}.$$

Illustrate with a Venn diagram.

10. If $\#(A_1) = \#(\bar{A}_1)$ and $\#(A_2) = \#(\bar{A}_2)$, where A_1 and A_2 are subsets of U, what relations exist among

$$\#(A_1 \cap A_2), \qquad \#(A_1 \cap \bar{A}_2), \quad \#(\bar{A}_1 \cap A_2), \qquad \#(\bar{A}_1 \cap \bar{A}_2)?$$

11. The cardinalities of a subset of the set of all fundamental intersections of n subsets of U are said to be **independent** if and only if they imply unique values for the cardinalities of all 3^n fundamental intersections. They are said to be **consistent** if and only if all 3^n cardinalities are non-negative. Show that a given set of independent cardinalities is consistent if and only if the implied cardinalities of the 2^n complete intersections are all non-negative.

12. If one knows the cardinalities of the complete intersections I_j and records these integers on the squares of a Veitch-Karnaugh map, what is the meaning of the total of the entries in the squares of a given k-dimensional subcube?

13. Show that if we define $A_i^* = U$, then the positive intersections are the set of all $A_1^{e_1} \cap A_2^{e_2} \cap \cdots \cap A_n^{e_n}$ where each $e_j = 1$ or $*$ while the fundamental intersections are those for which $e_j = 0, 1,$ or $*$.

A3.6   References

1.   H. J. Ryser, *Combinatorial Mathematics* (Carus Monograph number fourteen). New York: John Wiley, 1963.
   The treatment is mature and the subject matter is exciting.

2.   J. Riordan, *An Introduction to Combinatorial Analysis*. New York: John Wiley, 1958.
   This book treats series-parallel networks and linear graphs, among other problems.

3.   G. U. Yule and M. G. Kendall, *An Introduction to the Theory of Statistics* (Twelfth Edition). London: Griffin, 1940.
   Many statistical applications of the formulas in this appendix appear in this reference.

4.   M. Harrison, *Switching and Automata Theory*. New York: McGraw-Hill, 1965.
   This book treats most of the known counting problems of switching theory.

Index

Absorption laws, 20, 81, 123 (Ex. 1)
Addend, 149
Addition, 149, 151, 156
Adjacent Squares, 174
Algebra of subsets of a set, 80
Allowable values, 105
Alternation, 6, 109
AND-element, 143, 244, 254
AND-gate, 143
AND-operation, 6
Antisymmetric property, 36, 77, 134, 227
Arithmetic of zero and one, 3, 8, 9, 112, 113
Arrow function, 132
Associative laws, 11, 78, 120, 224
Augend, 149

Back contact, 2
Base of a transistor, 252
Biconditional, 130
Bilateral circuit element, 1
Binary arithmetic, 149, 151, 235
Binary connective, 109

Binary operation, 109
Binary system, 234
Binary to decimal conversion, 238
Bistable devices, 1
Boolean algebra
    definition, 39, 228
    of propositional functions, 135
    of set functions, 98
    of subsets of a set, 80
    of switching functions, 39
    of truth functions, 136
Boolean equations, solution of, 24, 38, 41 (Ex. 15), 66 (Ex. 12), 201 (Ex. 11)
Boolean functions
    definition, 228
    normal forms, 228
    of real numbers, 101 (Ex. 9)
    of set variables, 96
    of switching variables, 5
Both-or-neither circuit, 4
Both-or-neither function, 11, 164 (Ex. 12)
Bound variable, 108
Break-before-make-contact, 3

Break contact, 2
Bridge circuit, 16

Cancellation laws
  alternatives to, 24
  lack of, 24, 77, 82
Cardinality of a set, 259
Carry digit, 149
Carry-in, 150
Carry-out, 151
Circuit variable, 3
Class, 71
Closed state, 1
Closure, 223
Code, 158
Code point, 158
Code word, 158
Collector of a transistor, 252
Combinational circuit, 5, 19, 68
Commutative laws, 11, 78, 120, 224
Comparable functions, 36
Complement, 3, 74, 112, 224
  in minimization, 185
  of a circuit, 10
Complementarity, laws of, 13, 80, 225
Complementation, 3, 224
  laws of, 14
Complements, computation of, 26, 83
Complete
  intersection, 92
  product, 41
  union, 42
Conditional, 128
Conjunction, 6, 110, 113
Conjunctive normal form
  definition, 53, 97, 122
  method of obtaining, 51
  properties of, 66 (Ex. 14-18)
Consistency principle, 37, 77, 227
Consistent sets of cardinalities, 268
Constant propositional function, 106
Contact, 1
Containing (inclusion) relation, 73
Continuity transfer, 3
Contradiction, 109
Corresponding values, 107

Coverings, 216
Current, 242
Current amplification, 253

Dagger function, 132
Decimal representation of functions, 192
Decimal system, 234
Decimal to binary conversion, 239
DeMorgan's laws, 14, 80, 122, 225
  extended, 20
  generalized, 28 (Ex. 4), 89 (Ex. 23), 125 (Ex. 15), 226 (Ex. 4)
Denial, 109
Diode, 243
  AND-element, 214
  OR-element, 246
Disjoint sets, 74
Disjunction, 6, 109, 113
Disjunctive normal form, 46, 97, 122
  method of obtaining, 44
  properties of, 66 (Ex. 14-18)
Distributive laws, 12, 79, 121, 224
  extended, 20
  generalized, 28 (Ex. 4), 89 (Ex. 24), 125 (Ex. 15)
Dominant elements, 13, 80, 121, 224
Domains of functions, 105
  of variables, 105
Don't-care combinations, 55, 186, 213
Double stroke, 132
Dual pairs of laws, 15, 81
Duality, principle of, 15, 82, 122, 225
Dummy variable, 108

Element, 71
Emitter of a transistor, 252
Empty set, 73
Equal functions, 7, 96
Equal sets, 73
Equal-to-or-greater-than, 35
Equals, operations on, 7, 76
Equivalence relation, 115
Equivalent
  circuits, 7

defining properties of sets, 73
propositional functions, 114
Essential prime implicant, 204
Essential products, 182
Exclusive-or, 10
  circuit, 4, 145, 146
  function, 127
  identities, 33 (Ex. 28), 140 (Ex. 30)
  operation, 127
Existential quantifier, 107

Factoring using redundancies, 27
Field of subsets, 99, 135
Five-variable maps, 189
Free variable, 108
Front contact, 2
Full adder, 151, 152, 155
Functional decomposition, 221
Fundamental intersections, 263
Fundamental products, 94, 201

Generalized DeMorgan laws, 28 (Ex. 4), 89 (Ex. 23), 125 (Ex. 15), 226 (Ex. 4)
Generalized distributive laws, 28 (Ex. 4), 89 (Ex. 24), 125 (Ex. 15)
Generalized NAND, 153, 154, 257
Generalized NOR, 153, 154, 257
Generalized stroke element, 153, 154, 255
Gray code, 158

Half-adder, 150
Hamming code, 168 (Ex. 25)

Idempotent laws, 12, 79, 121, 224
Idempotent ring, 231
Identical functions, 7
Identity elements, 13, 80, 121, 224
  uniqueness of, 23
Identity function, 106
Implication, 129

properties of, 137 (Ex. 2, 3)
Implies, 129, 201
Inclusion (containment), 34, 73
  properties of, 77, 83, 88 (Ex. 21)
Inclusive-or, 6, 109
Inconsistency, 118
Independence of postulates, 14
Independent sets of cardinalities, 268
Inhibitor, 145
Input combination, 68
Input (*verb*), 142
Input leads, 141
Intersection of sets, 74
Inverses, lack of, 24
Inverter, 143, 253
Involution, law of, 14, 80, 122, 225

Join, 6, 223
Join normal form, 230
Joint denial, 131

Karnaugh map, 170

Law of involution, 14, 80, 122, 225
Laws of complementarity, 13, 80, 122, 225
Laws of complementation, 14, 122
Laws of operation
  with F and T, 121
  with Ø and U, 79
  with zero and one, 13, 224
Leads, 2, 141
Less than or equal to, 35
Literal, 201
Logic elements, 141
Logical functions, 108
Logical operations, 108
Logical product, 110
Logical sum, 109

McClusky's procedure, 208
  for finding all minimal forms, 212
  for handling don't-cares, 213

Make-before-break contact, 3
Make contact, 2
Map of a function, 172
Mathematical model of a system, xiv
Maximal polynomial, 43
Maxterm, 43
Meet, 223
Meet normal form, 230
Member, 71
Minimal polynomial, 42
Minimization procedure, 182, 187
Minterm, 42
Mixed logic, 248
Multiplication, 6

n-cube, 176
n-digit Gray code, 159
n-digit reflected binary code, 159
NAND-element, 145, 257
NAND full adder, 155
Negation, 109, 112
Negative logic, 248
NOR-element, 145, 257
Not comparable functions, 36
NOT-element, 143, 253
Null property, 73
Null set, 73
Number of switching functions, 47

One, 2, 224
Open sentence, 72, 104
Open state, 1
OR-element, 142, 246, 256
OR-gate, 142
OR-operation, 5
OR-polynomial, 181, 201
Order of a finite set, 259
Order of operations, 12
Order relations, 35
Output combination, 68
Output lead, 141

p-n junction diode, 251
p-n-p junction transistor, 252

p-squares, 172
p-subcubes, 176-178, 201 (Ex. 12, 13)
Parallel addition, 157
Parallel connection, 6, 9
Parentheses, rules for use of, 12
Partitioning of a set, 92
Perfect induction, 19
Place value, 233
Positive intersections, 261
Power of a finite set, 259
Prime implicant, 202
Principle of duality, 15, 82, 122, 225
Product, 6
Proper subset, 73
Proposition, 103
Propositional form, 104, 105
Propositional function, 104, 105

Quantifiers, 107
Quine's method, 201

Range of a propositional function, 105
Redundant factors, 27
Redundant terms, 27
Reflected binary code, 158
Reflexive property, 36, 115, 134, 223,
    227
Relation of
    equal-to-or-greater-than, 35
    equality of elements, 223
    equality of functions, 7
    equality of sets, 73
    equivalence of propositional
        functions, 114
    implication, 129
    inclusion, 77, 83, 88 (Ex. 21)
    less-than-or-equal-to, 35
Relay, 1
Relay tree, 94, 95
Resistance, 242
Ring sum, 127

Scheffer stroke, 131
Self-dual, 81

Semiconductor diode, 243
Serial addition, 156, 157
Series connection, 6, 9
Series-parallel circuit, 16
Set, 71
Shannon, 2
Shortest OR-polynomial, 181
Signal, 141
Simplicity, definition of, 148
Six variable maps, 191
Sneak path, 62, 63
Solution of Boolean equations, 24, 38, 41 (Ex. 15), 66 (Ex. 12), 201 (Ex. 11)
Spring, 2
Stone Representation Theorem, 100
Stroke-elements, 144, 254
Stroke full adder, 152, 155
Stroke half adder, 150
Subset, 73
Subsets of a finite set, 93
Substitution principle, 123
Subsume, 202
Sum digit, 149
Superset, 73
Switch, 1
Switching function, 5, 7
  as vertices on a cube, 75
Symmetric difference, 88 (Ex. 22), 90 (Ex. 30, 31), 91 (Ex. 32, 33)
Symmetric function, 49
Symmetric property, 115, 223

Tautology, 116, 117
Torus, 174
Transfer contact, 3, 4, 50
Transistor, 251
Transistor AND-element, 254
  NOT-element, 253
  off and on, 253
  OR-element, 256
  stroke-element, 254

Transitive property, 37, 77, 115, 134, 223, 227
Translators, 159, 160, 167 (Ex. 22), 168 (Ex. 25)
Truth function, 111
Truth set, 105
Truth table, 112
Truth value, 111
Two's complement, 236
Two-stage circuit, 250
Two-state devices, 1
Two-terminal circuit, 5

Unary operation, 109
Unilateral circuit element, 1
Union, 5, 6, 74
Uniqueness of complement, 225
Uniqueness of identity elements, 23
Uniqueness of zero and one, 23, 226 (Ex. 1)
Uniqueness quantifier, 107
Unit distance code, 161
Universal bounds property, 36, 77, 134, 227
Universal quantifier, 107
Universal set, 73
Universe of discourse, 73

Value of a propositional function, 105 105
Veitch-Karnaugh map, 170
Venn diagram, 74
Verification theorem, 97
Voltage, 242
Voltage pulse, 141

Word, 158

Zero, 2, 224
Zero set, 73